Publication No. 11
of the Mathematics Research Center
United States Army
The University of Wisconsin

NONLINEAR INTEGRAL EQUATIONS

NONLINEAR INTEGRAL EQUATIONS

Proceedings of an Advanced Seminar Conducted by the Mathematics Research Center, United States Army, at the University of Wisconsin, Madison, April 22-24, 1963

edited by

P. M. ANSELONE

MADISON · THE UNIVERSITY
OF WISCONSIN PRESS · 1964

Published by
THE UNIVERSITY OF WISCONSIN PRESS
Madison and Milwaukee
Mailing Address: P.O. Box 1379, Madison, Wisconsin 53701
Editorial Offices: 430 Sterling Court, Madison

Typescript by Technical Publication Staff,
Mathematics Research Center, U.S. Army
Printed in the United States of America by
North American Press, Milwaukee, Wisconsin

Library of Congress Catalog Card Number 64-17771

FOREWORD

This volume comprises the proceedings of the second advanced seminar conducted by the Mathematics Research Center, U. S. Army. It was held at the Wisconsin Center on the campus of the University of Wisconsin in Madison, April 22-24, 1963.

The advanced seminars were conceived originally as part of an educational program for Army mathematicians. In addition, they are designed to stimulate research and scholarship in the general mathematical community. In line with these objectives, the lectures are essentially expository surveys at an advanced level. The emphasis is on recent and current progress.

Although accurate mathematical formulations of physical processes are notoriously nonlinear, until recently it has been customary to deal with more tractable linear approximate formulations. But all too often linearization leads to results which are qualitatively or quantitatively unacceptable. In the past decade, the more fundamental nonlinear problems have received increasing attention. These problems are often expressed first in terms of nonlinear differential equations and then transformed into integral equations to facilitate their study and solution. Sometimes, physical theory leads directly to nonlinear integral equations.

The study of nonlinear integral equations is still in a relatively early stage; much remains to be done. It is earnestly hoped that this seminar will inspire research in the field as well as applications of existing theory.

The meeting was opened with words of welcome from Dr. R. E. Langer, the Director of the Mathematics Research Center. The mathematical program consisted of ten one-hour lectures by invited speakers. Each morning and afternoon session, consisting of two lectures and discussion periods, was presided over by an invited chairman. The chairmen were:

Prof. E. Hopf, Indiana University
Dr. Č. Masaitis, Aberdeen Proving Ground
Prof. A. T. Lonseth, Oregon State University
Prof. I. I. Kolodner, University of New Mexico
Dr. E. H. Bareiss, Argonne National Laboratory

Appreciation is extended to the speakers, chairmen and all the other participants for their efforts to make the seminar a success.

P. M. Anselone

PREFACE

We have tried to make this seminar on nonlinear integral equations reasonably comprehensive. Following is a brief indication of its scope.

Some of the early history and pre-history of the subject is traced by Dr. Wouk, the first speaker. He discusses the relations between nonlinear differential and integral equations. Initial value problems can lead to Volterra equations and boundary value problems to Hammerstein equations. Thus, much of the theory of nonlinear differential equations is really a part of the theory of nonlinear integral equations. The familiar Picard method of successive approximations falls into this category. Other connections between differential and integral equations are developed by several of the speakers. Of course, not all integral equations are equivalent to differential equations.

A nonlinear integral equation is ordinarily considered in an appropriate setting such as a linear space or partially ordered space of functions. The choice of the space is influenced by the form and properties of the integral operator. For example, on a certain domain, the operator may be continuous, completely continuous, contractive, positive, or differentiable. These properties can be exploited in the analysis and solution of the equation. Therefore, it is often advantageous to regard nonlinear integral equations as special cases of more general equations in abstract spaces. The process of generalization gives access to existing theories and methods of solution: fixed point theorems, variational methods, implicit function theorems, the abstract Newton's method. Several speakers treat nonlinear integral equations from abstract points of view. In this connection, the modern work of the Russians, especially Kantorovich, Krasnoselskii and Vainberg, is prominently featured.

Numerical methods of solution and applications to physical problems are discussed primarily in the last three talks. The applications are important and representative. Some others which might have been included in a longer conference pertain to elasticity, heat transfer, automatic control and communication theory.

Although there is considerable current interest in nonlinear integral equations, the subject does not really exist as a separate and unified field of study in this country. Instead, the equations are investigated principally in connection with the separate facets mentioned above: differential equations, abstract spaces, numerical solutions and physical applications. This is probably the first meeting in the United States and the first book in English devoted to nonlinear integral equations in their manifold aspects. So this seminar should help to promote the unification of the field and thereby enrich and advance the study of nonlinear integral equations.

P. M. Anselone

CONTENTS

NONLINEAR INTEGRAL EQUATIONS

ARTHUR WOUK

Direct Iteration, Existence and Uniqueness

Introduction

There is a continual development of mathematical ideas both in the simplicity of their description and in their generality of application. As a consequence of this process, we are now able to look back upon and summarize neatly and succinctly in a few abstract or concrete analytic principles, work which formerly was lost in much analytic detail. Those principles with which we shall concern ourselves are associated with the problems of existence and uniqueness of solutions and the related one of the convergence of successive approximations, for non-linear ordinary and partial differential equations and integral equations. The band will be limited on one side by those hypotheses on the problem which guarantee the differentiability in the Fréchet or Gateaux sense of some operator under discussion, while on the other side the limit will be the type of fixed point theorem associated with the name of Schauder. Later speakers will cover the two excluded directions.

In one sense, the method of exhaustion of the Greek geometers should be the starting point of any survey of iterative methods. This alone should emphasize the fact that in the actual discussion which follows we have selected highlights; what is presented is not to be thought of as being in itself complete. We will trace the development of the present views of these matters since Cauchy, leading to expositions of the recent abstract views of the methods together with recent analytic devices and their relation to abstract methods.

Two bibliographies are appended. The first consists of papers which are referenced in the text, the second of various direct or slightly indirect applications of successive approximations or the fixed point theorems of the text to assorted problems. Special attention should be called to the monographs by Kantorovich [21], [22], Krasnoselskii[31] and Miranda [44] which overlap in part with the present text.

Part I

1. Cauchy's Existence Proofs

The work of Cauchy* in the rigorization of mathematics during the first half of the nineteenth century marks a watershed in the theory of differential and integral equations. In it are to be found the sources of at least four major branches of the theory, as follows:

1. The Cauchy-Lipschitz-Peano existence and uniqueness theorems;
2. The Cauchy-Picard existence and uniqueness theorems;
3. The Cauchy Majorant method for analytic equations;
4. The Cauchy-Poincare small parameter methods (called by Cauchy the Variation of Constants).

The first method was known to Euler for numerical purposes at least as early as 1768; (we speak of this as the Euler integration method in numerical work) Cauchy first proved an existence and uniqueness theorem for ordinary differential equations $y' = f(x, y)$ by establishing the convergence of the Euler polygons when $f(x, y)$ is continuously differentiable. In 1876 Lipschitz [39], simplified Cauchy's proof while introducing the now well known Lipschitz condition to replace certain complicated arguments of Cauchy based on derivatives. Peano [48] at the end of the nineteenth century saw deeper into the problem and produced the existence theorem in a form spiritually related to later ideas based on fixed point theorems such as Schauder's. We recall that the central point of the Peano argument is the fact that if $f(x, y)$ is continuous on some set D including the point (x_0, y_0) in its interior, then the mapping $F(y)$, defined on the set of continuous functions whose graph lies in a uniformly bounded subset of D, where

$$F(y) = \int_{x_0}^{x} f(t, y(t))\, dt + y_0 ,$$

maps this set of bounded continuous functions into a uniformly bounded equicontinuous set of functions for $|x - x_0|$ sufficiently small. We shall see below that this is the essential condition of the Schauder fixed point theorem which can be used to imply the existence of a fixed point, or a solution of $y' = f(x, y)$, in a modern development. It is, of course, well known that under these conditions no uniqueness is implied. Somewhat after Schauder, E. Rothe [52] extended the use of the Schauder type arguments to obtain existence theorems for solutions of integral equations of the form

---

* (Cauchy did not publish his contributions in these areas; they appear in an 1844 treatise [45] by a student, Moigno, based on Cauchy's lectures. The announcements appear in the Comptes Rendu's during the 1820's.

$$y(P) = \int_D f(P, Q, y(Q))\, dQ$$

under rather light restrictions on f, where y and f are n-vectors, P and Q are points in D, a domain in an m-dimensional space. He also provided uniqueness theorems under rather more severe restrictions on f. For numerical purposes, this line of development is still fruitful. It is exploited for instance by Diaz [11, 12] for hyperbolic non-linear partial differential equations.

The Cauchy-Picard method also predates Cauchy, having been widely used in the eighteenth century by astronomers for the correction of orbital calculations. Liouville [37, 38] in 1836-7 used the method to solve the boundary value problem of heat conduction posed in the form

$$(ky')' + (\lambda g + m)y = 0; \quad y'(x_0) + hy(x_0) = 0, \quad y(x_1) + Hy(x_1) = 0$$

where x is a real variable, $x_0 \leq x \leq x_1$, k, g, m are functions of x, h and H are constants. He constructed the iteration

$$p_0 = A(1 + hk(x_0) \int_{x_0}^{x} dt/k(t))$$

$$\cdots$$

$$p_{n+1} = \int_{x_0}^{x} \int_{x_0}^{s} \frac{m(t) - \lambda g(t)}{k(s)} p_n(t)\, dt\, ds,$$

$$\cdots$$

which is the Volterra integral equation, solved by successive approximations. He used the now customary estimates to prove the uniform convergence of $p_0 + p_1 + p_2 + \ldots$, the Neumann series to a solution of the boundary value problem.

Minor uses of the method for linear problems were made during the period from Liouville to Picard's rediscovery of the method. In 1890, Picard [49, 50] applied the method to obtain existence and uniqueness theorems for systems of equations

$$y' = f(x, y), \quad y(x_0) = y_0$$

under the usual Lipschitz condition; he also applied it to partial differential equations of the form

$$u_{xx} + u_{yy} = f(x, y, u, u_x, u_y)$$

and

$$u_{xy} = f(x, y, u, u_x, u_y),$$

again under Lipschitz conditions uniform in x and y on the other arguments of f. He obtained for the ordinary and hyperbolic cases local existence theorems, as is to be expected. He worked, of course, with the Volterra integral equation of the problems. In the case of the elliptic problems he utilized the Greens function G for the domain D under discussion and considered successive approximations for integral equations of the type

$$u(x, y) = \iint_D G(x, y; \xi, \eta) f(\xi, \eta, u, u_x, u_y) \, d\xi \, d\eta$$

He obtained a "local" convergence, existence and uniqueness theorem (i. e., for sufficiently small domains D.) Lindelöf [36] concerned himself with the extent of the domain of definition of the solution guaranteed by successive approximations and gave essentially the current analytic form of the existence proof. I. Bendixson (1897), [3] started this method into a deeper direction. He showed that when the method of successive approximations converges, it yields a solution, even though the system of equations does not have a unique solution. He also gave the first of a long line of uniqueness theorems by showing for a single first order equation that if $f(x, y)$ is monotone increasing in y and $f(x_0, y_0) > 0$, then the solution is unique and successive approximations converge. The operator theoretic notion of positive monotone operators, to which we shall return, is foreshadowed here.

After Picard, the iterative method was well known and widely used. Abstraction began to set in and in 1920 Lamson [34] rephrased the problem as that of an implicit function theorem in an abstract space. He considered P an element of an abstract set D, $y(P)$ and $z(P)$ single-valued functions from D to a complete normed space E, and set up the implicit functional

$$y(P) = F[y, z; P]$$

where F maps triples y and z in E and P in D into E. He showed that if F is continuous in y and z and F satisfies a Lipschitz condition of constant < 1 with respect to y uniformly in z and P, and

$$y_o(P) = F[y_o, z_o; P]$$

is an identity in P, then there exists a unique mapping $y = y(P, z)$ satisfying $y \equiv F[y, z; P]$ which is continuous in z in a neighborhood of z_o and which is the limit of any sequence of the form

$$y_n(P, z) = F[y_{n-1}(P, z), z; P] .$$

This, of course, contains the Cauchy-Picard existence and uniqueness theorem for the initial value problem for ordinary differential equations as a special case. It also contains numerous other older and more recent existence and uniqueness theorems for differential and integral equations. The theorem is global, in the sense that convergence is assured for any starting value y_1. In 1927 Hildebrandt and Graves [17] provided their version of the implicit function theorem, which generalizes the Lamson theorem somewhat; it is a "local" theorem, in that convergence is assured for some neighborhood of the fixed point, and smoothness properties other than continuity are obtained. Error estimates for the approximations were given. In the same year Graves applied the result to generalized integro-differential equations of the form

$$\widetilde{F}(r, \int_{r_o}^{r} g(r, r', y(r'), x)\, dr', y(r), x) = 0$$

where $\widetilde{F}$, g, and y are bounded and Lebesgue measurable in r and r', while $\widetilde{F}$ satisfies a generalized uniform Lipschitz condition of the form

$$\| F(\cdot, y_1, \cdot) - F(\cdot, y_2, \cdot) \| \leq h \int^{r} \| y_1(r) - y_2(r) \|$$

$$(\text{where } \int^{r} \| y(r) \| = \text{g.l.b.}_{R(r) \geq \| y(r) \|} \int^{r} R(r)\, dr)$$

to obtain the existence locally of a unique fixed point obtained from successive approximations.

In a very general sense, the local theory of non-linear ordinary and hyperbolic partial differential equations and Volterra integral equations, subject to appropriate Lipschitz conditions, is obtainable by these theorems. In the case of non-linear integral equations generated by Greens functions, say, for elliptic equations, the results are also only local in the independent variables. In the case of a parameter, non-local theorems may be obtained say for

$$y(x) = \lambda \int_{x_0}^{x_1} K(x, s, y(s))\, ds$$

with K continuous provided λ is small enough (for this guarantees the Lipschitz constant < 1). The general nature of the available theory is that for any starting point y_1 in some suitable abstract sphere, the obvious iteration

$$y_n = F(y_{n-1})$$

converges in norm to a unique fixed point and the convergence rate is uniform on any sphere of fixed radius about the fixed point. Further, if F is smooth in some parameter, y will be too.

Neither the series method nor the last method need concern us much here; some illustrations of these ideas will be mentioned later. (However, the last method is worth noting for historical reasons alone. It seems to be original with Cauchy, which none of the preceding three are. Observing that the system $y' = 0$ has a known solution he expands the solutions of

$$y' = \epsilon f(x, x_0, y), \quad y(x_0) = y_0$$

in powers of ϵ and proves convergence as far as $\epsilon = 1$. He predated Poincaré's use of the idea by 50 years.)

2. Some ideas from uniqueness theorems

We may remark first that the distinction between the continuous formulation of the initial value problem for ordinary differential equations, and the Caratheodory type theory in which $f(x, y)$ is assumed only measurable in x for each fixed y and continuous in y for each fixed x and dominated by a Lebesgue integrable function of x, independent of y, is only the distinction between the particular term-by-term integration theorems to be used for a certain sequence of integrals

$$\int_{x_0}^{x} f(t, y_n(t))\, dt .$$

We can therefore with equanimity assume either of the two conditions for $f(x, y)$, in the discussion below. It is convenient to state matters in the continuous case, but no great effort is needed to rewrite everything in terms of the Caratheodory conditions. Further, the extension to systems of equations is in general trivial, requiring only the change from certain absolute value signs to a norm indication for vectors. Focus attention therefore on a single first order differential equation and its initial value problem

$$(2.1) \qquad y' = f(x, y), \qquad y(x_o) = y_o$$

with $f(x, y)$ defined and continuous on $|x - x_o| \le a$, $|y - y_o| \le b$. Starting with Bendixson, numerous criteria have been developed to assure the unique solvability of (2.1) in terms of the y variation of f; we recall the conditions associated with the names of Nagumo, Osgood and Perron:

(2.2N) $|f(x, y_1) - f(x, y_2)| \le c|y_1 - y_2| / |x - x_o|$, $c \le 1$;

(2.2O) $|f(x, y_1) - f(x, y_2)| \le w(|y_1 - y_2|)$ where $\int_{\epsilon} dy/w(y) \to \infty$, $\epsilon \to 0$;

(2.2P) $|f(x, y_1) - f(x, y_2)| \le w(|x - x_o|, |y_1 - y_2|)$, $x \ne x_o$, where the function $w(t, r)$ is continuous, non-negative on $0 < t < a$, $r \ge 0$ and non-decreasing in r for fixed t, while the only differentiable solution of $r' = w(t, r)$ for which $r(+0) = \lim_{t \to +0} r(t)/t$ exists and equals zero is $r \equiv 0$.

None of these criteria is associated with successive approximations. However, it was proven quite early (Rosenblatt, [51]) that (2.2N) for $c < 1$ implies that the successive approximations

$$y_n(x) = \int_{x_o}^{x} f(t, y_{n-1}(t))\, dt + y_o$$

converge uniformly for any starting $y_1(x)$ and uniformly on any sphere in the space of. (Later extensions showed this true also for $c = 1$ (VanKampen [62]) but false for $c > 1$.) Again the proof is by way of an appraisal of the rate of convergence (see also Nagumo [46].) Complicated variants of this condition have recently been obtained by Luxemburg [40, 41, 42], Brauer [4,5], Krasnoselskii and Krein [30], and Kooi [39], and Dinghas [13], among others.

In 1945 Dieudonné [14], and in 1946 Wintner [70] published distinct proofs of the following fact: there is an intermediary ground between Cauchy-Peano-type existence theorems based on the Arzela-Ascoli theorems, and Cauchy-Picard-type existence and uniqueness theorems based on the Banach fixed point theorem. Dieudonné showed for a slightly weakened form of the Kamke uniqueness conditions, and Wintner for the condition of Osgood (2.3-0) that if the initial choice, $y_1(x)$, is any continuous function, then the successive approximations y converge uniformly in x, and hence to a solution of (2.1); however no estimate of the rate of convergence is used, so that the second type of uniformity is not established. (However, there is no published example in which the second type of uniformity does not hold.) A slight generalization is to be found in LaSalle [35]. Viswanatham [63] (1952) removed Dieudonné's restrictions and showed by the method of Wintner that (2.3K) implies the uniform convergence in the above sense of the successive approximations, and simultaneously Coddington and Levinson [9] showed it for the Caratheodory equivalent form of (2.3K). Continuations of this line of thought for Volterra integral equations and partial differential equations exist in Sato [54, 55, 56]. Other special convergence properties may be found in Husty [18], Wintner [69], and Z. Danov [73].

Part II

3. Existence Via Fixed Point Theorems

We consider first the purely topological approach mentioned above in connection with work of Schauder [57] and Rothe [52]. We are concerned with certain mappings F of a Banach space E into itself about which we have the

Schauder Fixed Point Theorem: *If F is a continuous mapping from E into E which maps a closed convex set D (in E) into itself in such a way that the image of D is compact, then D contains at least one element y such that $F(y) = y$.*

We call F a compact operator. The following corollary of the Schauder fixed point theorem should be noted:

If there exist α and β, $0 < \alpha < 1$ and $\beta > 0$ such that

$$\|F(y)\| \leq \alpha \|y\| + \beta$$

then there exists a fixed point y satisfying

$$\|y\| \leq \beta/(1-\alpha) .$$

This corollary, due to Rothe [52], is true since the sphere $\|y\| \leq \beta/(1-\alpha)$ is mapped into itself via F.

In applications we require, for a given problem, the construction of an appropriate closed convex set D, usually some sphere in the norm sense, on which F is a compact operator mapping D into D. We will illustrate the domain of this theorem by obtaining the Peano existence theorem and by an application to the existence of periodic solutions.

Consider the system of differential equations given formally by (2.1). Let the norm be given by

$$\|y\| = \sum_{i=1}^{n} \max_{[x_o, x_{o+a}]} |y_i(t)|$$

while

$$|y| = \sum_{i=1}^{n} |y_i| .$$

Suppose that

$$|f_i(x, y)| \leq A_i |y| + B_i \quad \text{on} \quad |x-x_o| \leq a, \; |y-y_o| \leq b.$$

Then the mapping $F(y)$ determined by

$$F(y) = y_o + \int_{x_o}^{x} f(t, y(t))\, dt$$

is compact (maps the uniformly bounded equicontinuous functions into themselves) and satisfies

$$\|F(y)\| \leq \|y\| \; |x - x_o| \sum_{i=1}^{n} A_i + |x - x_o| \sum_{i=1}^{n} B_i + |y_o| .$$

Applying the Rothe corollary we see that

$$|x - x_o| \sum_{i=1}^{n} A_i < 1$$

implies the existence of a solution y of (2.1) satisfying

$$|y(t)| = \sum_{i=1}^{n} |y_i(t)| \leq \frac{|x - x_o| \sum_{i=1}^{n} B_i + |y_o|}{1 - |x - x_o| \sum_{i=1}^{n} A_i}$$

Here, the Schauder theorem replaces the Arzela-Ascoli theorems and the passage to the limit under the integrals in the Peano proof. Rothe in [52] has elaborated this idea via the Schauder methods to obtain very general existence theorems for integral equations

(3.1) $$y(x) + \int_{B} f(x, t, y(t))\, dt = 0$$

where y and f are n-vectors, x and t are points of a domain B in an m-dimensional space and f is continuous on $\{x \in B, t \in B, |y| \leq R\}$. On the domain y continuous and $\|y\| \leq R$ the integral in (3.1) exists, is uniformly bounded and equicontinuous. If

$$|f_i| \leq \widetilde{F}_i(x, t, |y_1|, \ldots, |y_n|)$$

where $\widetilde{F}_i$ is continuous, and increasing in the arguments $|y_1|, \ldots, |y_n|$ and

$$\| \int_B \widetilde{F}(x, t, r_1, \ldots, r_n)\, dt \| \leq r$$

whenever $r_j \geq 0$, and $\sum_{j=1}^{n} r_j = r \leq R$, then the Schauder fixed point theorem implies the existence of a solution of (3.1), continuous, and of norm $\leq R$. Rothe has made applications to equations with kernels of the form

$$f_i = K_i(x, t)\, g_i(t, y_1, \ldots, y_n)$$

and even to show the existence of continuous solutions for the single equations

$$y(t) + \int_B K(x, t)\, g(t, y(t))\, dt = 0$$

where K is absolutely integrable and

$$\int_B |K(x^*, t) - K(x, t)|\, dt \to 0, x^* \to x.$$

Rothe also goes beyond pure existence theorems into uniqueness theorems, by means of the Schauder-Leray topological methods.

In another direction, we can observe another fact about the fixed point method as we focus attention on the fact that it is a mapping of a set into itself; given a mapping it may be profitable to establish spaces on which certain desirable properties are preserved. One easy illustration of such a property is periodicity: let f(x, t) be continuous in x and t, $0 \leq x, t < \infty$, uniformly bounded by M there, and periodic, i.e. $f(x+1, t) \equiv f(x, t)$ for all x, t. Then the equation

$$F(y) = y(x) = f(x, t) + \int_{x - \frac{1}{2}t}^{x + \frac{1}{2}t} y(s)\, ds \tag{3.2}$$

can be shown to possess a continuous solution of period 1. To see this note that $F(y)$ maps the continuous periodic functions of period 1 into themselves, and the set

$$\|y\| = \max |y(x)| \leq M$$

into itself. On $\|y\| \leq M$, f is easily seen to be equicontinuous. Hence, there is a closed convex domain which F maps into a compact subset of itself. The Schauder theorem implies that (4.2) has a fixed point among the continuous functions of period 1.

Pure existence and possibly uniqueness theorems are available to us in this manner, but there is no prescription implied for finding the fixed point, or solution to our problem. We shall approach the problem from a more constructive point of view next, and shall see how narrow is the gulf between pure existence theorems of this type and constructive theorems.

Part III

4. Constructive Theorems

The usual formulation of what is known variously as the Banach fixed point theorem, or the Principle of the Contraction Mapping (among other titles) assumes that the space under consideration is a complete metric space with metric ρ. Then we have:

If a mapping F of a complete metric space R into itself satisfies, for all y and y^* in R,

$$\rho(F(y), f(y^*)) \leq \alpha \rho(y, y^*)$$

for some $\alpha < 1$, then the mapping F has one and only one fixed point y. The sequence $y_n = F(y_{n-1})$ converges to this fixed point and

$$\rho(y, y_n) \leq \alpha^n \rho(y, y_0)/(1-\alpha).$$

Thus the convergence is uniform on any sphere $\rho(y, y_0) \leq r$.

The classical proof of the existence theorem for ordinary differential equations, for Volterra integral equations, and for Fredholm equations of the second kind obtain the estimate $\alpha < 1$ from a Lipschitz condition in y uniform in t (and x) on the kernel of

$$y(x) = \int_{x_0}^{x} f(t, y(t))\, dt + y_0$$

or

$$y(x) = \int_{x_o}^{x} f(x, t, y(t))\, dt + y_o(x)$$

or

$$y(x) = \lambda \int_{x_o}^{x} f(x, t, y(t))\, dt + g(x) \; ;$$

in the first two cases the x range of the solution is restricted while in the third case the range of λ is restricted so as to make $\alpha < 1$. The proof and the estimates involved are essentially those of Liouville of 1837 as modified by Picard to utilize the Lipschitz condition for non-linear problems. The ideas involved are now too well known to require elaboration. Examples of the use of the method abound; see for instance [15], [23], [24], [25]. [26]. [27], and [28]. It is worth remarking that there is a relation between the Lipschitz condition and differentiability for functions of a real variable which should be kept in mind when other speakers discuss differentiability of operators. It is a theorem of Zygmund (generalized to functions of several variables by Rademacher,) that a function of a single real variable which is Lipschitz continuous is differentiable almost everywhere. The contraction property, which generalizes the Lipschitz condition of constant < 1, has not yet been shown to imply any operator differentiability of the type used, for instance, in applying Newton's method on a Banach space. But we can observe, by considering any two points, y, y^*, in R and the ray $y + \beta y^*$, that the Lipschitz property implies

$$\frac{\| F(y + \beta_1 y^*) - F(y + \beta_2 y^* \|}{\| y^* \| (\beta_2 - \beta_1)} \leq \alpha ;$$

hence we conclude the differentiability in the Gateaux sense almost everywhere along this and hence any line segment. The full nature of the relation between the contraction or Lipschitz property for operators and their differentiability (i.e., an abstract equivalent of Zygmund's theorem) remains unexplored.

Attempts to weaken the Banach fixed point theorem abound in the literature; the nature of the desired weakenings is always such as to retain the convergence of successive approximations to a unique solution of the functional equation; i.e., to stay this side of the Schauder fixed point theorem plus uniqueness. One of the earliest extensions, frequently rediscovered, (cf. e.g. [68]), is due to

Caccioppoli [7]. In 1930 he remarked that it is possible to replace the role of the contraction property in the proof of convergence of the Neumann series by the assumption of that convergence. His formulation is as follows.

Let F map a complete metric space R into itself in such a way that

$$\rho(F(y), F(y^*)) \leq \|F\| \rho(y, y^*) .$$

Let $F^n(y) = F(F^{n-1}(y))$. Suppose that $\sum_{n=1}^{\infty} \|F^n\| < \infty$. Then the sequence $y_{n+1} = F^n(y_1)$ converges to $y = F(y)$ and

$$\rho(y, y_{n+1}) \leq \sum_{j=n+1}^{\infty} \|F^j\| \rho(y, y_1)$$

If $\|F\| < 1$, this is the Banach fixed point theorem. This theorem has been applied by Caccioppoli [7] and Scorza-Dragoni [60] to integral equations, including the Hammerstein equation. The quantity of weakening is not great; the method still converges uniformly in any sphere about the fixed point.

Krasnoselskii [32] has joined the Schauder and Banach fixed point theorems into one overall statement.

Mann [44] has explored linear averaging: i.e., given an infinite triangular matrix (a_{ij}) such that $\sum_{j=1}^{i} a_{ij} = 1$, $a_{ij} \to 0$, $i \to \infty$; then the convergence of $y_{n+1} = F(y_n)$ and of $\sum_{k=1}^{n+1} a_{n+1,k} y_k = F(\sum_{k=1}^{n} a_{n,k} y_k)$ are equivalent facts. Other generalizations include [1], [2], [48], and [72].

Kantorovitch [19], and later Schroder [58, 59], have generalized the method in a different direction, that of the distance concept. Instead of a complete metric space, for instance, Schroder considers a mapping ρ from $R \times R$ into a partially ordered linear space N such that $\rho \geq 0$ and

$$\rho(F(y), F(y^*)) \leq P \rho(y, y^*)$$

where P is possibly nonlinear positive operator. If the Neumann series $\sum_{i=1}^{\infty} P^i \rho = (I - P)^{-1} \rho$ converges for every $\rho \epsilon N$ and if F maps some complete subspace R^* of R containing y_1 into itself, then the successive approximations $y_n = F(y_{n-1})$ converge to a solution $y = F(y)$ in R^*. If R^* is the set in R such that $r \epsilon R^*$ implies

$$\rho(r, y_2) \leq (I - P)^{-1} P \rho(y_2, y_1)$$

then the fixed point satisfies

$$\rho(y, y_2) \leq (I - P)^{-1} P \rho(y_2, y_1) .$$

Schroder has used this theorem to obtain many error bounds for approximate methods in numerical work, and for integral equations [59]. Kantorovich had also worked with such concepts earlier in a slightly different formulation, dealing with monotone majorant operators whose oscillation majorizes the oscillation of F. He used the ideas, among other ways, to prove the Cauchy-Picard existence theorem for systems of ordinary differential equations and also to give the Cauchy majorant proof for analytic differential equations.

Part IV

5. Nonuniform Approach

In 1945-6 Dieudonné and Wintner independently remarked that for the case of ordinary differential equations, the convergence of the successive approximations can be freed from the uniformity on which we have been dwelling above. The price of this freedom is the loss of estimates of the rate of convergence of the successive approximations. The method of Wintner to show in fact has become the source of numerous generalizations to Volterra integral equations, and partial differential equations; we shall consider this method and its generalizations.

Wintner considered the Osgood uniqueness theorem; suppose then that $f(x, y)$ is continuous on $|x - x_0| \leq a$, $|y - y_0| \leq b$ and that

$$|f(x, y) - f(x, y^*)| \leq \phi(|y - y^*|)$$

for all x, y, y^* in the domain, where $\phi(r)$ is a continuous monotone nondecreasing function on $r \geq 0$ such that

$$(5.1) \qquad \int_{\epsilon} \frac{dr}{\phi(r)} \to \infty , \quad \epsilon \to 0 .$$

For a fixed initial function $y_1(x)$ satisfying $y_1(x_0) = y_0$, we consider the successive approximations

$$y_n(x) = y_0 + \int_{x_0}^{x} f(t, y_{n-1}(t))\,dt$$

and the functions

$$\omega(x) = \limsup_{n\to\infty} |y_{n+1}(x) - y_n(x)|$$

and

$$|\Delta\,\omega(x)| = \omega(x+\Delta) - \omega(x) .$$

Since $y_n(x)$ is uniformly bounded and equicontinuous, $\omega(x)$ is continuous and an easy calculation shows

$$(5.2) \qquad |\Delta\omega| \le \int_{x_0}^{x} \phi(\omega(t))\,dt$$

From (5.2) we infer the absolute continuity of ω and the differential inequality

$$\frac{|d\omega|}{\phi(\omega)} \le dx$$

which violates (5.1) unless $\Delta\omega \equiv 0$. But $\omega(0) = 0$, and so $\omega \equiv 0$.

The key to the argument is the fact that $\omega(x)$ satisfies an integral inequality which has no solution other than the identically zero solution. This provides an essentially new tool for the investigation of existence and uniqueness via successive approximations, majorizing by equations with unique solutions. It is worth rephrasing somewhat, in order to relate the very analytic approach to more general ideas. Suppose as well that $\phi = \phi(x, |y - y^*|)$, the constraint on the oscillation depends upon x as well. Then by the monotonicity of ϕ as a function of its second variable we conclude

$$\delta_k(x) = \text{l.u.b}_{n\ge k} |y_{n+1}(x) - y_n(x)|$$

$$\le \int_{x_0}^{x} \phi(t, \text{l.u.b.}_{n\ge k-1} |y_{n+1}(t) - y_n(t)|)\,dt .$$

Since δ_k is a nonincreasing positive sequence (of equicontinuous functions) it converges to a limit function $\delta(x)$ and

$$(5.2') \qquad 0 \leq \delta(x) \leq \int_{x_0}^{x} \phi(t, \delta(t))\, dt .$$

Any condition which guarantees that the equation

$$(5.3) \qquad \eta(x) = \int_{x_0}^{x} \phi(t, \eta(t))\, dt$$

has as its only solution $\eta \equiv 0$ can be used to imply uniqueness for $y' = f(x, y)$ as follows. If we consider (6.3) as a functional equation $\eta = \widetilde{F}(\eta)$, and consider successive approximations with $\eta_\phi = \alpha$, then, since ϕ is increasing, we conclude $\eta_n \geq \eta_{n-1} \geq 0$; on any interval on which ϕ is bounded, the η_n are uniformly bounded, and hence η_n converges monotonely to a solution η of (5.3). But the only solution is zero, so $0 \leq \delta \leq \eta \equiv 0$, which implies $\delta \equiv 0$. This implies many results to be found in the literature.

This reworking of the proof is suggested by a proof by Sacksteder quoted in a paper of Shanahan [67]. Shanahan applies the idea in a two-dimensional form to obtain uniqueness, existence, and the convergence of successive approximations for the partial differential equation

$$z_{xy} = f(x, y, z, z_x z_y) ,$$

$$z(x,0) = \sigma(x), \quad z(0, y) = \tau(y) ,$$

where

$$\sigma(0) = \tau(0) = z_0 ,$$

on $0 \leq x \leq a$, $0 \leq y \leq b$, provided that σ and τ are Lipschitz continuous and f is bounded for all z, z_x, z_y and x and y in their intervals, while

$$|f(x, y, x, p, q) - f(x, y, z^*, p^*, q^*)| \leq \phi(x, y, |z-z^*| |p-p^*|, |q-q^*|).$$

Here $\phi = \phi(x, y, \delta_1, \delta_2, \delta_3)$ is a continuous function on $0 \leq x \leq 0$, $0 \leq y \leq b$, $0 \leq \delta_1$, $0 \leq \delta_2$, $0 \leq \delta_3$, nondecreasing in δ_1, δ_2, and δ_3 and such that

$$(5.4) \qquad \eta(x, y) = \int_0^x \int_0^y \phi(s, t, \eta(s, t), \eta_x(s, t), \eta_y(s, t))\, ds\, dt$$

has only the zero solution $\eta \equiv 0$, on some rectangle $0 \leq x \leq a' \leq a$, $0 \leq y \leq b' \leq b$. (Shanahan also obtains an analogue of the proof that Nagumo-like uniqueness criteria imply convergence of the successive approximations.) In two dimensions the role of the inequality (5.2') is replaced by a vector inequality

$$\delta_1(x, y) \leq \int_0^x \int_0^y \phi(s, t, \delta_1, \delta_2, \delta_3)\, ds\, dt,$$

$$\delta_2(x, y) \leq \int_0^y \phi(s, t, \delta_1, \delta_2, \delta_3)\, dt,$$

$$\delta_3(x, y) \leq \int_0^x \phi(s, t, \delta_1, \delta_2, \delta_3)\, ds.$$

This area is to be related to the work of Kantorovich and Schroder mentioned above; clearly we are constructing in (5.2') a monotone majorant for f along successive approximations. Other applications of these ideas to Volterra Integral Equations are to be found in papers of Sato [53, 54, 55] and to Partial Differential Equations of the same type as those Shanahan considers in the papers of Walter [64, 65, 66, 67], Conti [10], and Guglielmino [16], (who also provides a Peano-type existence proof.) An extension to third order equations is found in [33].

6. Abstract Uniqueness, Existence And Convergence Of Successive Approximations

These analytic devices may be related to the ideas of Kantorovitch and Schroder [58, 59] on operators on partially ordered spaces in the following manner:

We will use a partially ordered space of the following sort: it is a real normed linear vector space R containing a set K closed under addition and multiplication by real nonnegative scalars. Two elements x and y in R are said to be ordered if $y - x \in K$, and we write $x \prec y$. We will assume that the ordering has the following properties for elements of K:

i) For any finite set $x_1, \dots, x_k$ in R there exists an element y in R such that $x_i \prec y$, $i = 1, \dots, k$ while $x_i \prec z$, $i = 1, \dots, k$ implies $y \prec z$. We will call y "$\sup_k[x_k]$;"

ii) If $x_n \prec y_n$ for all n and $x_n \to x, y_n \to y$ in the norm topology as $n \to \infty$ then $x \prec y$;

iii) If $0 \prec x \prec y$ then $\|x\| < \|y\|$;

iv) If x_n is an infinite sequence with $x_n \prec x_{n+1} \cdots$ while $\|x_n\| \leq M$ for all n, then there is an element x to which x_n converges in the norm topology.

It is clear that it is both necessary and sufficient for i, ..., iv) to hold on R that they hold on K.

Given an arbitrary Banach space E, Schroder calls it R-metrized by the R-metric ρ provided that there exists a continuous function ρ on $E \times E$ into the positive cone K of R which satisfies

1°) $\rho(x, y) = 0$ if and only if $x = y$;

2°) $\rho(x, y) = \rho(y, x)$;

3°) $\rho(x, y) \prec \rho(x, z) + \rho(z, y)$.

3° will not actually be used below; we require only an R-valuation, ρ. We shall now provide uniqueness and existence theorems for mapping of E into E.

Uniqueness Theorem: Let F be a mapping of E into E satisfying

$$\rho(F(x), F(y)) \prec \Phi(\rho(x, y))$$

for all x, y in E, where Φ is a continuous mapping of K into K which satisfies

A) $\|\Phi(\rho)\| \leq M$ for all $\rho \in K$;

B) $\rho_1 \prec \rho_2$ implies $\Phi(\rho_1) \prec \Phi(\rho_2)$;

C) $\Phi(\rho) = \rho$ if and only if $\rho = 0$.

Then F has at most one fixed point.

Existence Theorem: Under the same hypotheses, the sequence defined by

$$x_n = F(x_{n-1})$$

converges, for arbitrary initial x_0, to a fixed point of F.

It is useful for ease of comprehension to break the proof up in the manner indicated by the statement of the theorems.

Proof of the uniqueness theorem: Suppose in fact that $F(x_1) = x_1$, $F(x_2) = x_2$ with $x_1 \neq x_2$. Then $\rho(x_1, x_2) \neq 0$ while

$$0 \prec \rho(x_1, x_2) = \rho(F(x_1), F(x_2)) \prec \Phi(\rho(x_1, x_2)).$$

Consider now the sequence defined by $\rho_1 = \rho(x_1, x_2) \neq 0$, $\rho_n = \Phi(\rho_{n-1})$. From B) and $\rho_1 \prec \Phi(\rho_1)$ we obtain $\rho_n \prec \rho_{n+1}$ for all n. On the other hand $\|\rho_n\| = \|\Phi(\rho_{n-1})\| \leq M$. By assumption iv) on K, this implies that ρ_n converges in the norm topology. Since Φ is continuous, the limit ρ satisfies $\rho = \Phi(\rho) \neq 0$. This is impossible, so we must have $\rho(x_1, x_2) = 0$, whence $x_1 = x_2$.

Proof of the existence theorem: Fix x_0 and consider the resultant sequence of successive approximations x_n. Set $\rho_{n,m} = \rho(x_n, x_m)$ and

$$\eta_{n,N} = \sup_{n \leq m \leq M+N} [\rho_{n,m}] .$$

Then it is easy to see that $\eta_{n,N} \prec \eta_{n,N+1}$. Using (iii) (for the first time,) we see that since

$$\rho_{n,m} = \rho(x_n, x_m) = \rho(F(x_{n-1}), F(x_{m-1})) \prec \Phi(\rho(x_{n-1}, x_{m-1})),$$

then

$$\|\rho_{n,m}\| \leq M$$

and so

$$\|\eta_{n,N}\| \leq M .$$

But $\eta_{n,N} \prec \eta_{n,N+1}$. Thus $\lim_{N\to\infty} \eta_{n,N} = \eta_n$ exists in K. It is easy to see by comparing $\eta_{n,N}$ with $\eta_{n+1,N-1}$ that $\eta_n \succ \eta_{n+1}$. Thus η_n is a decreasing sequence in K. This makes $\eta_1 - \eta_n$ an increasing sequence in K and uniformly bounded in norm by $2M$. Hence $\lim_{n\to\infty} \eta_n = \eta$ exists in K. Suppose that $\eta \neq 0$. From $\rho_{n,m} \prec \Phi(\rho_{n-1,m-1})$, the definition of sup, and the monotonicity of Φ we see that

$$\eta_{n,N} \prec \Phi(\eta_{n-1,N}) ;$$

the continuity of Φ implies

$$\eta_n \prec \Phi(\eta_{n-1})$$

and again

$$\eta \prec \Phi(\eta) .$$

If η is not zero, we may repeat the argument of the proof of the uniqueness theorem to imply the existence of a fixed point of Φ which is not 0. Thus we see that η must vanish. But for all $m \geq n$ we have

$$0 \prec \rho_{n,m} \prec \eta_n$$

while $\|\eta_n\| \to 0$, $n \to \infty$. Thus $\|\rho_{n,m}\| \to 0$, $n, m \to \infty$. We conclude $\|x_n - x_m\| \to 0$, $n, m \to \infty$, from the continuity of ρ. (Note that assumption $3°$ in the definition of the R-metric plays no role in the proofs.)

These theorems contain for example the Shanahan theorem [61], those of the Coddington-Levinson theorems [9], which utilize monotone majorants, the Dieudonné theorem [14], the Wintner theorem [70], and others such as [33] as special cases and can be used for multidimensional integral equations both of the Volterra type and of the type involving fixed domains of integration.

However, there exist as yet certain analytic uniqueness and convergence of successive approximation theorems which are not so contained in abstract theorems. A paper of Brauer and Sternberg [4] in fact provides an example of a uniqueness condition which does not imply convergence of the successive approximations. The authors assume the existence of a continuously differentiable function $V(x, y)$ vanishing if and only if $y = 0$ and uniformly bounded, such that

$$V_x[x, y-y^*] + V_y \cdot [f(x, y) - f(x, y^*)] \leq \omega[x, V[x, y-y^*]] \tag{6.1}$$

where $\omega \geq 0$, and $r' = \omega(t, r)$ has a unique solution vanishing at $t = 0$, such that $r'(+0) = 0$, namely $r \equiv 0$. They show that this implies uniqueness for equations $y' = f(x, y)$ for which successive approximations do not converge. They give a sufficient condition for convergence of successive approximations.

$$V[x, \int_{x-h}^{x} [f(t, y) - f(t, y^*)]\, dt)] \leq \int_{x-h}^{x} \{V_x[t, y-y^*]$$

$$+ V_y[t, y-y^*] \cdot [f(t, y) - f(t, y^*)]\}\, dt .$$

which is the analogue of (5.2') after insertion in (6.1). Here V plays the role of the valuation ρ in the theorem given above. However, the monotonocity required of the mapping Φ above is not the tool for the proof of uniqueness and convergence of successive approximations; the burden is carried in this case by the linear ordering of the real number. This linear ordering allows one to pass from a differential inequality $u' \leq \omega(x, u)$ with u not identically zero to the existence of a non-zero fixed point (solution of the equation) which lies in the interval $[0, u(x)]$ for all sufficiently small x. This is the reverse of the direction in which we go when we reach the contradiction above. It is not yet known what hypotheses on the mapping Φ will guarantee the passage from

$$0 \prec \eta \prec \Phi(\eta) \tag{6.2}$$

to

$$0 \prec \rho = \Phi(\rho) \neq 0. \tag{6.3}$$

It is not, however, the requirement that ρ be an R-metric which is the trouble; in particular condition 3° was never used in the proofs of this section. Thus these criteria of Brauer and Sternberg do not fit into any abstract scheme currently available.

It is easy to make other hypotheses about Φ which are equivalent to the desired passage from (6.2) to (6.3) but it seems hard to find hypotheses which translate, in concrete problems, to new existence and uniqueness theorems. For instance the hypothesis

$$\Phi(\rho) \prec \rho, \qquad \rho \in K,$$

which corresponds to a Lipschitz condition of constant ≤ 1, together with (6.2) implies

$$\eta = \Phi(\eta)$$

and the desired contradiction.

BIBLIOGRAPHY I

1. Bahtin, I. A. and Krasnoselskii, M. A., On the theory of equations with concave operators. Dokl. Akad. Nauk. SSSR 123 (1958), 17-20 (Russian).

2. Block, H. D., Construction of solutions and propagation of errors in nonlinear problems. Proc. Amer. Math. Soc. 4, 715-722 (1953).

3. Bendixson, I. O., Sur la convergence uniform des séries. Stock. Ofv. 54 (1897) 605-622.

4. Brauer, F. and Sternberg, S., Local uniqueness, existence in the large, and the convergence of successive approximations. Amer. J. Math. 80 (1958) 421-430.

5. Brauer, Fred, A note on uniqueness and convergence of successive approximations. Canad. Math. Bull 2 (1959) 5-8.

6. Brauer, Fred, Some results on uniqueness and successive approximations. Canad. J. Math. 11 (1959) 527-533.

7. Caccioppoli, R., Un teorema generale sull'esistenza di elementi uniti in una traetor-maxione funzionale. Atti. Accad. Naz. Lincei. Rend. Ci. Csi. Fis. Mat. Nat. (6) 11 (1930) 794-799.

8. Caccioppoli, R., Sugli elementi uniti delle transformazioni funzionali, Rendiconti del Sem. Mat. Padova 3 (1932) 1-15.

9. Coddington, E. A. and Levinson, N., Uniqueness and convergence of successive approximations. Jour. Indian Math. Soc. (N. S.) 16 (1952), 75-81.

10. Conti, Roberto. Sull'equazione integrodifferenziale di Darboux-Picard. Matematiche (Catania) 13 (1958) 30-39.

11. Diaz, J. B., On an analogue of the Euler-Cauchy polygon method for the numerical solution of $u_{xy} = f(x, y, u, u_x, u_y)$. Archive for Rat. Mech. Anal. 1 (1958), 357-390.

12. Diaz, J. B., On existence, uniqueness and numerical evaluation of solutions of ordinary and hyperbolic equations. Symposium on the numerical treatment of ordinary differential Equations, Int. and Integro-differential equations, Rome (1960) 581-602.

13. Dinghas, A., Zur existenz von fixpunkten bei abbildungen vom Abel-Liouvilleschen typus. Math. Z. **70** (1958) 174-189.

14. Dieudonné, Sur la convergence des approximations successives, Bull. Sci. Math. (2) **69** (1945) 62-72.

15. Foures-Bruhat, Y., Theoreme d'existence pour certains systemes d'equations aux derivees partielles non linearies. Acta. Math. **88** (1952) 141-225.

16. Guglielmino, Francesco, Sulla Risoluzione dei problema di Darboux per l'equazione $r = f(x, y, z)$. Boll. Un. Mat. Ital. (3) **13** (1958) 308-318.

17. Hildebrandt, T. H. and Graves, L. M., Implicit functions and their differentials in general analysis. Trans. Amer. Math. Soc. **29** (1922) 127-153.

18. Husty, Zdenek, Uber einige eigenschaften der Picards-Folgen. Mat. Fyz. Casopis. Slovensk. AKAD. Vied. **8** (1958) 7-19 (Czech.)

19. Kantorovitch, L. V., The method of successive approximations for functional equations. Acta. Math. **71** (1939) pp. 63-97.

20. Kantorovitch, L. V., Some further applications of the principle of majorants. Doklady Akad. Nauk. SSSR. (N. S.) **80** (1951) 849-852.

21. Kantorovich, L. V., Functional analysis and applied mathematics. Nat. Bur. of Stand., Los. Angeles, Calif. NBS Rep. 1509, ii + 202 pp. (1952).

22. Kantorovich, L. V., Vulih, B. Z., and Pinsker, A. G., Functional analysis in partially ordered spaces. Gosudarstu. Izdat. Tehn-Teor. Lit., Moscow-Leningrad. (1950). 548 pp. (Russian)

23. Kisynski, Jan, Sur l'existence des solutions d'un probleme de Mlle. Z. Szmydt relatif a l'equation $\partial^2 z/\partial x \partial y = f(x, y, z, \partial z/x, \partial z/\partial y)$. (Polish and Russian summaries). Ann. Univ. Mariae Curie-Sklodowska Sect. A **12** (1958) 67-109.

24. Kisynski, Jan., Sur le probleme de Picard pour l'equation hyperbolique aux derivees partielles du second order (Polish and Russian summaries) Ann. Univ. Mariae Curie-Sklodowska Sect. A. **13** (1959) 5-24.

25. Kisynski, Jan, Remarque sur l'existence des solutions en large de l'equation

$$\partial^2 z/\partial x\partial y = f(x_1 y_1 z_1 \partial z/\partial x, \ \partial z/\partial y).$$

(Polish and Russian summaries) Ann. Univ. Mariae Curie-Sklodowska Sect. A. 13 (1959) 25-32.

26. Kisynski, J., Sur la convergence des approximations successives pour l'equation

$$\frac{\partial^2 z}{\partial x \partial y} = f(x, y, z, \frac{\partial z}{\partial x}, \frac{\partial z}{y})$$

Ann. Polon. Math. 7 (1960), 233-240.

27. Kisynski, J., Sur les equations differentielles dans les espaces de Banach. Bull. Acad. Polon. Sci. Ser. Sci. Math. Astr. Phys. 7 (1959) 381-385.

28. Koselev, A. I., Convergence of the method of successive approximations for quasi-linear elliptic equations. (Russian). Dokl. Akad. Nauk SSSR 142 (1962), 1007-1010.

29. Kooi, O., The method of successive approximations and a uniqueness theorem of Krasnoselskii and Krein in the theory of differential equations. Nederl. Akad. Weten Sch. Proc. Ser. A 61 = Indag. Math. 20 (1958) 322-327.

30. Krasnoselskii, M. A. J. and Krein, S. G., On a class of uniqueness theorems for the equation $y' = f(x, y)$. Uspehi Mat. Nauk (NS.) 11 (1956) No. 1 (67) 204-213.

31. Krasnoselskii, M. A., Some problems of nonlinear analysis. Uspehi. Mat. Nauk (NS.) 9 (1954), No. 3 (61), 57-114.(Russian)

32. Krasnoselskii, M. A., Two remarks on the method of successive approximations. Usephi Mat. Nauk. (NS.) 10, No. 1 (63), (1955). 123-127. (Russian)

33. Kwadisz, H., Palczewski, B, and Pawelski, W., Sur l'existence et l'unicite des solutions de certaines equations differentielles du type

$$u_{xyz} = f(x_1 y_1 z_1 u, u_x, u_z, u_{xy}, u_{yz}, u_{xz})$$

Ann. Polon. Math. 11 (1961) 75-106.

34. Lamson, K. W., A general implicit function theorem with an application to problems of relative minima, Amer. J. Math. 42 (1920) 243-256.

35. LaSalle, J., Uniqueness theorems and successive approximation. Annals of Math. 50 (1949), 722-730.

36. Lindelöf, E., Sur l'application des methodes d'approximate successive a l'etude des integral neel de equations differentielles ordinaires, Jour. de Math. Pures et appliquees, Ser. 4 10 (1894) 117-128.

37. Liouville, J., Sur le development des fonctions ou parties de fonctions en séries dont les divers terms sont assujetti à satisfaire à une même équation différentielle du second ordre contenant un paramètre variable. J. de Math. (1) 2 (1937) 16-35.

38. Liouville, J., Sur la theore des équations différentielles lineaires et sur le development des fonctions en series. J. de Math. (1) 3 (1838) 561-614.

39. Lipschitz, R., Lehrbuch der analysis, Bonn (1877).

40. Luxemburg, W. A. J., On the convergence of successive approximations in the theory of ordinary differential equations. Canad. Math. Bull. 1 (1958) 9-20.

41. Luxemburg, W. A. J., On the convergence of successive approximations in the theory of ordinary differential equations II. Nederl. Akad. Wetensch. Proc. Ser. A 61 Indag. Math. 20 (1958) 540-546.

42. Luxemburg, W. A. J., On the convergence of successive approximations in the theory of ordinary differential equations III. Nieww. Arch. Wisk. (3) 6 (1958) 93-98.

43. Mann, W. Robert, Mean value methods in iteration. Proc. Amer. Math. Soc. 4, (1953) 506-510.

44. Miranda, Carlo, Problemi di esistenza in analisi funzionale. Scuola Normale Superiore, Pisa. (1950).

45. Moigno, F., Lecons sur le calcul différential et intégral (d'après Cauchy) Vol. 2, Paris (1844).

46. Nagumo, Mitio, Uber das Verfahren der Sukzessiven Approximationen Fur integration gewohn icher differential gleichungen und die eindeutigkeit ihrer integrale. Jap. Jour. Math. 7 (1930) 143-160.

47. Nevanlinna, Rolf, Uber die methode der sukzessiven approximationen. Ann. Acad. Sci. Fenn. Ser. A. I. No. 291 (190).

48. Peano, G., Démonstration de l'intégrabilité des équations différentielles ordinaires., Math. Ann. 37 (1890) 182-228.

49. Picard, E., Memoire sur la theorie des equations aux derivees partielles et la methode des approximations successives. J. de Math. (4) 6 (1890) 145-210.

50. Picard, E., Sur l'application des methods d'approximations successives a l'etude de certaines equations differentielles ordinaires., J. de Math. (4) 9 (1893) 217-271.

51. Rosenblatt, A., Uber die existenz von integralen gewohnlicher differential gleichungen. Arkiv for Mathematik, Astronomi och Fysik, Vol. 5, No. 2 (1909) 1-4.

52. Rothe, E., Zur theorie der topologischen ordung und der vektor felder in Banach schen raumen, Compositio Mathematica 5 (1937), 177-197.

53. Sato, Tokui, Sur l'equation integrale non-lineaire de Volterra. Composito Math. 11 (1953) 271-290.

54. Sato, Tokui, Sur l'application qui fait correspondre a une courbe une famille de courbes. Proc. Japan Acad. 31 (1955) 1-4.

55. Sato, Tokui, and Iwasaki, Akira, Sur l'equation integrale de Volterra. Proc. Japan Acad. 31 (1955), 395-398.

56. Schaefer, Helmut, Zur theorie nichtlinearer integralgleichungen. Math. Nachr. 11 (1954) 193-211.

57. Schauder, F., Der fixpunktsatz in funktionalraumen. Studia Math. (2) 1930.

58. Schroder, Johann, Das iterationsverfahren bei allgemeinerem abstandsbegriff. Math. Zeit. 66 (1956), 111-166.

59. Schroder, J., Nichtlineare Majoranten beim verfahren der schrittweisen naherung. Arch. Math. 7 (1957), 471-484.

60. Scorza-Dragoni, G., Sur Sistemi di Equazioni Integral Nonlineari. Rend. Del. Sem. Mat. Padova 7 (1930) 1-35.

61. Shanahan, John P., On uniqueness questions for hyperbolic differential equations. Pac. J. Math. 10 (1960) 677-688.

62. Van Kampen, E. R., Notes on systems of ordinary differential equations, Amer. J. Math., 63 (1941) 371-376.

63. Viswanatham, B., The general uniqueness theorem and successive approximations, J. of the Indian Math. Soc. 5 (1951) 69-73.

64. Walter, Wolfgang, Uber die differential gleichung $u_{xy} = f(x, y, u, u_x, u_y)$ I. Math. Zeit. 71 (1959) 308-324.

65. Walter, Wolfgang, Uber die differential gleichung $u_{xy} = f(x, y, u, u_x, u_y)$ II. Math. Zeit. 71 (1959) 436-453.

66. Walter, Wolfgang, Uber die differential gleichung $u_{xy} = f(x, y, u, u_x, u_y)$ III. Math. Zeit. 72 (1960) 268-279.

67. Walter, Wolfgang, Eindeutigkeitssatze fur gewohnliche, parabolische und hyperbolische differential gleichungen, Math.Zeit 74 (1960) 191-208.

68. Weissinger, Johannes, Sur theorie und anwendung des iterationsverfahrens. Math. Nach. 8 (1952) 193-212.

69. Wintner, A., The nonlocal existence problem of ordinary differential equations. Am. J. Math., 67 (1945) 277-284.

70. Wintner, A., On the convergence of successive approximations, Am. J. Math., 68 (1940) 13-19.

71. Yeh, J., Nonlinear Volterra functional equations and linear parabolic differential equations. Trans. Amer. Math. Soc. 95 (1960) 488-432.

72. Zitarosa, Antonio, Sulle equazioni funzionali di Volterra-Tonelli. Richerche Mat. 3, 108-126 (1954).

73. Zdanov, G. M., On the location of Picard approximations relative to an unknown solution of the equation $y^{(n)} = f(x, y)$. (Russian) Issled. Po. Mat. Analizui Mehanike V. Uzbekistane, pp. 127-132. Izdat. Akad. Nauk. Uzbek, SSSR, Tashkent 1960.

BIBLIOGRAPHY II

1. Abian, S. and Brown, A. B., "On the Solution of the Differential Equation $f(x,y,y') = 0$", Amer. Math. Monthly 60 (1959)192-199.

2. Abian, S. and Brown, A. B., "On the Solution of the Differential Equation $f(x,y,y^{(\prime)},\ldots,y^{(n)}) = 0$", Boll. Un. Mat. Ital. (3) 13 (1958), 383-394.

3. Abian, S. and Brown, A. B., "On the Solution of an Implicit First Order Partial Differential Equation", Rend. Circo. Mat. Palermo (2) 8 (1959), 271-296.

4. Abian, S. and Brown, A. B., "On the Solution of Simultaneous First Order Implicit Differential Equations, Math. Ann. 137, (1959), 9-16.

5. Bihari, I., "A generalization of a Lemma of Bellman and its Application to Uniqueness Problems of Differential Equations," Acta. Math. Acad. Sci. Hungar, 7 (1956), 81-94.

6. Baĭčorov, H. Ya., "Plane Parallel Flow of an Ideal Incompressible Liquid about a Porous Circular Cylinder with linear and Quadratic Law of Filtration", Vestnik Moskov Univ. Ser. Fiz-Mat. Estest. Nauk (1952), No. 8, 73-87. (Russian).

7. Dolidze, D. E., "On the existence of solutions of the nonlinear problem of Hydrodynamics", Bull. Acad. Sci. Georgian SSSR (4) (1943) 11-16 (Russian).

8. Dolidze, D. E., "Solution of Prandtl's Equation of the Non-stationary boundary Layer", Bull. Acad. Sci. Georgian SSSR (4) (1944) 867-876.

9. Ešukov, L. N., "On a Function Problem for ODE," Uspekhi. Mat. Nauk, (N. S.) 13 No. 3(81) (1958) 191-196.

10. Èbanoidze, T. A., "On a Clàss of Nonlinear Integral Equations", Soobšč. Akad. Nauk. Gruzin SSSR 15, (1954) 7-12 (Russian).

11. Egorov, A. I., "Existence Theorem for the Solution of an Integro-Differential Equation", Kirgiz. Gos. Univ. Trudy Fiz. Mat. Fak. (1953) No. 2, 119-123 (Russian).

12. Franchini, Lucia, "Un Problema al Limiti per una Particolare Classe di Equazioni Integro-differenziali", Ann. Univ. Ferrara, Sez. VII (N.S.) 3 (1954) 75-91.

13. Gagaev, B. M., "Existence Theorems for Solutions of Integro-Differential Equations," Doklady Akad. Nauk SSSR (N.S.) 85, (1952) 469-472 (Russian).

14. Guseǐnov, A. I., "On a Class of Nonlinear Integral Equations", Akad. Nauk. Azerbaidzan SSSR. Trudy Inst. Fiz. Mat. 4-5 (1952) 20-23, (Russian. Azerbaijani Summary).

15. Harazov, D. F., "Application of the Method of Successive Approximations to the Solution of some Functional Equations." Soobščeniya Akad. Nauk. Gruzin. SSSR 12, (1951) 3-9 (Russian).

16. Ko, Dya-Ha, "Über die existenz und Eindeutigkeit der Lösungen von Integro-differential Gleichungen." J. Chinese Math. Soc. 2, (1953), 275-278. (Chinese, Russian Summary).

17. Laasonen, Pentti, "Bemerkung Zur Iterativen Losung der Eigenwertaufgabe Einer Vektor Differential Gleichung," Ann. Acad. Sci. Fenn. Ser. A. I. No. 230 (1956) 8 pp.

18. Latterman, Karl, "Über die Nichtexistenz Periodischer Lösungen in der Nahe der Kritischen Kreise", Math. Ann. 121 (1950) 327-339.

19. Lotkin, Mark, "The Solution by Iteration of Nonlinear Integral Equations", J. Math. Phys. 33, (1955), 346-355.

20. Maǐorov, I. V., "Approximate Solutions of Equations of Elliptic Type", Izv. Vysš. Učebn. Zaved. Matematika (1958) No. 3(4) 160-162.

21. Mann, W. R., and Balckburn, J. F., "A Nonlinear Steady State Temperature Problem", Proc. AMS, 5, (1954) 979-980.

22. Merli, Luigi, "Esistenza e Unicita Degli Integrali di un'Equazione Alle Derivate Parziali della Forma

$$X_1(x_1, \ldots, x_n)\frac{\partial z}{\partial x_1} + \ldots + X_n(x_1, \ldots, x_n)\frac{\partial z}{\rho x_n} = f(x_1, \ldots, x_n z)"$$

Ann. Mat. Pura. Appl. (4) 46 (1958), 98-107.

23. Mlak, W., "Parabolic Differential Inequalities and Chaplighin's Method", Ann. Polon. Math. 8 (1960), 139-153.

24. Moser, Jurgen, "A New Technique for the Construction of Solutions of Nonlinear Differential Equations", Proc. Nat. Acad. Sic., USA 47 (1961), 1824-1831.

25. Musina, S. S., "Approximate Solution of a Class of Nonlinear Integral Equations", Mat. Sbornik, N. S. 27 (60) (1950), 171-174.

26. Navarro - Borrás, F. Conferencia Sobre la Teoria de las Ecuaciones Integrales (Lineles y No-Lineales), Consejo Superior de Investigaciones Cientificas, Madrid (1942).

27. Nazarov, N. N., "On One Class of Homogeneous Nonlinear Integral Equations", Acta (Trudy) Univ. Asiae Mediae Servia Fase, 28 12 pp (1939) (Russian).

28. Olech, L., "A Connection Between Two Certain Methods of Successive Approximations in Differential Equations", Ann. Palon. Math., 11 (1962), 237-245.

29. Panferov, V. M., "On the Convergence of a Method of Elastic Solutions for the Problem of Elastic-Plastic Bending of a Plate", Akad. Nauk. SSSR Prikl. Mat. Meh. 16, (1952) 195-212 (Russian).

30. Picone, M., "Sull'equazione Integrale Non Lineare di Volterra", Ann. Di Mat. Pura ed App. (4), 49 (1962) 1-10.

31. Picone, M., "Sull'equazione integrale non lineare di Seconda Speciedi Fredholm", Math. Zeit. 74 (1960), 119-128.

32. Picone, M., "Nuove determinazioni Concernenti l'equazione Integrale Non Lineare di Volterra", Ann. Mat. Pura Appl. (4) 50 (1960), 97-113.

33. Picone, M., "Sur les Equations Intégrales Lineaire de Deuxieme Espace de Volterra avec noyau de Translation", C. R. Acad. Sci. Paris 250 (1960, 46-48.

34. Pogorzelski, W., "Sur l'équation Intégrale Non Linéarie de Seconde Espece à Forte Singularité", Ann. Polon. Math., 1 (1954) 138-148.

35. Richard, Ubaldo-Breve Ricerca, "Sulla Risolubilita dell'equazione Integrale non Lineare

$$\phi(x) + \lambda \int_0^a k(x_1 y)\, \phi^n(y)\, dy = f(x)$$

Atti. Accad. Sci. Torino. Cl. Sci. Fis. Mat. Nat. (1943) 293-311.

36. Sadowska, D., "Sur Une Equation Intégro-Differentielle de la Théorie de la Conductibility", Ann. Polon. Math. 7 (1959) 81-92.

37. Sobolevskii, P. E., "Approximate Mathods of Solving Differential Equations in Banach Space", Dokl. Akad. Nauk. SSSR (N. S.) 115 (1957) 240-243.

38. Solodovnikov, V. V., "On an Application of Operational Calculus to Dynamical Systems with Varying Parameters", Izvestia Akad. Nauk. SSSR (1945) 1203-1212 (Russian).

39. Slezkin, N. A., "Plane Flow of an Ideal Fluid about a Gas-Filled Shell", Moskov, Cos. Univ. Učenye Zapiski 152 Mehanika 3, (1951), 61-75.

40. Wild, E., "On Boltzmann's Equation in the Kinetic Theory of Gases", Proc. Camb. Phil. Soc., 47 (1951) 602-609.

41. Wittich, Hans, "Konvergenzbetrachtung zum Abbildungsverfahren von Theodorsen-Garrick", Math. Ann. 122, (1950) 6-13.

42. Wolska, J., "Sur une Solution de l'équation du Mouvement Permanent du Fluide Visqueux", Ann. Polon. Math. 3 (1956), 13-18.

43. Wolska, J., "Sur Les Équations Intégrales et Intégrodifferentielles a Singularite Polaire", Prace Mat. -Fiz. 48 (1952) 27-44.

44. Pohozdev. S. I., "The Dirichlet Problem for the Equation $\Delta u = u^2$", Pokl. Akad. Nauk. SSSR (N. S.) 134 (1960) 769-772, Soviet Math. 1, No. 5 (1960) 1143-1146.

45. Przeworska-Rolewicz, D., "Sur L'application de la Méthode des Approximation Successive à une Equation Integrale à Forte Singularite", Ann. Polon. Math. 6 (1959), 161-170.

H. P. THIELMAN

Applications of the Fixed Point Theorem by Russian Mathematicians

In the absence of Dr. Thielman, this paper was presented by Prof. Carl E. Lagenhop.

1. Historical Background

The earliest investigators of nonlinear integral equations, A. M. Liapunov [1], E. Schmidt [2], and Lichtenstein [3] made use of analytical methods. During the last thirty years topological methods have been developed for the investigation of nonlinear equations. These methods were used at first mainly for the establishment of existence theorems of solutions, but at the present time they have found applications in problems of many types.

The earliest version of the fixed point theorem dates back to Brouwer (1911). Topological methods were used by Birkhoff and Kellogg for proving existence theorems. The basic idea of their proof was formulated later (in 1930) by J. Schauder [4] into what is now known as Schauder's principle. A generalization of it to linear non-normed topological spaces was given by A. N. Tikhonov [5].

With the aid of the fixed point principle and the idea of a contraction mapping, V. V. Nemytskii [6] proved a number of theorems on the existence and uniqueness of the solutions of integral equations. Some of these theorems were extensions of results obtained by analytical methods earlier. Nemytskii's method was used by V. M. Dubrovskii [7], N. S. Smirnov [8], and A. I. Guseinov [9] to establish the existence of solutions of various classes of nonlinear integral equations.

The object of this report is to show how the principle of the fixed point is used by Soviet mathematicians for the study of concrete problems. Following M. A. Krasnosel'skii [10] we shall introduce the concept of the resolvent of a nonlinear operator with the aid of the principle of contraction mapping. Before we can proceed with our main object, we need some preliminary definitions.

2. Fundamental Concepts

A Banach space is a complete linear normed space. We shall deal with operators in a real Banach space E, i.e., a space in which multiplication of the elements by real numbers is defined. The origin of the Banach space will be denoted by θ .

Let $\underline{A}$ be an operator acting from a Banach space E_1 into a Banach space E_2 . The operator $\underline{A}$ is said to be continuous if it transforms every convergent (in the norm of E_1) sequence of elements into a convergent (in the norm of E_2) sequence of elements. If the operator $\underline{A}$, defined on $M \subset E_1$, is such that from every bounded sequence of elements $\varphi_n \in M$ one can select a subsequence φ_{n_i} such that the elements $\underline{A}\varphi_{n_i}$ converge in E_2 , then the operator $\underline{A}$ is said to be compact. (In other words, $\underline{A}$ is compact if it transforms every bounded set into a compact set.)

An operator is said to be completely (or totally) continuous if it is continuous and compact.

An element, or a vector $\varphi \in E$ $(\varphi \neq \theta)$ will be called an eigenvector of an operator $\underline{A}$ if there exists a number λ such that

$$\underline{A}\varphi = \lambda\varphi \quad .$$

The number λ will be called an eigenvalue of the operator $\underline{A}$. This eigenvalue will be said to belong to the eigenvector φ . The reciprocal of the eigenvalue will be called a characteristic value (of the operator $\underline{A}$) belonging to the eigenvector φ .

A concept frequently used in Soviet literature on operators is that of the rotation (or winding) of a vector field Φ . Let a continuous simplicial mapping Ψ of an n-dimensional closed oriented polyhedron T into an n-dimensional oriented unit sphere S^n be given. Here S^n is assumed to lie in an $(n+1)$-dimensional Euclidean space R^{n+1} . This means that there exists a simplicial division K of the polyhedron T, and a simplicial division K_1 of the sphere S^n such that by the mapping Ψ each simplex of the complex K is affinely transformed into some simplex of the complex K_1 . Let us pick some n-dimensional simplex Σ of the complex K_1 , and let us consider all the n-dimensional simplexes of the complex K which go into Σ under the mapping Ψ . Suppose that among them s simplexes go into Σ with the orientation preserved, and that t of these simplexes are transformed into Σ with the orientation changed; then $t-s$ is called the degree (or index) of the simplicial mapping Ψ .

Let Ψ now be any continuous mapping of T onto the sphere S^n . It is found that the degrees of all simplicial mappings near to the mapping Ψ are the same. This common degree of the simplicial mappings close to Ψ is called the degree of the continuous mapping Ψ .

Krasnosel'skii and a number of other Soviet mathematicians have replaced this concept of the degree of a mapping by the concept of the rotation of a vector field. Let an $(n+1)$-dimensional vector field Φ, without the null vector, be given on T. (This means that at every point $x \in T$ there is given an $(n+1)$-dimensional vector $\Phi(x)$). The rotation of a vector field Φ is the degree of the mapping

$$\Psi_x = \frac{\Phi(x)}{\|\Phi(x)\|} \qquad (x \in T) .$$

3. Contraction Mappings

Let T be a closed sphere in a Banach space E, and let $\underline{A}$ be an operator defined on T, and satisfying the Lipschitz condition

$$(3.1) \qquad \|\underline{A}x_1 - \underline{A}x_2\| \leq \alpha \|x_1 - x_2\| \qquad (x_1, x_2 \in T)$$

where $\alpha < 1$. (The transformation of T by $\underline{A}$ is called a contraction mapping.) Suppose that the operator $\underline{A}$ transforms T into itself. We have the following result.

The equation

$$(3.2) \qquad x = \underline{A}x$$

has a unique solution x^* in T. This solution can be computed by the method of successive approximations by the formula

$$(3.3) \qquad x_n = \underline{A}x_{n-1}, \qquad (n = 1, 2, \dots)$$

where x_0 is an arbitrary element of the sphere T. The rate of convergence is given by

$$\|x_n - x_n^*\| \leq \frac{\alpha^n}{1-\alpha} \|x_1 - x_0\| \qquad (n = 1, 2, \dots) .$$

Proof. Let $x_0 \in T$, and let $x_1, x_2, \dots$ be the sequence given by (3.3). By (3.1) we have

$$\|x_{m+1} - x_m\| = \|\underline{A}x_m - \underline{A}x_{m-1}\| \leq \alpha \|x_m - x_{m-1}\| \dots \leq \alpha^n \|x_1 - x_0\| .$$

Hence,

$$\|x_{n+k} - x_n\| = \|x_{n+k} - x_{n+k-1} + x_{n+k-1} - x_{n+k-2} + \dots + x_{n+1} - x_n\| \leq$$

$$\leq \|x_{n+k} - x_{n+k-1}\| + \|x_{n+k-1} - x_{n+k-2}\| + \dots + \|x_{n+1} - x_n\| \leq$$

$$\leq (\alpha^{n+k-1} + \dots + \alpha^n)\|x_1 - x_0\| \leq \frac{\alpha^n}{1-\alpha}\|x_1 - x_0\| ,$$

or

$$\|x_{n+k} - x_n\| \leq \frac{\alpha^n}{1-\alpha}\|x_1 - x_0\| \tag{3.5}$$

$$(n = 0, 1, 2 \dots ; \; k = 1, 2, \dots) .$$

Hence, the sequence $x_1, x_2, \dots$ is a Cauchy sequence. We denote the limit of this sequence by x^*. Obviously, $x^* \in T$.

Next we show that x^* is a solution of (3.1)

$$\|\underline{A}x^* - x^*\| = \|\underline{A}x^* - x_{n+1} + x_{n+1} - x^*\|$$

$$= \|\underline{A}x^* - \underline{A}x_n + x_{n+1} - x^*\|$$

$$\leq \|\underline{A}x^* - \underline{A}x_n\| + \|x_{n+1} - x^*\|$$

$$\leq \alpha\|x^* - x_n\| + \|x_{n+1} - x^*\| .$$

Each of the last two terms tends to zero as n goes to infinity. Hence, $\|\underline{A}x^* - x^*\| = 0$, i.e., $\underline{A}x^* = x^*$.

The uniqueness of the solution of the equation (3.2) is established very simply. Let x^* and x^{**} be two solutions of (3.2). Then

$$\|x^* - x^{**}\| = \|\underline{A}x^* - \underline{A}x^{**}\| \quad \alpha\|x^* - x^{**}\| ,$$

and since $0 < \alpha < 1$, $x^* = x^{**}$.

In order to obtain the rate of convergence given by (3.4) we need only to let k go to infinity in (3.5).

This simple proof establishes the so-called principle of contraction mappings for operators acting in complete metric spaces.

The principle of contraction mappings, and Schauder's principle, which states that if a continuous operator $\underline{A}$ transforms a closed convex set T of a Banach space into a compact subset of T, then there exists a point $x \in T$ such that $\underline{A}x = x$, are related but independent of each other. Both principles are particular cases of the following fixed point theorem, as was pointed out by Krasnosel'skii [10].

Let T be a closed, bounded convex set of a Banach space E_1. Let $\underline{A}$ and $\underline{B}$ be operators defined on T, and satisfying the conditions:

a) $\underline{A}x + \underline{B}y \in T$, when $x, y \in T$.

b) The operator $\underline{A}$ satisfies the condition (3.1) for some positive $\alpha < 1$.

c) The operator $\underline{B}$ is completely continuous.

Under these conditions there exists at least one point x^* in T such that $\underline{A}x^* + \underline{B}x^* = x^*$.

4. Resolvent of a Nonlinear Operator

Let $\underline{D}$ be a nonlinear operator that is defined in a Banach space E and satisfies on the sphere T of radius ρ about θ the Lipschitz condition

$$\|\underline{D}\varphi_1 - \underline{D}\varphi_2\| \leq q\|\varphi_1 - \varphi_2\|, \qquad (\varphi_1, \varphi_2 \in T) \tag{4.1}$$

where q is some positive number. We shall assume that $\underline{D}\theta = \theta$. In this case

$$\varphi = \alpha D\varphi + f \tag{4.2}$$

has in T a unique solution φ_0 as can be established on the basis of the principle of contraction mappings, provided that $|\alpha| < 1/q$, and that $f \in E$ such that

$$\|f\| \leq (1 - |\alpha q|)\rho . \tag{4.3}$$

Indeed, under the stated condition, the operator $\underline{A}$ defined by

$$\underline{A}\varphi = \alpha\underline{D}\varphi + f \tag{4.4}$$

transforms the sphere T into a part of itself, since

$$\|\underline{A}\varphi\| \leq |\alpha|\ \|\underline{D}\varphi - \underline{D}\theta\| + \|f\| \leq |\alpha q|\ \|\varphi\| + \|f\| \leq \rho ,$$

$$(\varphi \in T)$$

and $\underline{A}$ satisfies also the Lipschitz condition, with a constant less than 1,

$$\|\underline{A}\varphi_1 - \underline{A}\varphi_2\| \leq |\alpha| \, \|\underline{D}\varphi_1 - \underline{D}\varphi_2\| \leq |\alpha q| \, \|\varphi_1 - \varphi_2\| .$$

With Krasnosel'skii ([10] p. 149) we define the operator $\underline{R}_\alpha$ as the relation which associates with every element f, whose norm satisfies (4.3), the solution φ_0 of the corresponding equation (4.2), namely,

$$\underline{R}_\alpha f = \varphi_0 . \tag{4.5}$$

This operator is called the resolvent of the operator $\underline{D}$. Since $\underline{D}\theta = \theta$ and (4.2) has a unique solution, $\underline{R}_\alpha \theta = \theta$.

By the definition of $\underline{R}_\alpha$,

$$\underline{R}_\alpha f = \alpha \underline{D}(\underline{R}_\alpha f) + f . \tag{4.6}$$

From this identity it follows that

$$\|\underline{R}_\alpha f_1 - \underline{R}_\alpha f_2\| \leq |\alpha| \, \|\underline{D}(\underline{R}_\alpha f_1) - \underline{D}(\underline{R}_\alpha f_2\| + \|f_1 - f_2\| \leq \tag{4.7}$$

$$\leq |\alpha q| \, \|\underline{R}_\alpha f_1 - \underline{R}_\alpha f_2\| + \|f_1 - f_2\|$$

for any f_1 and f_2 such that

$$\|f_1\|, \ \|f_2\| \leq (1 - |\alpha q|)\rho .$$

From (4.7) we deduce an important property of the resolvent:

$$\|\underline{R}_\alpha f_1 - \underline{R}_\alpha f_2\| \leq \frac{1}{1 - |\alpha q|} \|f_1 - f_2\| . \tag{4.8}$$

This equation shows, in particular, that the resolvent $\underline{R}_\alpha$ is a continuous operator. From (4.8) and $\underline{R}_\alpha \theta = \theta$ it follows also that

$$\|\underline{R}_\alpha f\| \leq \frac{\|f\|}{1 - |\alpha q|} . \tag{4.9}$$

The identity (4.6) implies that

$$f_1 - f_2 = \underline{R}_\alpha f_1 - \underline{R}_\alpha f_2 - \alpha[\underline{D}(\underline{R}_\alpha f_1) - D(\underline{R}_\alpha f_2)] \;;$$

from which it follows that

$$\|f_1 - f_2\| \leq (1 + |\alpha q|)\|\underline{R}_\alpha f_1 - \underline{R}_\alpha f_2\| \;,$$

that is,

$$\|\underline{R}_\alpha f_1 - \underline{R}_\alpha f_2\| \geq \frac{1}{1+|\alpha q|} \|f_1 - f_2\| \;. \tag{4.10}$$

Let α and β be given such that $|\alpha| < 1/q$, and $|\beta| < 1/q$. Then the resolvents $\underline{R}_\alpha$, and $\underline{R}_\beta$ will be defined for all elements such that

$$\|f\| \leq [1 - \max\{|\alpha q|, \; |\beta q|\}]\rho \;.$$

From the identity (4.6) it now follows that

$$\underline{R}_\alpha f - \underline{R}_\beta f = \alpha[\underline{D}(\underline{R}_\alpha f) - \underline{D}(\underline{R}_\beta f)] + (\alpha - \beta)\underline{D}(\underline{R}_\alpha f) \;, \tag{4.11}$$

and, hence,

$$\|\underline{R}_\alpha f - \underline{R}_\beta f\| \leq |\alpha q| \, \|\underline{R}_\alpha f - \underline{R}_\beta f\| + |\alpha - \beta| \, \|\underline{D}(\underline{R}_\beta f)\| \;. \tag{4.12}$$

By (4.1), (4.8) and $\underline{R}_\alpha \theta = \theta$,

$$\|\underline{D}(\underline{R}_\beta f)\| = \|\underline{D}(\underline{R}_\beta f) - \underline{D}(\underline{R}_\beta \theta)\| \leq \tag{4.13}$$

$$\leq q\|\underline{R}_\beta f - \underline{R}_\beta \theta\| \leq \frac{q}{1 - |\beta q|} \|f\| \;.$$

Combining (4.12) and (4.13), we find that

$$\|\underline{R}_\alpha f - \underline{R}_\beta f\| \leq \frac{q\|f\|}{(1-|\alpha q|)(1-|\beta q|)} |\alpha - \beta| \;, \tag{4.14}$$

which shows that the resolvent $\underline{R}_\alpha$ is a continuous operator function of the parameter α.

The identity (4.6) can be rewritten in the form

$$\underline{R}_\alpha f - f \leq \alpha \underline{D}(\underline{R}_\alpha f) ,$$

which together with (4.1) and (4.9) yields

$$(4.15) \qquad \|\underline{R}_\alpha f - f\| \leq \frac{|\alpha q|}{1 - |\alpha q|} \|f\| .$$

We have thus established a number of properties of the resolvent operator $\underline{D}$ under the condition that $\underline{D}\theta = \theta$. This is the case considered most frequently in the literature.

If $\underline{D}\,\theta \neq \theta$, the resolvent $\underline{R}_\alpha$ will be defined on the sphere

$$\|f + \alpha \underline{D}\theta\| \leq (1 - |\alpha q|)\rho .$$

The inequalities (4.8) and (4.10) remain valid. The inequality (4.14) goes over into

$$(4.16) \qquad \|\underline{R}_\alpha f - \underline{R}_\beta f\| \leq \frac{q\|f\| + \|\underline{D}\theta\|}{(1 - |\alpha q|)(1 - |\beta q|)} |\alpha - \beta| ,$$

which is true for all elements f such that

$$\|f + \alpha \underline{D}\theta\| , \quad \|f + \beta \underline{D}\theta\| \leq [1 - \max\{|\alpha q| , \ |\beta q|\}]\rho .$$

We note one more obvious property of the resolvent of a nonlinear operator: The resolvent $\underline{R}_\alpha$ of an odd operator $\underline{D}$, $\underline{D}(-\varphi) = -\underline{D}(\varphi)$, is an odd operator, $\underline{R}_\alpha(-f) = -\underline{R}_\alpha f$.

The concept of a resolvent of a nonlinear operator is used for the investigation of vector fields which are not completely continuous, but which are, in a sense, near to completely continuous vector fields.

5. Not Completely Continuous Vector Fields

On the boundary L of some bounded region G of a Banach space E, let there be given a vector field $\Phi = \underline{I} - \underline{A} - \epsilon\underline{D}$, where $\underline{A}$ is a completely continuous operator; $\underline{D}$ is an operator satisfying the Lipschitz condition

$$\|\underline{D}\varphi - \underline{D}\Psi\| \leq q\|\varphi - \Psi\|$$

in a sufficiently large part of E.

For a sufficiently small positive ϵ there will be defined on $\underline{A}L$ a resolvent $\underline{R}_\epsilon$ of the operator $\underline{D}$. Let us consider on L a vector field $\Psi = \underline{I} - \underline{R}_\epsilon \underline{A}$. This field will be completely continuous since the operator $\underline{R}_\epsilon \underline{A}$ is completely continuous. If the field Φ has no null vector on $\overline{L}$, then the field Ψ will have no null vector on L, for

$$\varphi = \underline{R}_\epsilon \underline{A}\varphi$$

would imply, in view of (4.6), that

$$\varphi = \underline{A}\varphi + \epsilon \underline{D}\varphi \ .$$

Suppose that the field $\Phi_0 = \underline{I} - \underline{A}$ has no null vector on L. Then one can find an $\alpha > 0$ such that

$$\| \Phi_0 x \| > \alpha \ (x \in L) \ .$$

Let $\epsilon > 0$ be chosen so that

$$\| \epsilon \underline{D}x \| < \alpha \ (x \in L) \ .$$

Then the vector field $\Phi_t = \underline{I} - \underline{A} - t \epsilon \underline{D}$, for $0 \leq t \leq 1$, will have no null vector on L. This means that the completely continuous vector field $\Psi_t = \underline{I} - \underline{R}_{t\epsilon} \underline{A}$ will have no null vector on L. The completely continuous operator $\underline{R}_{t\epsilon} \underline{A}$ is uniformly continuous in t in view of the relation (4.16).

Thus the vector fields $\Psi_0 = \underline{I} - \underline{A}$, and $\Psi_1 = \underline{I} - \underline{R}_\epsilon \underline{A}$ are homotopic and, hence, their rotations on L are the same. This result can be formulated in the following way.

Suppose that on a region G there is given a completely continuous vector field with a nonzero rotation on the boundary. If this field is disturbed by a small smooth operator, then the disturbed field will have at least one fixed point in G.

Here the term "small disturbance" means a disturbance by means of an operator of sufficiently small norm satisfying the Lipschitz condition with a sufficiently small constant.

6. Existence of Solutions

The principle of contraction mapping lends itself very well to the establishment of existence and uniqueness theorems of solutions. Many theorems of this type are contained in the works of V. V. Nemytskii [6]. A typical example of his results is the following.

Suppose that the operator $\underline{D}$ satisfies the Lipschitz condition, with some constant q, in a sphere $\|\varphi\| \leq \rho$ of a Banach space. Then the equation

$$\varphi = \mu \underline{D}\varphi$$

has a solution if μ is small enough.

This assertion is a direct consequence of the principle of contraction mappings. It has a direct application to the equation of P. S. Uryson, $\varphi = \mu\underline{A}\varphi$, where

$$\underline{A}\varphi(s) = \int_G K[s,t,\varphi(t)]\,dt ,$$

and G is a closed bounded set in an n-dimensional space.

We shall assume that $K[s,t,u]$ is continuous in all of its variables $s, t \in G$, $|u| \leq \rho$ (ρ some positive number), and that K has a bounded partial derivative with respect to u, i.e.,

$$\left| \frac{\partial K(s,t,u)}{\partial u} \right| \leq M \qquad (s,t, \in G; \ |u| < \rho).$$

The Uryson operator is defined on a sphere of radius ρ of the space C of continuous functions on G, and it satisfies the Lipschitz condition

$$\|\underline{A}\varphi - \underline{A}\Psi\| = \max_{s\in G} \left| \int_G \{K[s,t,\varphi(t)] - K[s,t,\Psi(t)]\}\,dt \right| \leq$$

$$\leq M \int_G |\varphi(t) - \Psi(t)|\,dt \leq M \text{ meas } G \|\varphi - \Psi\| .$$

Suppose, furthermore, that

$$\|\underline{A}\varphi\| \leq N \qquad (\|\varphi\| \leq \rho) ,$$

where N is some positive number. The last condition will be satisfied, for example, when

$$\max_{s,t\in G;\ |u| \leq \rho} |K(s,t,u)| \leq \frac{N}{\text{meas } G} .$$

Under these hypotheses we have the following result. The equation $\varphi = \mu\underline{A}\varphi$ has a unique solution in the sphere $\|\varphi\| \leq \rho$ if

$$|\mu| M \text{ meas } G < 1, \quad |\mu| N \leq \rho .$$

Krasnosel'skii [10] has used the method of successive approximations based on the principle of contraction mappings for the evaluation of eigenvalues and eigenfunctions of disturbed linear operators. His method is closely related to Newton's method for the approximate solution of nonlinear operator equations, as it has been developed by L. V. Kantorovich [11] and his pupils.

7. Reviews of Special Papers

Most of the material presented thus far can be found in a book by Krasnosel'skii [10]. We shall now indicate some works on nonlinear integral equations found in recent Soviet periodicals.

V. K. Ivanov [12] considers the equation $\underline{A}x_0 = y_0$, where x_0 is an unknown element of a Banach space, and y_0 is a given element in another Banach space. He treats this equation under the assumption that the inverse operator $\underline{A}^{-1}$ is not continuous. He reduces the determination of an approximate solution of the given equation to the finding of the minimum of a function of a finite number of variables within a given region. The construction of the suggested convergence process is illustrated by finding an approximate solution of the inverse of a potential theory problem.

B. P. Demidovič [13] investigates the problem on the existence of, and of the properties of bounded oscillations of a quasilinear system of the saddle-point type in the presence of a rapidly changing external force. The obtained results generalize a theorem of Farnell, Langenhop and Levinson [J. Math. and Phys. 29 (1951), 300-302; MR 12, 706].

V. V. Pokornyi [14] and P. P. Rybin [15] consider the Nekrasov-Nazarov method. This method is actually an analytic method. It consists in seeking the solutions $\phi(x, \lambda)$ of certain nonlinear integral equations in the form

$$\phi(x, \lambda) = \sum_{k \geq 1} \phi_k(x) \lambda^k .$$

Pokornyi shows in his article that this method is equivalent in a certain sense to the so-called Liapunov-Schmidt method. [2]. Wang, Sheng-Wang [16] proves the existence and uniqueness of a solution of the integral equation

$$\varphi(s) = \int_G K(s,t) f(s, \varphi(t))\, dt ,$$

where G is an L-measurable set in a finite Euclidean space; K(s,t), defined for $s, t \in G$, is a quasinegative symmetric kernel which yields a completely continuous operator in L. He makes the usual assumptions that f(t, u) is measurable in t for every u, and is continuous in u for almost all t.

S. I. Pohožaev [17] gives an analogue of Schmidt's method for solving nonlinear integral equations. He reduces the solution of these equations to the solution of equations with degenerate kernels.

N. V. Marčenko [18] establishes the existence of solutions of a certain class of nonlinear integral equations on the basis of ideas given by J. Leray and J. Schauder [Ann. Sci. Ecole Norm. Sup. (3) 51 (1934), 45-78].

T. A. Ebanoidze [19] proves the existence of solutions of certain nonlinear systems of integral equations by means of Tikhonov's fixed point theorem.

O. Yu. Vasilenko [20] has used nonlinear integral equations in hydrology. He not only has proved the existence and uniqueness of positive solutions of his nonlinear equations, which arise in the theory of non-steady flow of ground water, but he also gives an iteration method for finding them.

There is a school headed by M. M. Vainberg on the study of the Hammerstein operator. A number of research papers have appeared in recent years [21] based on the ideas given in a book by Vainberg [22]. (Cf. the article by L. B. Rall in this book.)

A. N. Baluev [23] has solved certain types of nonlinear integral equations by approximating them with finite systems of algebraic equations. He gives conditions under which the solutions of the finite approximating systems will be near the solutions of the original systems.

BIBLIOGRAPHY

1. Liapunov, A. M., Sur les figures d'equilibre peu différentes des ellipsoides d'une masse liquide homogéne douée d'un mouvement de rotation, Premiér partie. Etude générale du probléme. Zapiski nauk, St. Petersburg, 1906, 1-125.

2. Schmidt, E., Zur Theorie der linearen und nichtlinearen Integralgleichungen, III Teil, Über Auflösungen der nichtlinearen Integralgleichungen und die Verzweigung iherer Lösungen. Math. Ann. 65 (1908), 370-399.

3. Lichtenstein, L., Volesungen uber einge Klassen nichtlinearen Integralgleichungen und Integro-Differentialgleichungen nebst Anwendungen. Berlin, 1931.

4. Schauder, Der Fixpunktsatz in Funktionalräumen. Studia Math. (2) 1930.

5. Tihonov, A. N., Ein Fixpunktsatz, Math. Ann. 111 (1935).

6. Nemytskii, V. V., Fixed Point Methods in analysis UMN, vyp. 1 (1936)(Russian).

7. Dubrovskii, V. M., On some nonlinear integral equations, Učennye zap. MGU 30 (1939)(Russian).

8. Smirnov, N. S., A theorem on the existence of a solution of a nonlinear integral equation. DAN 3 (1936)(Russian).

9. Guseinov, A. I., Theorems on the existence and uniqueness of solutions of nonlinear singular integral equations. Matem. sbornik, 20, No. 2 (1947)(Russian).

10. Krasnosel'skii, M. A., Topological methods in the theory of nonlinear integral equations. Gosudarstvennoe Izdatel'stvo Tekhniko-teoreticheskoi literatury, Moscow, 1956. (Russian).

11. Kantorovich, L. V., Functional analysis and applied mathematics. UMN 3, vyp. 28 (1948). (Russian).

12. Ivanov, V. K., Integral equations of the first kind and approximate solutions of the inverse problem of potential theory. Dokl. Akad. Nauk SSSR, 142 (1962), 998-1000 (Russian).

13. Demidovič, B. P., Forced oscillations of a quasilinear system in the presence of a rapidly changing external force. Prikl. Mat. i Meh. 25 (1961), 705-715 (Russian). Translated as J. Appl. Mathematics and Mechanics. 25 (1962), 1044-1059.

14. Pokornyi, V. V., Two analytic methods in the theory of small solutions of nonlinear integral equations. Dokl. Akad. Nauk SSSR, 133 (1960), 1027-1030 (Russian). Translated as Soviet Math. Doklady, 1 (1961), 939-942 MR 24, A406.

15. Rybin, P. P., A formula in the Nekrasov-Nazarov method. (Russian). Izv. Vysš. Uveb. Zaved. Matematika 1959, No. 6(13), 131-137. MR 23, A3980.

16. Wang, Shen-Wang, On the solutions of the Hammerstein integral equation. Bull. Acad. Polon. Sci. Ser. Sci. Math., Astron., Phys. 8 (1960) 339-342 (Russian summary).

17. Pohožaev, S. I., Analogue of Schmidt's method for nonlinear equations. Dokl. Akad. Nauk SSSR 136 (1961), 546-548 (Russian). Translated as Soviet Math. Doklady 2, 103-105.

18. Marčenko, N. V., Existence of solutions of a certain class of nonlinear integral equations. Dokl. Akad. Nauk SSSR, 137 (1961), 515-518 (Russian). Translated as Soviet Math. Doklady 2, 305-308.

19. Ebanoidze, T. A., On infinite systems of certain nonlinear regular and singular integral equations. Akad. Nauk Gruz. SSR 22 (1959), 648-656 (Russian).

20. Vasilenko, O. Iu., Concerning a certain integral equation. Dopovodi Akad. Nauk Ukrain. SSR (1959), 942-944 (Ukrainian, Russian and English summaries) MR 22, 2869. Solutions of an integral equation. The same journal pages 1184-1188. MR 22, 2870.

21. Vainberg, M. M., Kasurovskii, R. I., On the variational theory of nonlinear operators and equations. Dokl. Akad. Nauk SSSR, 129 (1959) 1199-1202. (Russian).

22. Vainberg, M. M., Variatsionnye metody issledovaniia nelineinykh operatorov, Gosudarstv. Izdat. Tekhn.-Teor. Lit., Moscow, 1956; MR 19, 567.

23. Baluev, A. N., Approximate solution of nonlinear integral equations. Leningrad Gosud. Univ. Uč. Zap. Ser. Mat. Nauk 33 (1958), 28-31 (Russian). MR 22, 3959.

HANS F. BUECKNER

Equations in Partially Ordered Spaces

Introduction

When we pose a problem in the form of an integral equation, we frequently interpret the equation with the aid of a normed linear space of functions. By now the merits of this procedure are well established. The geometrical and topological concepts of the theory of metric linear spaces enable us to describe most of the relevant phenomena with clarity and transparency; a typical example is that of a Fredholm integral equation $y = \lambda Ky + f$ with some linear integral operator K. If we choose a suitable Banach space B, containing f as an element, and if we can interpret K as a completely continuous linear operator mapping B into itself, then we can establish the fundamental results of Fredholm's classical theory without recourse to any other properties which K may have. It is obvious that this convenient situation results from two favorable circumstances. One of them is that we can classify K in an abstract way, which uses the topological concepts of the space B; secondly, the characterization of K (as completely continuous operator) is narrow enough so that none of the important classical results are lost through a process of dilution.

It is not difficult to also find rather problematic examples. For certain linear singular integral equations, in particular for those with Cauchy integrals, it is not easy to decide on a suitable space. Furthermore, it is a problem to characterize Cauchy-type integral operators in an abstract way. To assume that they represent bounded operators is certainly quite correct in a great number of cases. But boundedness alone is too broad a description in order to yield the special results which we associate with the theory of singular integral equations. The situation becomes aggravated when we turn to nonlinear integral equations. In order to develop their theory and methods for their numerical solution, we frequently cannot disregard individual features of the nonlinear operators involved. Sometimes these cannot be adequately expressed in whatever abstract language is available in order to describe a nonlinear mapping from a Banach space into a Banach space. But this situation is challenging rather than discouraging. In the last decades remarkable progress has been achieved with regard to the feature of positivity of functions as well as of kernels which define nonlinear integral operators. Perron's theorem, that a matrix with positive elements has a positive eigenvalue together with an eigenvector of nonnegative components, is now a special case of the theory of positive operators acting in partially ordered spaces. This brings me to the subject of this lecture, namely, to operator equations in such spaces. Since it is impossible to fully mention the results that have been found so far, I must restrict my remarks to a few typical examples. Also, I cannot quote all of the relevant literature. For this reason I only refer to two books about the subject: namely, the book by G. Birkhoff, "Lattice Theory" (Amer. Math. Soc. Colloquium Publication XXV, revised edition, 1948); and the recent book by M. A. Krasnoselskii, "Positive Solutions of Operator Equations" (Moscow 1962). Both of them list the pertinent literature. A translation of the table of contents of Krasnoselskii's book is attached for the convenience of the reader.

Since I feel that the Russian book strikes an excellent balance between abstract theory and practical applications, I shall confine my remarks to the description of examples as they appear in Krasnoselskii's book. For the sake of identification the examples will be quoted as theorems, which represent as a whole or in part free translations of theorems of the book. For the sake of reference there will be shown in parentheses the enumeration under which they can be found in the book.

1. Basic Definitions

We assume familarity with the concepts of: linear spaces, normed linear spaces, completeness, weak completeness, compactness, weak compactness, Banach spaces, open and closed sets in them, operators (linear or nonlinear) mapping a Banach space B into itself and, finally, certain special properties of the operators such as boundedness, continuity, complete continuity, differentiability in the sense of Gateaux or Fréchet.

Let E be a real Banach space with the null element θ. A subset $K \subset E$ is called a cone, if the following conditions are met:

a) $u \in K$, $v \in K$ imply $\alpha u + \beta v \in K$ for arbitrary scalars $\alpha \geq 0$, $\beta \geq 0$;

b) $u \in K$, $-u \in K$ imply $u = \theta$;

c) K is closed.

The elements (vectors) $u \neq \theta$ of K are called the positive elements of E.

EXAMPLES: 1) $E = R_1$, the Euclidean space of all real numbers x. As cone K may serve the set of all nonnegative numbers.

2) $E = R_2$, the Euclidean space of all ordered pairs (x, y) of real numbers x, y; as cone K we may take the pairs of the "first quadrant", i.e., all pairs for which both $x \geq 0$ and $y \geq 0$.

3) $E = C\langle 0,1\rangle$, the Banach space of all real valued continuous functions defined on the closed interval $\langle 0,1\rangle$; all nonnegative functions form a cone.

With the aid of the cone K a partial ordering of E can be introduced. The definition of a partial ordering assumes that to certain pairs of elements u, v of E a relation $u \leq v$ is assigned such that:

i) $u \leq v$ and $v \leq w$ imply $u \leq w$.
ii) $u \leq v$ and $v \leq u$ imply $u = v$.
iii) $u_1 \leq v_1$ and $u_2 \leq v_2$ imply $u_1 + u_2 \leq v_1 + v_2$
iv) $u \leq v$ implies $tu \leq tv$ for $t \geq 0$ and $tv \leq tu$ for $t \leq 0$.

Given a cone K, we define a partial ordering by the criterion: $u \leq v$ if $v - u \in K$; it satisfies all of the preceding axioms of partial ordering. Since K is closed, two converging infinite sequences $\{u_n\}$, $\{v_n\}$ of E with the property $u_n \leq v_n$ imply $u \leq v$ for the corresponding limits.

Certain cones of special properties play an important role. Among them are:

A) Spacelike cones: K contains at least one inner point.

B) Reproducing cones: Every $w \in E$ admits a representation $w = u - v$ with $u, v \in K$.

C) Normal cones: Let $u, v \in K$ and $\|u\| = \|v\| = 1$; then $\|u+v\| \geq \epsilon > 0$ with ϵ independent of u, v.

D) Cones that admit embedding: A cone $K' \supset K$ exists such that for $u \neq \theta$ and $u \in K$, a ball of center u and radius $r = p \cdot \|u\|$ with $p > 0$ independent of u lies in K'.

We call $x \in E$ an order bound of a subset E' of E, if $u \leq x$ for all $u \in E'$. An order bound y of E' is called a supremum of E' ($\sup E'$) if $y \leq x$ with regard to all order bounds x of E'. The supremum, if it exists, is unique. These concepts enable us to define:

E) Regular cones: Every order bounded sequence $\{x_n\}$ of E which is monotonic in the sense $x_k \leq x_{k+1}$ converges.

F) Completely regular cones: Every sequence $\{x_n\}$ which is bounded in the ordinary sense, i.e., by norm, and monotonic in the sense $x_k \leq x_{k+1}$ converges.

G) Minihederal cones: Each pair x, y of elements of E has a supremum.

H) Strongly minihedral cones: Every order bounded subset E' of E has a supremum.

To some extent there is a hierarchy among some of the preceding concepts. Strongly minihedral cones are minihedral in the ordinary sense. Completely regular cones are regular in the ordinary sense. Regular cones are normal. A cone which admits embedding is also completely regular.

Turning now to operators mapping some domain $D \subset E$ onto some set $D' \subset E$, we assume that the intersection $\hat{D} = D \cap K$ is not empty. An operator A with domain D and range D' is called positive if $Au \in K$ for all $u \in \hat{D}$; it is called monotonic if $Au \leq Av$ whenever $u \leq v$ and $u, v \in D$. If A is linear then positivity implies monotonicity. In the case of nonlinear operators their derivatives (if they exist) can be expected to play an important role. Let x be an inner point of the domain D of A and let φ be any element of E. If we can write $A(x + t\varphi) - Ax = tA_x\varphi + t\omega(\varphi, x; t)$ such that A_x is a linear operator and $\|\omega\| \to 0$ as $t \to +0$ for all φ, then A_x is known as the Gateaux derivative of A at the point x. If $\|\omega\| \to 0$ when $t \to +0$ uniformly for all φ of unit norm, then A_x is known as the Fréchet derivative of A at x. We can reduce the condition that φ be arbitrary. If we only insist that $\varphi \in K$, the preceding definitions lead to the concepts of a Gateaux derivative with respect to K and to the Fréchet derivative with respect to K. We shall also speak of derivatives along the cone K.

A vector valued function $y(t)$ ($y \in E$, $t \in R_1$) is called differentiable at infinity if it is defined for sufficiently large $t > 0$ and if $\lim_{t \to \infty} y(t)/t = y'(\infty)$ exists. Let now $h \in E$ and $th \in D$ for sufficiently large $t > 0$. Let $y(t) = A(th)$ be differentiable at infinity for every h such that $y'(\infty) = A'(\infty)h$ with $A'(\infty)$ as a linear and continuous operator. Then we call A differentiable at infinity and $A'(\infty)$ the derivative of A at infinity. If we restrict h to belong to the cone K, then we characterize $A'(\infty)$ as the derivative of A with respect to or along the cone K.

In the preceding definitions "convergence" means, of course, convergence in the metric of the space E. If we substitute for convergence the concept of weak convergence, then we obtain the definitions of weak Gateaux and weak Fréchet derivatives. For the sake of distinction the ordinary derivatives are frequently referred to as strong Gateaux and strong Fréchet derivatives respectively.

We shall not present more definitions at this place but rather supplement the preceding ones where later necessary.

2. Positive Linear Operators

Let A be a linear operator defined on all of E and leaving K invariant. A is called strongly positive if K is spacelike and if $A^p x$ is an inner point of K for $x \neq \theta$, $x \in K$ and a suitable positive integer p (depending on x).

EXAMPLE: Set $Ax(t) = \int_0^1 k(t,s)x(s)\,ds$, where $x(t)$ is a function of the real Banach space $C\langle 0,1\rangle$; if $k(t,s)$ is positive and a continuous function of its arguments and if K consists of all non-negative functions, then A is strongly positive.

The eigenvalue problem $Ax = \lambda x$ for a positive operator A need not have a positive solution $x \neq \theta$; suitable examples are presented by Volterra integral operators. The following theorem however makes an affirmative statement under supplementary assumptions on A. We have

Theorem I: (2.5)

Let A be positive, completely continuous and let there exist elements u, v, w of E as well as a positive number α and a positive integer p such that $u = v - w$, $v \in K$, $w \in K$, $-u \notin K$ (read $-u$ not in K) and $\alpha u \leq A_u^p$. Then A has as at least one positive eigenvector, the corresponding eigenvalue of which is greater than or equal to $\alpha^{1/p}$.

This theorem generalizes the already mentioned result by Perron and also the well-known result by R. Jentzsch about Fredholm integral equations with a square integrable kernel $K(s,t)$, nonnegative in the domain $a \leq s, t \leq b$ of its definition and vanishing at most on a set of zero measure.

A result of similar nature appears in

Theorem II: (K 2.6)

Let A be completely continuous, positive and even uniformly positive, i.e. $\|Ax\| \geq b\,\|x\|$ for all $x \in K$, where $b > 0$. Then A has at least one positive eigenvector.

Of both theoretical and practical importance is the concept of v-positivity. Here $v \neq \theta$ denotes an element of K. The operator A is called v-positive if for $x \in K$, $x \neq \theta$ there exists a positive integer n such that $\alpha v \leq A^n x \leq \beta v$ where α, β are suitable positive numbers. Here we mention only

Theorem III: (K 2.10 and K 2.11)

Let A be a v-positive operator. Then a positive eigenvalue λ of A is simple and the related eigenvector is (its norm disregarded) uniquely identified as an element of K.

From here on we turn to not necessarily linear operators.

3. Fixed Point Theorems

The following theorems can be partially proved with the aid of the well known fixed point theorems by Schauder and Tikhonov. Let x_0, y_0 be elements of E such that $x_0 \leq y_0$ and let $\langle x_0, y_0 \rangle$ denote the set of all elements u for which $x_0 \leq u \leq y_0$; this set is also referred to as a cone interval.

Theorem IV: (K 4.1)

Let A transform $\langle x_0, y_0 \rangle$ into itself and let A be monotonic in x_0, y_0 . In order to find at least one fixed point of A in $\langle x_0, y_0 \rangle$ any one of the following conditions is sufficient:

a) K is strongly minihedral;
b) K is regular and A is continuous;
c) K is normal, A is completely continuous;
d) K is normal, E is weakly complete, the unit ball in E is weakly compact, A is weakly continuous.

Condition (a) of this theorem goes back to G. Birkhoff*. It is remarkable that A does not have to be continuous; the reader may find it interesting to consider the special case $E = R_1$ with real numbers $x \geq 0$ forming the cone K; A is an ordinary monotonically increasing function f(x), which transforms the closed interval $x_0 \leq x \leq y_0$ into itself. As for the other statements of the theorem, the reader is referred to Bakhtin and Krasnoselskii, and the pertinent literature is quoted in the latter's book.

Of practical importance is

Theorem V: (partially K 4.4)

Let (b) or (c) of Theorem IV be satisfied, and let x^* be the only fixed point of A in $\langle x_0, y_0 \rangle$. Then any iterative sequence $y_n = Ay_{n-1}$ with an arbitrary element y_1 in $\langle x_0, y_0 \rangle$ converges to x^*.

---

* See page 54 of the book on "Lattice Theory". In a recent report by Ignace I. Kolodner "On Completeness of Partly Ordered Sets and Fixed Point Theorems for Isotone Mappings" (The University of New Mexico, Department of Mathematics, Technical Report No. 20, November 1962) Birkhoff's result is extended.

Krasnoselskii's book lists this theorem in a more general form. From here on differentiable operators and their derivatives will be considered. To this end we supplement the concept of a derivative at infinity by means of the nature of the convergence when the approach to the limit takes place. Let A be an operator differentiable at infinity. If

$$\lim_{R \to \infty} \sup_{\|x\| \geq R} \frac{\|Ax - A'(\infty)x\|}{\|x\|} = 0$$

then $A'(\infty)$ is called a strong asymptotic derivative and A itself strongly asymptotically linear. If the preceding limit relation holds for all x of K only or at least for all x of K of sufficiently large norm, then we speak of a strong asymptotic derivative with respect to or along the cone; likewise we say, that A is strongly asymptotically linear with respect to or along the cone K. We quote:

Theorem VI: (K 3.3)

Let A have a weak Gateaux derivative $A'(x)$ at every point x of sufficiently large norm. Let B be some linear operator such that $\|A'(x) - B\| \to 0$ when $\|x\| \to \infty$; then B is a strong asymptotic derivative of A.

Theorem VII: (K 3.4)

If x in Theorem VI is confined to K, then B is a strong asymptotic derivative of A with respect to the cone K.

Theorem VIII: (K 4.5)

Let K be completely regular. Let the operator A be defined in K and let it be continuous, positive, monotonic and strongly asymptotically linear, such that the derivative $A'(\infty)$ has a spectral radius $\rho_0 < 1$. Then there exists at least one fixed point of A in K.

Remarks: The fixed point can be θ. It is useful to interpret the theorem for the case $E = R_1$ (see Fig. 1); here Ax is a function $f(x)$, which is continuously defined for $x \geq 0$, which increases monotonically and which has a derivative $f'(\infty) < 1$ at infinity. The existence of a fixed point $x^* = f(x^*)$ is geometrically plausible.

Theorem IX: (K 4.6)

Under the assumptions of Theorem VIII let there be an element $x_0 \in K$, $x_0 \neq \theta$, such that $x_0 \leq Ax_0$. Then A has at least one fixed point $x^* \neq \theta$ in K.

Again Fig. 1 may serve to make the theorem plausible.

Figure 1

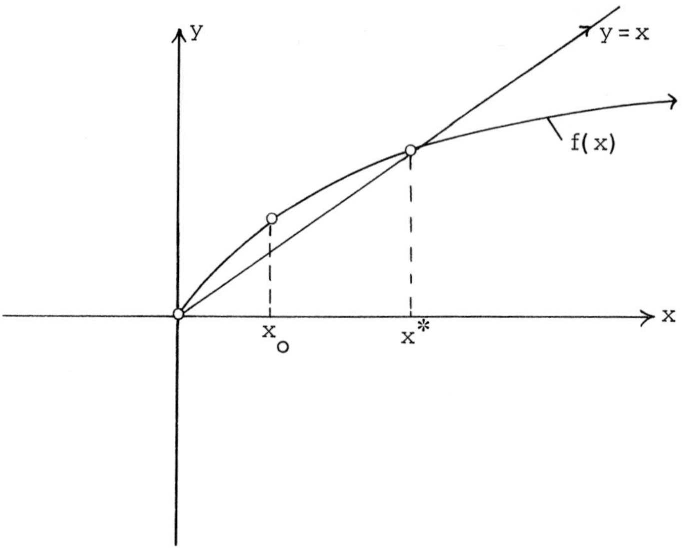

In Theorem VIII the assumptions of a completely regular cone K and of the continuity and monotonicity of A can be replaced by any one of the following conditions:

a) A is completely continuous;
b) E is weakly complete, the unit ball weakly compact and A weakly continuous.

Again with reference to Fig. 1 let us consider the case $E = R_1$. If the function $f(x)$ is also differentiable at $x = 0$ with $f'(x) > 1$ and $f(0) = 0$ then we would expect $x = f(x)$ to have a positive solution. The corresponding generalization is in

Theorem X: (K 4.11)

Let A be defined on K as a positive operator with $A\theta = \theta$; Let A have a Fréchet derivative $A'(\theta)$ at θ and a strong asymptotic derivative $A'(\infty)$, both with respect to K. Let the spectrum of $A'(\infty)$ be in a circle of radius $\rho < 1$; assume $A'(\theta)$ to have an eigenvector $h_o \in K(A'h_o = \lambda_o h_o)$ with an eigenvalue $\lambda_o > 1$, and let there be no other eigenvectors of $A'(\theta)$ in K with corresponding eigenvalues equal to 1. In order that A have at least one fixed point $x^* = Ax^*$ in K with $x^* \neq \theta$, either of the two following conditions suffices:

1) A is completely continuous
2) A is weakly continuous, E is weakly complete, the unit ball of E weakly compact and K admits embedding.

Theorem XI: (K 4.16)

Let the conditions of the preceding theorem be changed inasmuch as the spectra of $A'(\theta)$ and $A'(\infty)$ are concerned. Let $A'(\theta)$ not have eigenvalues equal to or greater than one; let $A'(\infty)$ have an eigenvector g_o, such that λ_∞ in $A'(\infty)g_o = \lambda_\infty g_o$ is greater than one and let it be assumed that $A'(\infty)$ has no eigenvalue equal to one. Then A has in K at least one fixed point different from θ.

Figure 2

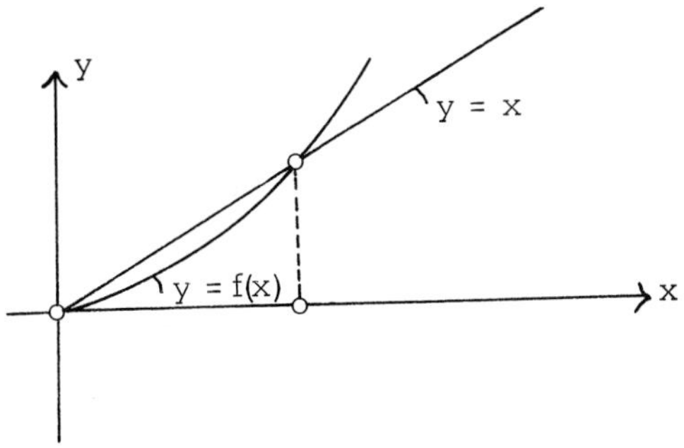

The situation is illustrated in Fig. 2 for $E = R_1$.

Figure 3

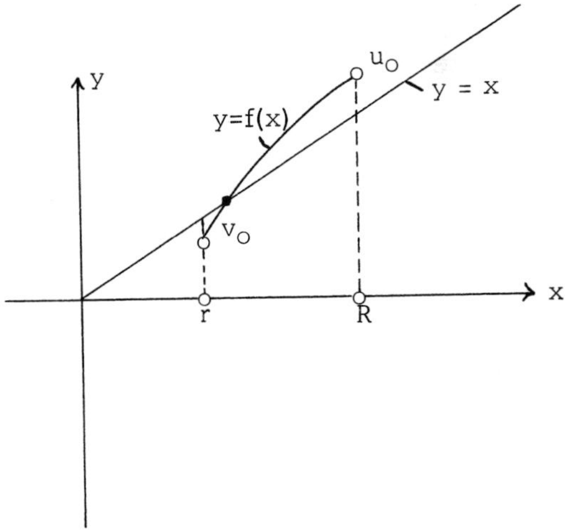

Theorem XII: (Lemma K 4.5)

Let A be defined for the intersection of K and the shell $0 < r \leq \|x\| \leq R$, such that A is positive and completely continuous. Let furthermore $Ax = v_o$ for $\|x\| = r$ and $Ax = u_o$ for $\|x\| = R$, such that $\|v_o\| < r < R < \|u_o\|$. Then A has at least one fixed point.

The application of this theorem to the case $E = R_1$ is illustrated in Fig. 3.

4. Equations With A Parameter

We conclude the list of examples with remarks about the equation

$$x = A(x, \mu)$$

where $x \in E$, $\mu \in R_1$ and $A(x, \mu)$ denotes a mapping of some domain $D \subset E$ into E; the mapping depends on μ and takes the familiar form $A(x, \mu) = \frac{1}{\mu} A(x)$ in the case of eigenvalue problems. We shall assume that D comprises all of K and that $A(x, \mu)$ is a positive operator, i.e., $A(x, \mu) \geq \theta$ for $x \in K$. Furthermore, $A(x, \mu)$ is assumed to continuously depend on μ and to be completely continuous in $R_1 \times E$. The preceding equation formulates a fixed point problem for the operator $A(x, \mu)$. Here we are interested not in certain fixed points belonging to one value of μ or to another but, rather, in the behavior of vector-valued functions $x(\mu)$, defined on some interval $\mathfrak{M} = (\mu' < \mu < \mu'')$, and solving the equation above. In particular we focus our attention on continuous dependence of $x(\mu)$ on μ.

Theorem XIII: (K 5.1)

For $\mu \in \mathfrak{M}$ (some finite or infinite interval) let $A(\theta, \mu) = \theta$ and let $A(x, \mu)$ have a strong asymptotic derivative $A'(\infty, \mu)$, having no eigenvalue equal to or exceeding one; let also the Fréchet derivative $A'(\theta, \mu)$ at $x = \theta$ exist. Furthermore, assume $A'(\theta, \mu) = \mu A'(\theta)$, $A'(\infty, \mu) = \mu A'(\infty)$; let $A'(\theta)$ and $A'(\infty)$ admit uniquely determined eigenvectors h_o, g_o of unit norm in K; write $A'(\theta) h_o = \lambda_o h_o$, $A'(\infty) g_o = \lambda_\infty g_o$. Then $x = A(x, \mu)$ has at least one nonzero solution in K for all μ of the interval $(\lambda_o^{-1}, \lambda_\infty^{-1})$.

The concepts of a majorant and a minorant will be used in the next theorem. The operator B is a majorant of A is $Ax \leq Bx$ for all $x \in D \cap K$; B is a minorant of A if $Bx \leq Ax$ for all $x \in D \cap K$. If B is a linear operator, we speak of a linear majorant or minorant respectively.

Theorem XIV: (K 5.2)

Assume $A(\theta, \mu) = \theta$. Let two linear and positive operators $A_-(\theta)$ and $A_+(\infty)$ exist, such that $\mu A_-(\theta)$ is a minorant to $A(x, \mu)$ for $\|x\| \leq r(\mu)$ and $\mu A_+(\infty)$ a majorant of $A(x, \mu)$ for $\|x\| \geq R(\mu)$. Assume $u_0 \neq \theta$, $v_0 \neq \theta$ of K with the properties $\lambda_0 u_0 \leq A_-(\theta) u_0$, $A_+(\infty) v_0 \leq \lambda_\infty v_0$; $\alpha u_0 \leq A_-^n(\theta) x$, $A_+^m(\infty) x \leq \beta v_0$ for $x \neq \theta$ in K and with positive integers m, n and positive numbers α, β, which may depend on x. Then for $\lambda_0 > \lambda_\infty$ and $\mu \in (\frac{1}{\lambda_0}, \frac{1}{\lambda_\infty})$ the equation $x = A(x, \theta)$ has in K at least one solution $x \neq \theta$.

Theorem XV: (K 5.3)

Let $A(\theta, \mu) = \theta$; let two linear positive operators $A_+(\theta)$ and $A_-(\infty)$ exist, such that $\mu A_+(\theta)$ is a majorant for $\|x\| \leq r(\mu)$ and $A(\infty)$ is a minorant for $\|x\| \geq r(\mu)$; furthermore, we assume two elements $u_0, v_0 \in K$, both different from θ, with the properties $A_+(\theta) u_0 \leq \lambda u_0$, $A_+^m(\theta) x \leq \alpha u_0$; $\lambda_\infty v_0 \leq A_-(\infty) v_0$, $\beta v_0 \leq A_-^n(\infty) x$ where $x \neq \theta$ in K and where $\alpha, \beta > 0$; m, n are suitable positive integers, and α, β, m, n may depend on x. If $\lambda_0 < \lambda_\infty$ and μ is in the interval $(\frac{1}{\lambda_\infty}, \frac{1}{\lambda_0})$, then $x = A(x, \mu)$ has at least one solution in K which is different from θ.

If $x = A(x, \mu)$ for every $\mu \in \mathfrak{M}$ has exactly one solution in some given ball, then $x = x(\mu)$ depends continuously on μ. A set $\mathfrak{M} \subset E$ is called a continuous branch, connecting a bounded and closed set $F \subset E$ with a set $F_1 \subset E$ if the intersection of $\mathfrak{M}$ with the boundary Γ of an arbitrary domain E', which contains F but has no points with F_1 in common, is nonempty. Let X_μ denote the set of all solutions x of $x = A(x, \mu)$ for a given μ, where $x \in K$. Continuity of $A(x, \mu)$ with respect to x implies closedness of X_μ; if $A(x, \mu)$ is completely continuous then X_μ is locally compact.

Theorem XVI: (K 5.4)

Let the completely continuous operator $A(x, \mu)$ satisfy the conditions of Theorem XIII (K 5.1). Assume $[\mu_1, \mu_2] \subset (\frac{1}{\lambda_0}, \frac{1}{\lambda_\infty})$ and for $x \in K$, $\mu \in [\mu_1, \mu_2]$:

$$\lim_{\|x\| \to 0} \sup_{\mu} \frac{\|A(x, \mu) - \mu A'(\theta) x\|}{\|x\|} = 0,$$

$$\lim_{\|x\| \to \infty} \sup_{\mu} \frac{\|A(x, \mu) - \mu A'(\infty) x\|}{\|x\|} = 0.$$

Then the set $\mathfrak{N}$ of all solutions to $x = A(x, \mu)$ for the values $\mu \in [\mu_1, \mu_2]$ represents a continuous branch connecting X_{μ_1}, and X_{μ_2}.

M.A. Krasnoselskii, Positive Solutions Of Operator Equations
Chapters of Nonlinear Analysis
A Translation of the Table of Contents

Chapter 3. Differentiability Along A Cone.

Chapter 4. Existence of Positive Solutions.

R. H. MOORE

Newton's Method and Variations

Contents

1. Introduction

Our topic is the application of Newton's method to equations of the form

(1.1) $$P(x) = 0$$

where P is a non-linear operator on a Banach space or, more generally, a space with norm in a partially ordered space. Not only does the method produce approximate solutions, but the accompanying theory yields statements on the existence of a true solution. These may apply where the fixed-point methods do not.

The idea, as is well known, is that of solving a given non-linear equation by solving a sequence of linearized local approximating equations. For the real equation $f(x) = 0$, the formula for the successive approximations to a solution is $x_{n+1} = x_n - [f'(x_n)]^{-1}f(x_n)$, where x_0 is an initial approximation to a solution. Using a generalized concept of derivative one can write a precisely analogous formula for equation (1.1), (see (2.2) and (4.1)).

The method has a long history, with contributions by Cauchy, Runge, Faber and Blutel among others. The theorem of Fine [30] in 1916 seems to be the first in n-dimensional space which, under conditions given for an initial approximate solution, asserts the existence of a solution of (1.1) to which the iterates in the Newton method converge. In the same year, Bennett[23] proved a convergence and existence theorem in more general spaces. Ostrowski [58] in 1937 gave error estimates in n-dimensional space (see also[59,60,61]). In 1939 Kantorovič [40] gave theorems for equations in a space with norm in a partially ordered space. As a basis for the present exposition, we shall use the fundamental theorem given by Kantorovič [43] in 1948 for Banach spaces. (Reported preliminarily in [41, 42]; also in [44] with some applications. See also Mysovskih [54]; and Vainberg [73], Appendix).

The formulation here, for the most part, will be for equations in a Banach space, with specific formulas in $C[0,1]$ and $L_2[0,1]$ being given for non-linear integral equations of Urysohn type

$$x(s) - \int_0^1 H(s,t,x(t))\,dt = b(s) . \tag{1.2}$$

This includes the important case of Hammerstein equations where

$$H(x,t,u) \equiv L(s,t)f(u) .$$

The theorems are useful, whenever a sufficiently good initial approximate solution x_0 can be found. This may be available from physical considerations, empirical data or related simpler problems. If a parameter is involved, it may be possible to solve approximately a sequence of equations obtained by successive small increments in the parameter, the approximate solutions from preceding equations supplying an initial guess for the current equation; one starts from a parameter value for which a solution can be obtained. In some instances this technique together with an appropriate local change of parameter permits investigation of solutions at and near "critical values" of the given parameter. (cf. § 7 and § 8).

In the remainder of this section we define the Fréchet derivative, state some of its fundamental properties, and exhibit its form in some examples. (cf. Hille-Phillips [II], Luisternik-Sobolev [III], Dieudonné [I].)

We shall use the notation $:=$ to mean the quantity on the left is <u>defined</u> to be equal to the quantity or expression on the right.

Let X and Y be (real or complex) Banach spaces, $\mathbf{L}(X;Y)$ the Banach space of bounded linear maps from X to Y. We say a map P from an open set G of X into Y is (Fréchet) <u>differentiable</u> at $x_0 \in G$, if there is $P'(x_0) \in \mathbf{L}(X;Y)$ such that

$$\lim_{\|h\| \to 0} \frac{1}{\|h\|} \, \| P(x_0 + h) - P(x_0) - P'(x_0)h \| = 0 \tag{1.3}$$

The norm of $P'(x_o)$ is that in $\mathfrak{L}(X;Y)$. The map P is <u>differentiable on a subset</u> G_1 of G is differentiable at each point of G_1; P is <u>continuously differentiable in</u> G_1, $P \in C'(G_1)$, if the map P' from G_1 into $\mathfrak{L}(X;Y)$ is defined and continuous at each point of G_1. If P' is differentiable at x_o then P is twice differentiable at x_o; we write $P''(x_o) \in \mathfrak{L}(X; \mathfrak{L}(X;Y))$. Thus, for $h \in X$, $P''(x_o)h$ is in $\mathfrak{L}(X;Y)$ and so acts on elements $k \in X$: $P''(x_o)hk \in Y$. The norm $\|P''(x_o)\|$ is that in $\mathfrak{L}(X; \mathfrak{L}(X;Y))$; that is,

$$\|P''(x_o)h\| \leq P''(x_o)\| \; \|h\| ,$$

and thus

$$\|P''(x_o)hk\| \leq \|P''(x_o)\| \; \|h\| \; \|k\| . \tag{1.4}$$

In a natural manner $P''(x_o)$ may be viewed as an element of $\mathfrak{L}(X,X;Y)$, the space of bounded bilinear maps from $X \times X$ into Y. Higher order derivatives are defined analogously.

Several properties of the Fréchet derivative will be of use.

I) If P is itself linear, then $P'(x) = P$ and $P''(x) = 0$ for all $x \in X$.

II) If $R: = P + Q$ then $R'(x_o) = P'(x_o) + Q'(x_o)$.

III) If P maps X into Y, and Q maps Y into Z, Q defined on the range of P, then for $R: = QP$,

$$R'(x_o) = Q'(P(x_o))\,P'(x_o) .$$

IV) if P is continuously differentiable on $\{x : x=x_o + th,\ 0 \leq t \leq 1\}$ then

$$\|P(x_o + h) - P(x_o)\| \leq \sup_{0 \leq t \leq 1} \|P'(x_o + th)\| \; \|h\| ,$$

and if twice continuously differentiable on the same set then

$$\|P(x_o + h) - P(x_o) - P'(x_o)h\| \leq \sup_{0 \leq t \leq 1} \tfrac{1}{2} \|P''(x+th)\| \; \|h\|^2$$

V) If P is continuously differentiable on $\{x: x = x_o + th,\ 0 \leq t \leq 1\}$ then

$$P(x + h) - P(x) = \int_0^1 P'(x + th)h \, dt$$

where the integral is in the Riemann sense. (cf. Graves [31]; Liusternik and Sobolev [III], Chap. VI.)

VI) If X is a Hilbert space and Y is the scalar field, then $P'(x)$ is a bounded linear functional and as such is representable by a gradient vector $\nabla P(x)$ in X:

(1.5) $$P'(x)h = (\nabla P(x),\ h).$$

Example 1. Let $X = R^n$, $Y = R^m$, with elements $x = (\xi_1, \dots, \xi_n)$, $y = (\eta_1, \dots, \eta_m)$, and let $P(x) \equiv y$ be defined by

(1.6) $$\eta_i = f_i(\xi_1, \dots, \xi_n), \qquad i = 1, \dots, m.$$

Then the first derivative is the Jacobian matrix,

(1.7) $$P'(x_0) = \left(\frac{\partial f_i}{\partial \xi_j}\right) \quad \begin{matrix} i = 1, \dots, m \\ j = 1, \dots, n \end{matrix}$$

and

(1.8) $$P''(x_0) = \left(\frac{\partial^2 f_i}{\partial \xi_j \partial \xi_k}\right) \quad \begin{matrix} i = 1, \dots, m \\ j, k = 1, \dots, n \end{matrix}$$

where the derivatives are evaluated at $(\xi_{01}, \dots, \xi_{0n})$.
Thus, $g := P''(x_0)hk$ is given by

(1.9) $$\gamma_i = \sum_{j,k} \frac{\partial^2 f_i}{\partial \xi_j \partial \xi_k} \vartheta_j \kappa_k$$

where $g = (\gamma_1, \dots \gamma_m)$, $h = (\vartheta_1, \dots, \vartheta_n)$, $k = (\kappa_1, \dots, \kappa_n)$.

Example 2. Let $X = Y = C[0,1]$, the space of real valued continuous functions on $[0,1]$ with the supremum (uniform) norm and let $H(x) \equiv y$ be the Urysohn operator defined by

(1.10) $$y(s) = \int_0^1 H(s, t, x(t))\, dt, \qquad 0 \leqq s \leqq 1,$$

where $H(s, t, u)$ is continuous in s and t and twice continuously differentiable with respect to its third argument u. Then

(1.11) $$H'(x_0)h = g \text{ where } g(s) = \int_0^1 \frac{\partial H}{\partial u}(s, t, x_0(t))\, h(t)\, dt,$$

and

$$(1.12)\quad H''(x_o)hk = g \quad \text{where} \quad g(s) = \int_0^1 \frac{\partial^2 H}{\partial u^2}(s,t,x_o(t))\, h(t)\, k(t)\, dt.$$

For later use, we recall that if K is a linear integral operator on $C[0,1]$ with continuous kernel $K(s,t)$,

$$(1.13)\qquad (Kx)(s) = \int_0^1 K(s,t)\, x(t)\, dt$$

then

$$\|K\| = \max_{0 \leqq s \leqq 1} \int_0^1 |K(s,t)|\, dt.$$

Example 3. Let $X = Y = L_2[0,1]$, the space of real valued Lebesgue square integrable functions on $[0,1]$ with norm $\|x\|^2 = \int_0^1 [x(t)]^2 dt$, and let $H(x) \equiv y$ again be given by (1.10). Let

$$R(x_o, h; s,t) := H(s,t,x_o(t) + h(t)) - H(s,t,x_o(t)) - \frac{\partial H}{\partial u}(s,t,x_o(t))\, h(t).$$

If given $\epsilon > 0$ there is a $\delta > 0$ such that for $\|h\| < \delta$

$$\int_0^1 \Big[\int_0^1 R(x_o, h; s,t)\, dt\Big]^2 ds < \epsilon^2 \|h\|^2$$

then $H'(x_o)$ exists and is defined by (1.11). This does not require $H(s,t,u)$ to be differentiable with respect to u for all points $(s,t,x_0(t))$, $0 \le s,t \le 1$. However, it is certainly sufficient if $H(s,t,u)$ is twice continuously differentiable in u, and

$$\Big|\frac{\partial^2}{\partial u^2} H(s,t,u)\Big| \leqq M \quad \text{for} \quad 0 \leqq s,t \leqq 1, \; -\infty < u < \infty,$$

since then by the ordinary mean value theorem

$$\Big|\int_0^1 R(x_o, h; s,t)\, dt\Big| \leqq \tfrac{1}{2} M \int_0^1 |h(t)|^2 dt = \tfrac{1}{2} M \|h\|^2,$$

and hence we can take $\delta = \frac{2\epsilon}{M}$. For the Hammerstein operator, in which $H(s,t,u) = L(s,t) f(u)$, it is enough that f have a bounded continuous second derivative for all u and that $L(s,t)$ be an L_2 kernel.

Similar conditions apply for the validity of (1.12) determining $H''(x_0)$.

2. Newton's Method In Banach Spaces

Let X and Y be (real or complex) Banach spaces, and P a nonlinear map from X into Y which is twice differentiable in a suitable domain as required below. Starting with an approximate solution x_0 of

$$P(x) = 0 \tag{2.1}$$

we consider the sequence defined by

$$x_{n+1} := x_n - [P'(x_n)]^{-1} P(x_n), \quad n = 0, 1, 2, \dots . \tag{2.2}$$

We denote by $S(x_0, \rho)$ the sphere $\{x \in X : \|x - x_0\| < \rho\}$.

Theorem 1. (Kantorovič; existence and convergence). Suppose the following conditions are satisfied:

1) P is twice differentiable in $S(x_0, \rho_0)$ where ρ_0 is defined by (2.3) below, and in this sphere

$$\| P''(x) \| \leqq \kappa ;$$

2) $P'(x_0)$ maps X onto Y and has an inverse $\Gamma_0 := [P'(x_0)]^{-1}$ (i.e. is one-to-one) for which

$$\| \Gamma_0 \| \leqq \beta_0 ;$$

3) x_0 is an approximate solution of $P(x) = 0$ such that

$$\| \Gamma_0 P(x_0) \| \leqq \eta_0 \qquad (\text{equivalently, } \|x_1 - x_0\| \leqq \eta_0);$$

4) $h_0 := \beta_0 \eta_0 \kappa \leqq \frac{1}{2}$.

Here

$$\rho_o := N(h_0)\eta_0, \qquad N(h) := \frac{1 - \sqrt{1-2h}}{h} \tag{2.3}$$

Then $P(x) = 0$ has a solution x^* in the closed sphere $\bar{S}(x_0, \rho_0)$, and the successive approximations defined by (2.2) converge to x^*. Further,

$$(2.4) \qquad \|x_n - x^*\| \leq \frac{1}{2^{n-1}} (2h_o)^{2^n - 1} \eta_o .$$

Remark 1. We may assume without loss of generality that $h_o > 0$ since $h_o = 0$ if and only if $\beta_o = 0$ (impossible for bounded $P'(x_o)$) or $\eta_o = 0$ (then x_o is already a solution) or $\kappa = 0$ (in which case P is linear in $S(x_o, \rho_o)$).

Remark 2. From the definition (2.3) of $N(h)$ and the restrictions on h, viz. $0 < h \leqq \frac{1}{2}$, we find $1 < N(h) \leqq 2$. Thus condition 1) holds if $\|P''(x)\| \leqq \kappa$ in $S(x_o, 2\eta_o)$.

Remark 3. If $\|P(x_o)\| \leqq \hat{\eta}$ then $\|\Gamma_o P(x_o)\| \leqq \beta_o \hat{\eta}_o$, so condition 4) is satisfied if $\beta_o^2 \hat{\eta}_o \kappa \leqq \frac{1}{2}$.

Remark 4. It is to be emphasized that the satisfaction of conditions 1) - 4) for some x_o guarantees the existence of a solution (which might not be demonstrable otherwise).

The proof uses induction to show that similar conditions hold at $x_1, x_2, \ldots,$ and that the points x_n remain in $S(x_o, \rho_o)$. The sequence of approximate solutions is a Cauchy sequence; x^* is a limit assured by the completeness of X. (A concise form of Kantorovič's proof is given in [19].)

In the course of the proof one encounters the operator $F_o(x) := x - \Gamma_o P(x)$; x^* is a solution of $P(x) = 0$ if and only if it is a fixed point of F_o. The proof in essence uses the fact that F is contractive for x near x_o, and maps the sphere $S(x_o, \rho_o)$ into itself when the conditions of the theorem are satisfied (cf. the article by Thielman in these Proceedings). Besides the existence thus obtained also by the contractive mapping theorem, Kantorovič's theorem gives the rate of convergence and an error estimate in (2.4).

On the assumption that a common bound for $[P'(x)]^{-1}$ holds in a suitable neighborhood of x_o, Mysovskih [56] gives an easier proof.

The local uniqueness of the solution x^* depends on the bound K holding in a larger sphere:

Theorem 2. (Kantorovič; uniqueness). Let conditions 1) -4) of Theorem 1 hold with $\|P''(x)\| \leqq \kappa$ in the open sphere $S(x_o, \sigma)$ where

$$(2.5) \qquad \sigma := L(h_o)\eta_o , \qquad L(h) := \frac{1 + \sqrt{1 - 2h}}{h} .$$

Then the x^* of Theorem 1 is the unique solution of $P(x) = 0$ in the same sphere.

Remark 5. For $0 < h \leqq \frac{1}{2}$ we have $\frac{1}{\beta_0 \kappa} \leqq \sigma < \frac{2}{\beta_0 \kappa}$, and $\sigma \to \frac{2}{\beta_0 \kappa}$ as $h_0 \to 0$ (or $\eta_0 \to 0$ [or $\hat{\eta}_0 \to 0$ in Remark 3]).

In order to avoid inverting the operator $P'(x_n)$, one sometimes uses the modified Newton Method:

$$\hat{x}_{n+1} := \hat{x}_n - [P'(x_0)]^{-1} P(\hat{x}_n), \qquad n = 0, 1, 2, \ldots . \tag{2.6}$$

For this procedure the above theorems hold* except that there is a slower rate of convergence:

$$\|x_n - x^*\| \leqq q^{n-1} \|x_1 - x^*\|, \qquad q := 1 - \sqrt{1 - 2h_0} < 1.$$

To illustrate the optimal nature of the conditions in Theorems 1 and 2 Kantorovič [43] considers the real valued quadratic equation defined on the real line

$$P(x) := \tfrac{1}{2} x^2 - x + h = 0 \text{ with } h > 0 \text{ and } x_o = 0. \tag{2.7}$$

$$P'(x_0) = -1, \qquad \Gamma_0 = 1, \qquad \beta_0 = 1;$$

$$P''(x) \equiv 1, \qquad \kappa = 1;$$

$$\|\Gamma_0 P(x_0)\| = h, \qquad \eta_0 = h; \qquad h_0 = h.$$

This equation has the roots $x^*_{1,2} := 1 \pm \sqrt{1 - 2h}$, that is,

$$x^*_1 = N(h_0)\eta_0 \quad \text{and} \quad x^*_2 = L(h_0)\eta_0 .$$

The roots are real only if $h_0 \leqq \frac{1}{2}$, in which case $\overline{S}(x_0, \rho_0)$ must be as large as stated to include a solution, while $S(x_0, \sigma)$ may not be larger without containing another solution.

In actuality, this equation arises from the study of Newton's method in partially ordered spaces. See §4, in particular the Corollary to Theorem 5.

For the integral equations

$$x(s) - \int_0^1 H(s, t, x(t))\, dt = b(s) \tag{2.8}$$

* Although in 1948 Kantorovič had to require $h_0 < \frac{1}{2}$, in [46], using partially ordered spaces and the method of majorants, he showed $h_0 \leqq \frac{1}{2}$ was sufficient; the error estimate above fails for $h_0 = \frac{1}{2}$.

where H is an integral operator as in Example 2 or 3 in § 1, and $b(s)$ is a given function, we define the operator P by

$$P(x) := (I - H)x - b. \tag{2.9}$$

With derivatives of H exhibited in (1.11) and (1.12), we have

$$P'(x_o)h = (I - H'(x_o))h$$

$$P''(x_o)hk = H''(x_o)hk. \tag{2.10}$$

In $C[0,1]$, Theorem 1 becomes (cf. Remark 3):

Theorem 1'. If

1) $\left|\frac{\partial^2 H}{\partial u^2}(s,t,x(t))\right| \leqq \kappa,\quad 0 \leqq s,t \leqq 1,\quad |x(t) - x_o(t)| < \rho_o$;

2) the kernel $L(s,t) := \frac{\partial H}{\partial u}(s,t,x(t))$ has the resolvent kernel

$R(s,t)$ and $\sup_{0 \leqq s \leqq 1} \int_o^1 |R(s,t)|\,dt \leqq \hat{\beta}$;

3) $\|P(x_o)\| = \max_{0 \leqq s \leqq 1} \left|x_o(s) - \int_o^1 H(s,t,x_o(t))\,dt - b(s)\right| \leqq \hat{\eta}$

4) $h_o := (1 + \hat{\beta})^2\, \hat{\eta}\, \kappa \leqq \frac{1}{2}$

then there is a solution x^* of $(I - H)x = b$ to which the successive approximations converge, and

$$\max_{0 \leqq x \leqq 1} |x^*(s) - x_o(s)| \leqq N(h_o)(1 + \hat{\beta})\hat{\eta} = \rho_o$$

where $N(h)$ is defined by (2.3).

In $L_2[0,1]$ we suppose again that the derivative operators are defined using the integral operators in (1.11) and (1.12) (cf. Example 3). Then Theorem 1 becomes

Theorem 1''. If

1) $\left|\frac{\partial^2}{\partial u^2} H(s,t,u)\right| \leqq \kappa \quad 0 \leqq s,t \leqq 1, \quad -\infty < u < \infty$;

2) in case $L(s,t) := \frac{\partial}{\partial u} H(s, t, x_0(t))$ is symmetric with proper values λ_n, then $\max\limits_n \frac{|\lambda_n|}{|1-\lambda_n|} \leqq \beta_0$,

or, in case $L(s,t)$ is general and Λ_n are the proper values of

$$\widetilde{L}(s,t) := L(s,t) + L(t.s) - \int_0^1 L(u,s)\, L(u,t)\, du$$

then $\max\limits_n \left[\frac{\Lambda n}{1-\Lambda_n}\right]^{\frac{1}{2}} \leqq \beta_0$;

3) $\| P(x_0) \|^2 = \int_0^1 [x_0(s) - \int_0^1 H(s,t,x_0(t))dt - b(s)]^2 ds \leqq \hat{\eta}_0^2$;

4) $h_0 := \beta_0^2 \hat{\eta}_0 \kappa \leqq \frac{1}{2}$

then there is a solution x^* of $(I-H)x = b$ to which the x_n converge, and $\|x^* - x_0\| \leqq N(h_0)\beta_0\hat{\eta}$.

For actual practice, we remark that not infrequently one has available an initial approximation for which condition 4) of Theorem 1 fails, thus $h_0 > \frac{1}{2}$. The procedure may, and often does, still converge; that is, an iterate is obtained for which the conditions are satisfied, so that convergence is then assured. (cf. an application of this in § 8; also Examples 2 and 3 of § 9).

For applications see also Mysovskih [56].

3. Less Restrictive Assumptions

In this section we give two generalizations of the foregoing which use weaker hypotheses. In the first, operators are permitted which are just once continuously differentiable; in the second, the derivative operators $P'(x)$ may fail to have a (left) inverse, although the requirement that they map X onto Y is kept.

The first is due to R. G. Bartle [22], and depends for its statement and proof on the following

Lemma. Let $P \in C'(S(x_0, \rho))$ and let $P'(x_0)$ have a bounded inverse, and

$$\beta_0 := \| [P'(x_0)]^{-1} \| .$$

If $\gamma > \beta_0$ then there is a $\delta \leqq \min\{1, \rho\}$ such that

1) $\|x-x_o\| \leqq \delta$ implies $P'(x)$ has an inverse and $\|[P'(x)]^{-1}\| < \gamma$;

2) $\|x_i-x_o\| \leqq \delta$, $i = 1, 2, 3$, implies

$$\|P(x_1) - P(x_2) - P'(x_3)(x_1-x_2)\| \leqq \frac{1}{2\gamma}\|x_1 - x_2\| .$$

Bartle's short proof of this uses Property V of §1.

Theorem 3. (Bartle). Let P map the sphere $S(x_o, \rho) \subset X$ into Y, and let the following conditions hold:

1) $P \in C'(S(x_o, \rho))$;

2) $P'(x_o)$ has an inverse, and for a number γ satisfying

$$\|[P'(x_o)]^{-1}\| < \gamma < \infty$$

δ is chosen as in the Lemma ;

3) $\|P(x_o)\| \leqq \hat{\eta}_o$;

4) $\hat{\eta}_o < \frac{\delta}{2\gamma}$;

5) z_n, $n = 0, 1, 2, \ldots$ are arbitrary points in $S(x_o, \delta)$.

Then $P(x) = 0$ has a unique solution in $S(x_o, \delta)$ and the successive approximations defined by

$$x_{n+1} = x_n - [P'(z_n)]^{-1} P(x_n) , \qquad n = 0, 1, 2, \ldots ,$$

converge to x^*. Further,

$$\|x_n - x^*\| < \frac{1}{2^n}\delta . \tag{3.1}$$

Remark. One need not use any particular operators $[P'(z_n)]^{-1}$ (which already are allowed to be distinct from those in (2.2)). In fact, from the proofs of the Lemma and Theorem 3, convergence will hold for the iteration

$$x_{n+1} := x_n - T_n^{-1} P(x_n) , \qquad n = 0, 1, 2, \ldots ,$$

where T_n is any sequence of bounded linear operators satisfying

$$\|T_n - P'(x_o)\| < \frac{1}{4\gamma} \quad \text{and} \quad \|T_n^{-1}\| < \gamma .$$

This remark is particularly applicable in mumerical work since the correct inverses of the operators are almost never precisely computed. In this connection we mention also the paper [25] by Borisovič on the influence of error on the convergence of Newton's method.

To compare with Theorem 1, we use $\beta_0 := \|[P'(x_0)]^{-1}\|$ and suppose again that P is twice differentiable with $\|P''(x)\| \leqq \kappa$. Using simple estimates, we find that in order for a δ to be such that the first condition of the foregoing Remark should hold for $T_n = P'(z_n)$ with $z_n \in S(x_0, \delta)$, it is necessary that $\delta < \frac{1}{4\kappa\gamma}$. Inserting this into condition 4) of Theorem 3, we obtain the requirement $\gamma^2\hat{\eta}\kappa < \frac{1}{8}$. This is to be compared with $\beta_0^2\hat{\eta}\kappa \leqq \frac{1}{2}$ in Remark 3 following Theorem 1, and evidences a stricter requirement on $\hat{\eta}_0$(i.e. a better first approximation), as is to be expected. The convergence may be slower also, as shown by (3.1).

In the same direction of generalization is the article by I. Fenyö [28] in which it is supposed that the derivative satisfies a Lipschitz condition, $\|P'(x) - P'(x_0)\| \leq k\,\|x - x_0\|$ (k constant), in a suitable sphere about x_0.*

Another relaxation of the hypothesis of Theorem 1, investigated by M. Altman [1, 4], is that $P'(x)$ need not have a left inverse (be one-to-one), although it must still map X onto Y. Let $\overline{X}$ and $\overline{Y}$ be the dual spaces of X and Y, resp., i.e. the spaces of bounded linear (scalar valued) functionals $\overline{x}$ and $\overline{y}$ defined on X and Y, resp. For $K \in \mathbf{L}(X, Y)$ let $\overline{K}$ denote its dual in $\mathbf{L}(\overline{Y}, \overline{X})$ defined by $(\overline{K}\overline{y})(x) := \overline{y}(Kx)$. Altman's development depends on the observation that if K maps X onto Y then $\overline{K}$ is one-to-one and so has a left inverse $\overline{K}_L^{-1}$. The proof uses a slight generalization of a theorem of Banach's, viz., that if H is a linear operator having a left inverse H_L^{-1} and if $\|G - H\| < \frac{1}{\|H_L^{-1}\|}$ then G has a left inverse and

$$\|G_L^{-1}\| \leq \frac{\|H_L^{-1}\|}{1-\|H_L^{-1}\|\,\|G-H\|}.$$

For the description of Newton's method, we suppose that P maps a sphere $S(x_0, \rho) \subset X$ into Y in such manner that for $x \in S(x_0, \rho)$ $P'(x)$ maps X onto Y. Let θ_x denote the null space of $P'(x)$: $\theta_x = \{z \in X : P'(x)z = 0\}$. Consider the coset spaces X/θ_x, and let

* We note the paper by Stein [65], but also his Erratum [66] indicating one of the conditions of his theorem cannot be fulfilled.

$\mathbf{Z}$ denote the coset of θ_x containing z. Define the norm by $\|\mathbf{Z}\| := \inf_{z \in \mathbf{Z}} \|z\|$, and assume for simplicity that for each $\mathbf{Z}$ there is an element $z \in \mathbf{Z}$ for which $\|\mathbf{Z}\| = \|z\|$. For each x in $S(x_0, \rho)$, $P'(x)$ induces naturally an invertible linear map $\mathbf{P}_x : X/\theta_x \to Y$, and $\|\mathbf{P}_x^{-1}\| = \|[\overline{P'(x)}]^{-1}\|$. Given an initial approximation x_0 to a solution of $P(x) = 0$, let $\mathbf{X}_1 := \mathbf{X}_0 - \mathbf{P}_0^{-1} P(x_0)$ and choose $x_1 \in \mathbf{X}_1$ such that $\|x_1 - x_0\| = \|\mathbf{X}_1 - \mathbf{X}_0\|$; here and below $\mathbf{P}_i := \mathbf{P}_{x_i}$, $i = 0, 1, \ldots$. In general

(3.2) $$\mathbf{X}_{n+1} := \mathbf{X}_n - \mathbf{P}_n^{-1} P(x_n), \qquad \|x_{n+1} - x_n\| = \|\mathbf{X}_{n+1} - \mathbf{X}_n\|.$$

For this procedure there is the following

Theorem 4. (Altman). Suppose the following conditions are satisfied:

1) P is twice differentiable in $S(x_0, \rho_0)$, where ρ_0 is defined by (3.3) below, and in this sphere

$$\|P''(x)\| \leqq \kappa ;$$

2) $P'(x_0)$ maps X onto Y and $\|[\overline{P'(x_0)}]^{-1}\| \leqq \beta_0$;

3) $\|x_1 - x_0\| \leqq \eta_0$;

4) $h_0 := \beta_0 \eta_0 \kappa \leqq \frac{1}{2}$.

Here (as in (2.3))

(3.3) $$\rho_0 = N(h_0)\eta_0 .$$

Then $P(x) = 0$ has a solution x^* in $\bar{S}(x_0, \rho_0)$ and the successive approximations x_n defined by (3.2) above converge to x^*. Further, the estimate (2.4) holds.

4. Newton's Method In Spaces With Partially Ordered Norm.

Somewhat more precise results are obtainable using the concept of a linear space X normed by means of a partially ordered linear space Z. In outline, this means that the "norm" $\|x\|$ is in Z, and for each x there is a z for which $\|x\| \leqq z$, where $\leqq$ is the order relation in Z.* This norm is to satisfy the conditions 1) $\|x\| \leqq 0$ if and only if $x = 0$; 2) if $\|x\| \leqq z$ and $z \leqq z'$ then $\|x\| \leqq z'$; 3) if $\|x_1\| \leqq z_1$, $\|x_2\| \leqq z_2$, then $\|x_1 + x_2\| \leqq z_1 + z_2$;

* Here we follow Kantorovitch [46]; see also Kantorovič [45, 49]. Cf. as well the papers and references by H. Bueckner and by G. Minty in these Proceedings.

4) if $\|x\| \leqq z$ then $\|\lambda x\| \leqq |\lambda| z$. We write $\|x\| \leqq \|x'\|$ if $\|x'\| \leqq z$ implies $\|x\| \leqq z$; and we write $\|x\| = \|x'\|$ if $\|x\| \leqq \|x'\|$ and $\|x'\| \leqq \|x\|$. Convergence in X, $x_n \to x$, means that $\|x_n - x\| \leqq z_n$ where $z_n \geqq 0$ and $z_n \to 0$ in the order sense in Z. Finally X is supposed complete in the sense that $\|x_n - x_m\| \leqq z_{n,m}$, where the order limit of $z_{n,m}$ is 0, implies the existence of an x such that $x_n \to x$. Suppose X and Y are such spaces, normed respectively by means of Z and W, and suppose U is an additive, homogeneous map from X into Y. We say that a map V from Z into W is a majorant for U, and write $\|U\| \leqq V$, if V is a positive ($z \geqq 0$ implies $Vz \geqq 0$) linear operator, and $\|Ux\| \leqq V(\|x\|)$, thus $\|x\| \leqq z$ implies $\|Ux\| \leqq Vz$. We consider only those U having an order continuous majorant in the space of linear maps from Z into W.

An operator P will be called differentiable if there is a linear map $U = P'(x)$ such that $\lim\limits_{t \to 0} \frac{1}{t}[P(x+th) - P(x) - P'(x)h] = 0$. (This corresponds to the weak or Gateaux derivative; cf, e.g. Hille-Phillips [II]). The second derivative is defined analogously. Kantorovič states that property V of § 1 continues to hold if P is uniformly differentiable on the segment $(x, x+h)$, i.e. if there is a monotone function $w(\delta)$ from the real line to W with $\inf\limits_{\delta > 0} w(\delta) = 0$ such that $\|\frac{1}{\Delta t}[P(x+(t+\Delta t)h) - P(x+th) - P'(x+th)h\| \leqq w(|\Delta t|)$ for $0 \leqq t$, $t + \Delta t \leqq 1$.

As a linear operator the first derivative may have a majorant. With analogous definitions, there may be a majorant of the second derivative.

For P mapping X into Y, the Newton formula for solving $P(x) = 0$ continues to read

$$x_{n+1} := x_n - [P'(x_n)]^{-1} P(x_n), \qquad n = 0, 1, 2, \ldots . \tag{4.1}$$

Parallel to this we consider an equation $Q(z) = 0$, where Q maps Z into W, and we define by the Newton formula a corresponding sequence $z_0, z_1, z_2, \ldots$. In this setting we have the

Theorem 5. (Kantorovič). Let P and Q be twice differentiable operators satisfying the conditions

1) there exist $\Gamma_0 := [P'(x_0)]^{-1}$ and $\Delta_0 := [Q'(z_0)]^{-1}$ such that Δ_0 is order continuous and $\|\Gamma_0\| \leqq -\Delta_0$;
2) $\|\Gamma_0 P(x_0)\| \leqq -\Delta_0 Q(z_0)$;
3) $\|\Gamma_0 P''(x)\| \leqq -\Delta_0 Q''(z)$ for $\|x - x_0\| \leqq z - z_0 < z' - z_0$.

Then the (feasibility and) convergence of the Newton process for

$Q(z) = 0$ to a solution z^*, $z_0 \leqq z^* \leqq z'$, implies the (feasibility and) convergence of the Newton process for $P(x) = 0$ to a solution x^*, and $\|x^* - x_n\| \leqq z^* - z_n$.

If $Q(z') \leqq 0$ and the equation $Q(z) = 0$ has at most one solution in the interval $z_0 \leqq z < z'$, then there is not more than one solution of $P(x) = 0$ in the domain $\|x - x_0\| < z' - z_0$.

A straight forward application of this theorem to Banach spaces results from taking $Z = W = R$ and $\|x\|$ to be the usual norm.

Corollary. Let X and Y be Banach spaces, and suppose $\|\Gamma_0\| \leqq \beta$, $\|P(x_0)\| \leqq \eta$, and $\|P''(x)\| \leqq \kappa(r)$ for $\|x - x_0\| \leqq r$. Consider the equation in R

$$(4.2) \qquad Q(r) := \int_0^r ds \int_0^s \kappa(t)\,dt - \frac{1}{\beta} r + \eta = 0,$$

and suppose it has two positive roots r_1 and r_2 with $r_1 < r_2$. Then the equation $P(x) = 0$ has a solution x^* such that $\|x^* - x_0\| \leqq r_1$, and only that one solution in the sphere $\|x - x_0\| < r_2$.

Note that the example (2.7) is exactly the above equation (4.2) with suitably chosen constants.

Sometimes a less direct application is appropriate. As an illustration of the general situation, consider the integral equation $P(x) = 0$ given by (2.8) and (2.9) with $X = Y = C[0,1]$, and let $Z = W = R^n$. In Z there is the natural ordering: $z \leqq z'$ if and only if $z_i \leqq z_i'$, $i = 1, \ldots, n$, where $z = (z_1, \ldots, z_n)$, $z' = (z_1', \ldots, z_n')$. Let $[0,1]$ be subdivided into n subintervals J_i, $i = 1, \ldots, n$, and let $\|x\| := (\max_{s \in J_1} |x(s)|, \ldots, \max_{s \in J_n} |x(s)|)$. An integral operator K in $C[0,1]$, with kernel $K(s,t)$, is majorized by a matrix $\hat{K}$ in $Z = R^n$, with elements $k_{ij} := \max_{s \in J_i, t \in J_j} |K(s,t)|$; thus $\|Kx\| \leqq \hat{K}\|x\|$. The conditions of Theorem 5 then concern the relation between the equation $P(x) = 0$ in $C[0,1]$ and an equation $Q(z) = 0$ in R^n; the latter is of the form considered in Example 1 of § 1. The convergence of Newton's method for Q may be discussed using Theorem 1. For this purpose, any norm may be used in R^n since norm convergence is equivalent to order convergence.

Additional applications and examples are given in Kantorovič [49] and Baluev [20].

The work of Schröder [63] using partially ordered spaces is somewhat more general in that the derivative operators need not be bounded. His paper has applications thus to non-linear differential equations. The conditions of his theorems are too complicated to develop here.

5. Newton's Method For Functionals. Application To Operator Equations In Hilbert Spaces.

Since in § 2 it is assumed that $P'(x_0)$ is invertible, the theorem given there does not apply to non-linear functionals (unless X is simply the scalar field itself.) We give now a procedure developed by Altman [2, 3, 9, 10, 11] (cf. also Szeptycki [68]).

Consider the equation $F(x) = 0$ where F maps the real Banach space X into R. To define the sequence of approximate solutions, given an initial approximation x_0, we seek a solution x_1, of $F(x_0) + F'(x_0)(x_1 - x_0) = 0$. For this we choose $y_0 \in X$ such that $\|y_0\| = 1$ and $F'(x_0)y_0 = \|F'(x_0)\|$ when this is possible, and set $x_1 = x_0 - \frac{F(x_0)}{\|F'(x_0)\|} y_0$. In general,

$$(5.1) \qquad x_{n+1} := x_n - \frac{F(x_n)}{\|F(x_n)\|} y_n, \qquad \|y_n\| = 1, F'(x_n)y_n = \|F'(x_n)\|.$$

(Such y_n can be found in reflexive Banach spaces.)

Consider also a majorant equation $Q(z) = 0$ where Q maps R into R, and is twice differentiable on $[z_0, z']$. (Cf. § 4). Let $z_{n+1} := z_n - [Q'(z_n)]^{-1} Q(z_n)$.

<u>Theorem 6.</u> (Altman). Let F be twice differentiable in $S(x_0, \rho)$ where $\rho = z' - z_0$. Suppose $Q'(z_0) < 0$ so that $\beta_0 = -\frac{1}{Q'(z_0)} > 0$.

Suppose

1) $\frac{1}{\|F'(x_0)\|} < \beta_0$,

2) $|F(x_0)| \leqq Q(z_0)$,

3) $\|F''(x)\| \leqq Q''(z)$ for $\|x - x_0\| \leqq z - z_0 \leqq z' - z_0$.

Under these conditions, if $Q(z) = 0$ has a real root z^* in $[z_0, z']$, then $F(x) = 0$ has a solution x^* in $\overline{S}(x_0, \rho)$, $\rho = z' - z_0$, and the successive approximations defined by (5.1) converge to x^*. Further, $\|x_n - x^*\| \leqq z^* - z_n$.

For general Banach spaces Altman has shown [12, 17] that it is both sufficient and possible to chose the y_n in (5.1) satisfying only

$$\|y_n\| \leqq 1 \text{ and } |Q'(z_n)| \leqq |F'(x_n)y_n| \leqq \|F'(x_n)\|.$$

Now suppose X is a Hilbert space with inner product (x,y). Then (cf. VI in § 1) for each x at which F is differentiable there is $\nabla F(x) \in X$ such that $F'(x)y = (\nabla F(x), y)$. For the elements y in (5.1) we thus may take

$$y_n := \frac{\nabla F(x_n)}{\|\nabla F(x_n)\|} .$$

Consider again the equation $P(x) = 0$ where P maps the Hilbert space X into X. Let

$$F(x) := \|P(x)\|^2 = Q(P(x)) \quad \text{where} \quad Q(y) := (y, y) .$$

We see that the derivative of Q is given by $Q'(y_0)h = (2y_0, h)$ (Note $Q(y+h) = Q(y) + 2(y,h) + (h,h)$ so

$$\frac{1}{\|h\|} |Q(y+h) - Q(y) - (2y, h)| = \|h\|).$$

Thus

$$F'(x_0)h = Q'(P(x_0))P'(x_0)h = (2P(x_0), P'(x_0)h) = (2\overline{P'(x_0)}P(x_0), h)$$

so

$$\nabla F(x_0) = 2\overline{P'(x_0)}P(x_0) .$$

In $L^2[0,1]$, with P defined by (2.9), we have $\overline{P'(x_0)} = I - \overline{H'(x_0)}$. Thus, for the F above,

$$\nabla F(x_0) = 2[P(x_0) - \overline{H'(x_0)}P(x_0)] = 2[P(x_0) - T(x_0)] \quad \text{where}$$

$$(T(x_0))(s) := \int_0^1 \frac{\partial}{\partial u} H(t, s, x_0(s))[x_0(t) - \int_0^1 H(t, \tau, x_0(\tau))d\tau - b(t)]dt.$$

The Newton iterates are given by (Altman [5, 12])

$$x_{n+1} = x_n - \frac{\|P(x_n)\|^2}{\|\nabla F(x_n)\|^2} \nabla F(x_n), \qquad n = 0, 1, 2, \ldots .$$

A related iteration

$$x_{n+1} = x_n - P(x_n) \frac{\| P(x_n) \|^2}{2(P'(x_n)P(x_n), P(x_n))}, \qquad n = 0, 1, 2, \ldots,$$

is considered in [6, 7].

6. Higher Order Methods In Banach Spaces

Newton's method results from approximating $P(x) = 0$ by the linear equation $P(x_0) + P'(x_0)(x_1 - x_0) = 0$. Using the next approximation, $P(x_0) + P'(x_0)(x_1 - x_0) + \frac{1}{2} P''(x_0)(x_1 - x_0)(x_1 - x_0) = 0$, one may obtain the Tchebycheff method of "tangent parabolas". Namely, $P''(x_0)$ is made to act on $\Gamma_0 P(x_0)$ (the first approximation to $x_1 - x_0$), where $\Gamma_0 := [P'(x_0)]^{-1}$, and the second approximating equation is solved for $x_1 - x_0$. We obtain thus the iteration formula

$$(6.1) \qquad x_{n+1} - x_n = -\Gamma_n [P(x_n + \tfrac{1}{2} P''(x_n)\Gamma_n P(x_n)\Gamma_n P(x_n)]$$

$$= -[I + \tfrac{1}{2}\Gamma_n P''(x_n)\Gamma_n P(x_n)]\Gamma_n P(x_n).$$

where $\Gamma_n = [P'(x_n)]^{-1}$. This procedure has been investigated by Nečepurenko [57], who proved the following

Theorem 7. (Nečepurenko). Let the conditions 1), 2), 3) of Theorem 1 be satisfied, and suppose

4) $h_0 := \beta_0 \eta_0 \kappa \leqq \sqrt{\frac{3}{2}} - 1$.

Then there is a solution x^* of $P(x) = 0$ in $S(x_0, \rho_0)$ and the sequence defined by (6.1) converges to x^*.

Letting $g_0 = h_0(1 + \frac{h_0}{2})$ and $\theta = \frac{256}{81}$ one has further

$$(6.2) \qquad \| x_n - x^* \| \; 4 \left(\tfrac{3}{4}\right)^n (\theta g_0)^{2^n - 1}\left(1 + \frac{h_0}{2}\right)\eta_0 .$$

[That $g_0 \leqq \frac{1}{4}$ follows from 4), so that $\theta g_0 \leqq \frac{64}{81} < 1$].
The estimate (6.2) may be compared with (2.4) for Newton's method.

Another procedure, the method of tangent hyperbolas, was investigated by Mertvetsova [53]. With the above notation his iterations are given by

$$(6.3) \qquad x_{n+1} := x_n - Q_n \Gamma_n P(x_n), \qquad Q_n = [I - \tfrac{1}{2}\Gamma_n P''(x_n)\Gamma_n P(x_n)]^{-1}.$$

Theorem 8. (Mertvetsova). Let the conditions 1) - 4) of Theorem 1 hold in $S(x_0, 2\eta_0)$, and suppose further that P is three times differentiable with $\| P'''(x) \| \leqq \lambda$ in $S(x_0, 2\eta_0)$, and

$$\mu_0 = \left[\frac{\lambda}{\kappa^2 \beta_0} (2+h_0) + 3\right](1+h_0) \leqq 9 .$$

Then $P(x) = 0$ has a solution x^* in $S(x_0, 2\eta_0)$ to which the iterates defined by (6.3) converge. Further

$$\|x_n - x^*\| \leq \frac{1}{2^{n-1}} (2h_0)^{3^n - 1} \eta_0 . \tag{6.4}$$

The exponent $3^n - 1$ in (6.4) describes the higher rate of convergence of this method over the Newton method (cf. (2.4)).

More complicated methods have been investigated by Kaazik [35, 36, 37, 38] and Tamme [69, 70]. One such is given by

$$x_{n+1} : = x_n + F_n \Gamma_n P(x_n) , \qquad \Gamma_n : = [P'(x_n)]^{-1} ,$$

$$F_n : = - [I+\alpha R_n]^{-1} [I+(\alpha+1) R_n], \qquad R_n : = \tfrac{1}{2} \Gamma_n P''(x_n) \Gamma_n P(x_n), \alpha \text{ real.}$$

For functional equations, higher order methods in the spirit of those in § 5 are discussed by Altman in [14, 15, 16, 17].

7. Equations With Parameters

Consider now an equation

$$P(\mu, x) = 0$$

where μ is a parameter. Adapting the notation of Theorem 1 to this instance, we let $\Gamma_0 : = [P'_x(\mu_0, x_0)]^{-1}$, $\|\Gamma_0\| \leqq \beta_0$, $\|\Gamma_0 P(\mu_0, x_0)\| \leqq \eta_0$, $\|P''_{xx}(\mu_0, x)\| \leqq \kappa$, where we have used a subscript to emphasize differentiation with respect to x. If we suppose that $h_0 : = \beta_0 \eta_0 \kappa < \frac{1}{2}$ (strict inequality) and if P, P'_x and P''_{xx} depend continuously on μ (for P''_{xx} the dependence is to be uniform for $x \in S(x_0, 2\eta_0)$), then for μ in a suitable neighborhood of μ_0, the corresponding product $h : = \beta \eta \kappa$ will remain $< \frac{1}{2}$, and thus for such μ, the Newton iterates beginning with x_0 will converge to a solution of $P(\mu, x) = 0$. (This yields an implicit function result. Cf. Hildebrandt and Graves [33], Liusternik and Sobolev [III], F.A. Ficken [29]; also Block and Rosenbloom [24]).

In the context of the partially ordered spaces of § 4, Kantorovič

[47] has proved the following (in which μ may be belong to a space M normed by the partially ordered space N to which ν belongs):

Theorem 9. Let $P(\mu, x)$ and $Q(\nu, z)$ be twice differentiable with respect to x and z, resp., and once differentiable with respect to μ and ν, resp., and let the following conditions be satisfied:

1) there exist $\Gamma_o := [P'_x(\mu_o, x_o)]^{-1}$, $\Delta_o := [Q'_z(\nu_o, z_o)]^{-1}$, and $\|\Gamma_o\| \leqq -\Delta_o$;
2) $\|P(\mu_o, x_o)\| \leqq Q(\nu_o, z_o)$;
3) $\|P''_{xx}(\mu_o, x)\| \leqq Q''_{zz}(\nu_o, z)$ for $\|x - x_o\| \leqq z - z_o$;
4) $\|\frac{\partial}{\partial \mu} P(\mu\ x_o)\| \leqq \frac{\partial}{\partial \nu} Q(\nu, z_o)$ for $\|\mu - \mu_o\| \leqq \nu - \nu_o$;
5) $\|\frac{\partial}{\partial \mu} P'_x(\mu, x_o)\| \leqq \frac{\partial}{\partial \nu} Q'_z(\nu, z_o)$ for $\|\mu - \mu_o\| \leqq \nu - \nu_o$;
6) $\|\frac{\partial}{\partial \mu} P''_{xx}(\mu, x)\| \leqq \frac{\partial}{\partial \nu} Q''_{zz}(\nu, z)$ for $\|x - x_o\| \leqq z - z_o$ and $\|\mu - \mu_o\| \leqq \nu - \nu_o$.

Suppose for $\nu_0 \leqq \nu \leqq \nu_1$ the equation $Q(\nu, z)$ has a solution $z^*(\nu) \geqq z_0$ which can be obtained by Newton's method (or the modified method (2.5)). Then the equation $P(\mu, x) = 0$ has a solution $x^*(\mu)$ satisfying $\|x^*(\mu) - x_0\| \leqq z^*(\nu) - z_0$ if $\|\mu - \mu_0\| \leqq \nu - \nu_0$, and this solution may be obtained by the Newton or modified method.

To specialize this theorem directly to Banach spaces, take $Z = W = R$ and $\|x\|$ as usual. Similarly one often takes $M = N = R$.

For functional equations (§5) depending on a parameter, see Altman [13].

8. Curves Of Solutions And Critical Values

Throughout the following let μ be a real parameter. Suppose a solution of $P(\mu, x) = 0$ is obtained for $\mu = \mu_0$, say $x = x(\mu_0)$. As μ increases (or decreases) from μ_0 there will be, under conditions such as given in § 7, for each μ a solution $x(\mu)$, so that a curve of solutions is formed in the space X. It is convenient to use Newton's method to approximate this curve. Namely, with $\mu_1 = \mu_0 + \Delta\mu$, where $\Delta\mu$ is a small increment, one uses $x(\mu_0)$ as a first approximate solution of $P(\mu_1, x) = 0$, and applies Newton's method to obtain a solution $x(\mu_1)$. In practice one accepts one of the iterates, say $\bar{x}(\mu_1)$, as an approximate solution at $\mu = \mu_1$. Then, incrementing again, with $\mu_2 = \mu_1 + \Delta\mu$, one again applies Newton's method using $\bar{x}(\mu_1)$, or an extrapolation from it, as an initial approximation. One obtains thus the solution $x(\mu_2)$, or an approximation

$\overline{x}(\mu_2)$. This process may be repeated so long as the iterates converge, solutions $x(\mu_k)$ or approximations $\overline{x}(\mu_k)$ being found. (Cf. the comment at the end of § 2).

A particularly interesting aspect of this technique is that one may be able to find solutions $x(\mu_k)$, or approximate solutions with a guarantee on the existence of a true solution nearby, when in no other way can the existence of a solution be demonstrated for certain ranges of μ. It is common, for example, to depend on the contractive mapping principle or the Schauder-Leray fixed point principle to conclude that a solution exists. But also commonly, these principles fail for μ outside of some range, say $\mu > \overline{\mu}$. If the curve can be approximated for $\mu_k > \overline{\mu}$ as above, then the existence is constructively demonstrated.

Consider now the frequently occurring equation (cf. (2.8))

$$P(\mu, x) := (I - \mu H)x - b = 0. \tag{8.1}$$

We see $P'_x(\mu, x) = I - \mu H'(x)$. It may happen that as μ approaches some critical value, μ_c, the derivative operator $P'_x(\mu, x(\mu))$ becomes singular (cf. Tricomi [71] p. 201); the above technique fails in the neighborhood of such a value. In some cases the difficulty can be obviated by a change of parameters. Thus, we let $\mu = g(w, x)$ and define $\hat{P}(w, x) := P(g(w, x), x)$. Then, with $P'_\mu := \frac{\partial}{\partial \mu} P$,

$$\hat{P}'_x(w,x) = P'_x(g(w,x), x) + P'_\mu(g(w,x),x) g'_x(w,x) = I - \mu H'(x) + H(x) g'_x(w,x).$$

This means, for a vector $h \in X$, that

$$\hat{P}'_x(w, x)h = h - \mu H'_x(x)h + g'_x(w, x)h \cdot H(x), \tag{8.2}$$

since $g'_x(w, x)h$ is a real number. Suppose $x(\mu) \to x_c$ as $\mu \to \mu_c$, and suppose $P'_x(\mu_c, x_c)$ has a null space of dimension one. Then unless the null space of $g'_x(w, x)$ contains that of $P'_x(\mu_c, x_c)$, we see from (8.2) that $\hat{P}'_x(w_c, x_c)$ has only the trivial null vector 0, and is thus invertible. (We assume $H(x_c) \neq 0$). If $P'_x(\mu_c, x_c)$ has range with deficiency (codimension) one, so that it does not map X onto X, then unless $H(x_c)$ is already in that range, we see from (8.2) that $\hat{P}'_x(w_c, x_c)$ does map X onto X. Hence, when such a $g(w, x)$ can be found the procedure of advancing approximations described above can be applied to $\hat{P}(w, x)$ with w playing the rôle of μ.

An investigation of the circumstances which allow such a $g(w, x)$ to exist begins with the linear approximation

$$P(\mu+\delta, x+h) \approx P(\mu, x) + P'_\mu(\mu, x)\delta + P'_x(\mu, x)h. \tag{8.3}$$

If $x = x(\mu)$ then $P(\mu, x) = 0$. We achieve also $P(\mu+\delta, x+h) \approx 0$ if $h = -[P'_x(\mu, x(\mu))]^{-1} P'_\mu(\mu, x)\delta$ in case $P'_x(\mu, x(\mu))$ is not singular. If this derivative is singular, as at (μ_c, x_c) and has null space of dimension one we still achieve $P(\mu+\delta, x+h) \approx 0$ by taking $\delta = 0$, $h \in$ null space of $P'_x(\mu_c, x_c)$. But for the actual determination of x_c we employ the change of parameters.

An intuitive geometric view of the situation is suggested by considering the curve C of points $(\mu, x(\mu))$ in $R \times X$. Then each point $x(\mu)$ is determined by the intersection of C with the "horizontal" hyperplane $\mu =$ const. in $R \times X$. The vector (δ, h) in $R \times X$

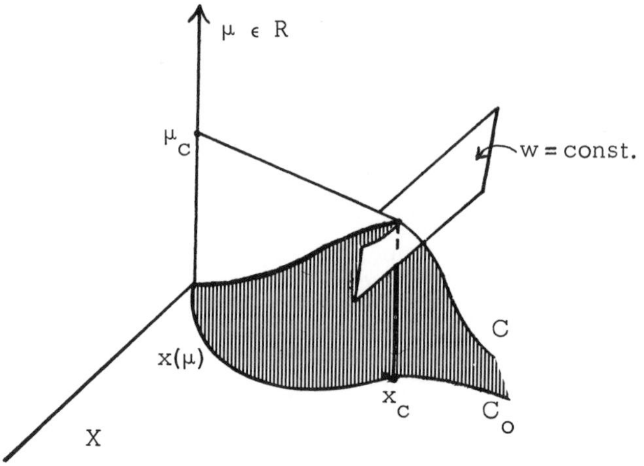

considered in (8.3) represents the tangent vector to C. Such a vector with $\delta = 0$ is horizontal. The statements following (8.3) mean that C has a horizontal tangent vector at (μ_c, x_c). If the null space of $P'_x(\mu_c, x_c)$ is one dimensional then the direction of horizontal component is well defined. But the intersection of C with the horizontal hyperplane $\mu = \mu_c$ degenerates to a tangency. By introducing $g(w, x) = \mu$ and applying Newton's method to $\hat{P}(w, x)$ with fixed values of w, we are seeking the intersection of C with hypersurfaces in $R \times X$ on which w is constant. That this can be done as suggested by the figure is the content of the discussion following (8.2).

The above considerations have been employed in the consideration of a buckling problem in elasticity theory (papers to appear by Bueckner and Johnson, and Anselone and Moore). By use of numerical methods a curve as suggested was in fact obtained.

9. Newton's Method And The Solution Of Nonlinear Integral Equations By Numerical Computation

We consider here the Urysohn equation in $C[0,1]$ (cf. (2.8) and (2.9))

$$x(s) - \int_0^1 H(s, t, s(t))\,dt - b(s) = 0, \tag{9.1}$$

or

$$P(x) = 0. \tag{9.2}$$

For computation it is convenient to replace the integration by a numerical quadrature, and so use the method of discrete ordinates. Thus, let the quadrature abscissas be s_i, $i = 1, \dots, m$, $0 \leqq s_1 < s_2 < \dots < s_m \leqq 1$, with associated weights $w_1, \dots, w_m$, respectively, and let $x_i = x(s_i)$, $b_i = b(s_i)$, $\overline{x} = (x_1, \dots, x_m)$, $\overline{b} = (b_1, \dots, b_m)$, to obtain the system in R^m analogous to (9.1)

$$x_i - \sum_{k=1}^{m} H(s_i, s_k, x_k)\, w_k - b_i = 0, \qquad i = 1, \dots, m, \tag{9.3}$$

or

$$\overline{P}(\overline{x}) = 0, \qquad \overline{P}(\overline{x}) := (\overline{I} - \overline{H})\,\overline{x} - \overline{b}. \tag{9.4}$$

An approximate solution in $C[0,1]$ of (9.1) is obtained from a solution or approximate solution, $\overline{x} = (\overline{x}_1, \dots, \overline{x}_m)$ of (9.3) by the formula

$$\widetilde{x}(s) := \sum_{k=1}^{m} H(s, s_k, \overline{x}_k)\, w_k + b(s). \tag{9.5}$$

Alternatively, one may use a standard interpolation scheme, e.g. Lagrangian, to obtain an element of $C[0,1]$ from $\overline{x}$. However such interpolation is less natural to the problem than that in (9.5); the second example below illustrates the advantages of (9.5).

To the equation (9.4) we may apply Newton's Method. (The derivatives $\overline{H}'(\overline{x}_0)$ and $\overline{H}''(x_0)$ are given, in this case, by the analogs in R^n of (1.11) and (1.12)). In particular, Theorem 1 applies. Baluev [21] has shown that if (9.2) has a solution x^*, and if the kernel $K(s,t) := \frac{\partial H}{\partial u}(s, t, x^*(t))$ has a bounded resolvent, while $H(s,t,u)$ and $b(s)$ have bounded third derivatives in $0 \le s, t \le 1$, $x^*(t) - h \le u \le x^*(t) + h$, then by using Gauss quadrature of sufficiently high order a system (9.3) is obtained which has a solution

$\overline{x} = (x_1, \ldots, \overline{x}_m)$ and $|\overline{x}_k - x^*(s_k)| = \theta(\frac{1}{m^2})$. The converse question has been considered by the author for Hammerstein integral operators, i.e. in case $H(s,t,u) = L(s,t)f(u)$, based on a result with P. M. Anselone [18]. Provided L is differentiable and f twice differentiable, conditions can be given, depending only on the norms computed in R^m, which insure that the conditions of Theorem 1 are satisfied in $C[0,1]$, and thus whose satisfaction guarantees the existence of a solution of $P(x) = 0$. It is expected that a similar statement holds for the Urysohn equation.

Kwan and Lin [51] have applied to nonlinear equations the approximation theory developed by Kantorovič in [43] for linear equations, with conditions being given under which the modified Newton method for the approximating equation (e.g. (9.3)) will converge.

We conclude with three examples of the computational scheme.*

Example 1. Let $H(s,t,u) = stu^2$ and $b(s) = \frac{3}{4}s$ so (9.1) becomes

$$x(s) - \int_0^1 st(x(t))^2 dt = \frac{3}{4}s ;$$

this has the solution $x(s) = s$ in $C[0,1]$. For computation a two point Gaussian quadrature was used, so $R^m = R^2$, with the norm $\|x\| = \max_{i=1,2}(|x_i|)$. Since $|\frac{\partial^2}{\partial u^2} H(s,t,u)| \leqq 2$ for $0 \leqq s,t,u \leqq 1$ we have $\|\overline{H}''(\overline{x})\| \leqq 2$ in the sphere $\|\overline{x}\| \leqq 1$; this is satisfactory for the computations (cf. Theorem 1). As initial vector we use $\overline{x}_0 = \overline{b}$, i.e. $\overline{x}_{0,1} = \frac{3}{4}s_1$, $\overline{x}_{0,2} = \frac{3}{4}s_2$, where s_1, s_2 are the quadrature abscissas. In tabular form below are given the results of the successive iterations in R^2, where, in the notation of Theorem 1, the quantities $h_0 := \beta_0 \eta_0 \kappa$ and $\rho_0 := N(h_0)\eta_0$ for the analog equation (9.3) are recomputed at each step.

The last values for $\overline{x}_1, \overline{x}_2$ are the correct (Legendre zeros) s_1, s_2. Another iterative sequence with initial vector $\overline{x}_0 = (\frac{1}{2}, \frac{1}{2})$, corresponding to $x_0(s) \equiv \frac{1}{2}$, also converged in five iterations. From the computed $\overline{x}$, Lagrangian interpolation for other values of $x(s)$ is, of course, fully accurate for the polynomial $x(s) = s$.

* The computational work was executed by Mr. Ken Atkinson, of the University of Wisconsin, using a CDC 1604 digital computer.

Iteration	h_o	ρ_o	$\bar{x}_1$	$\bar{x}_2$
1	.28941	.21522	.158 493	.591 506
2	.038958	.01987	.206 042	.768 958
3	$.4931 \times 10^{-3}$	$.2405 \times 10^{-3}$	.211 260	.788 434
4	$.7517 \times 10^{-7}$	$.3664 \times 10^{-7}$	.211 324 8560	.788 675 0975
5	$.38 \times 10^{-11}$	0.0	.211 324 8658	.788 675 1342

Example 2. The equation

$$x(s) - \int_0^1 e^{st} e^{-[x(t)]^2} dt = \sqrt{s} - \frac{1}{s-1}[e^{s-1} - 1]$$

has the solution $x(s) = \sqrt{s}$. Using 5-point Gaussian quadrature and the procedure outlined above, the final iterates of the Newton method yielded ten-digit accuracy for $\bar{x}$, that is $\bar{x}_k = \sqrt{s_k}$ to ten places. For the first step, $h_o = 158.98$; although this much exceeded $\frac{1}{2}$ the procedure converged rapidly, having for the sixth iteration $h_o = .174 \times 10^{-8}$.

Interpolation using (9.5) shows here to be much better than Lagranian interpolation, even when the latter is based on a computation using 25 points in the quadrature. This may be expected here, of course, because of the difficulty of fitting $s^{\frac{1}{2}}$ with a polynomial. Since this difficulty may occur in general, the formula (9.5) proves highly appropriate. The table following gives sample results.

s	Lagr. interp. 25 pt. Gauss quadr. $\tilde{x}(s)$	Interp. by (9.5) 5-pt. Gauss quadr. $\tilde{x}(s)$	$\sqrt{s}$
.00	.026 034	.00	.00
.20	.447 193	.447 213 5955	.447 213 5955
.60	.774 606	.774 596 6693	.774 596 6692
.80	.894 433	.894 427 1911	.894 427 1910

Example 3. We consider the equation for the H-function in the theory of radiative transfer

$$\frac{1}{H(\mu)} = 1.0 - \tfrac{1}{2}\,\bar{w}\int_0^1 \frac{\mu}{\mu+\mu'}\,H(\mu')\,d\mu' ,$$

which we write in the form,

$$x(s) + \tfrac{1}{2}\,\bar{w}\int_0^1 \frac{s}{s+t}\,\frac{1}{x(t)}\,dt = 1 .$$

Using the method of discrete ordinates and Newton's method as described, with the initial approximation $x_0(s) = 1 + 2s$, we obtain the results tabulated below. The final values of h_0 and ρ_0 for the analog equation (9.3) are included; these were obtained in four or five iterations, with the initial h_0 being 13.6 and 3.3 in the two case presented here. For comparison are given also the results of Chandrasekhar and Breen [26] and of Stibbs and Weir [67] obtained in a quite different manner.

$\bar{w}_0 = .95$	Chandrasekhar Breen	Stibbs Weir	Newton (6 pt. Gauss)
$\mu = 0$	1.0000	1.000 000	1.000 000
0.05	1.1117	1.111 508	1.111 063
0.10	1.1952	1.195 232	1.195 159
0.30	1.4604	1.460 454	1.460 465
0.60	1.7647	1.764 711	1.764 719
1.00	2.0771	2.077 123	2.077 129
	Final $h_0 = 1.3 \times 10^{-9}$, $\rho_0 = 1.4 \times 10^{-11}$		
$\bar{w}_0 = 1.00$			(12 pt. Gauss)
$\mu = 0$	1.0000	1.000 000	1.000 000
0.05	1.1368	1.136 575	1.136 573 5
0.10	1.2474	1.247 350	1.247 351 0
0.30	1.6425	1.642 522	1.642 522 5
0.60	2.1941	2.194 133	2.194 133 2
1.00	2.9078	2.907 809	2.907 810 7
	Final $h_0 = 2.8 \times 10^{-9}$, $\rho_0 = 2.6 \times 10^{-11}$		

10. Supplementary Remarks

We mention here some papers not included in the foregoing. W. Chen [27] has considered iterations of the general type $x_{n+1} = x_n - T_n^{-1} P(x_n)$, where T_n is linear, in Banach spaces.

Slugin [64] considers $x_{n+1} = x_n - L\,P(x_n)$ where L need not have an inverse, and obtains two sets of successive approximations converging monotonically from above and below (a Chaplygin method) when the space is a vector lattice.

Hirasawa [34] has given a generalization of Newton's method to convex linear topological spaces over the complex field. For this purpose he develops briefly enough theory of analytic functions in such spaces to obtain a Taylor expansion (cf. IV of § 1 above).

Newton's method may be used for the computation of eigenvalues and eigenvectors of a linear operator: cf. Kantorovič [43], Rall [62].

Hart and Motzkin [32] have investigated a composite of the Newton and gradient methods for systems of equations.

The articles [48] by Kantorovič and [52] by Masaitas are surveys.

The chapter on Newton's method from the book by Kantorovič and Akilov, Functional Analysis in Normed Spaces, appears in translation as an appendix to the recently published translation of Vainberg's book [73].

At the end of the bibliography we have appended supplementary references to papers dealing with Newton's method applied to differential equations.

GENERAL REFERENCES

I Dieudonné, J., Foundations of Modern Analysis. Academic Press, New York, 1960.

II Hille, E., and Phillips, R. S., Functional Analysis and Semi-groupes. Amer. Math. Soc. Colloquium Publ., Vol. 31, 1957.

III Luisternik, L. A., and Sobolev, V. J., Elements of Functional Analysis (Transl. Labarre, Izbicki, Crowley), Ungar, New York, 1961.

BIBLIOGRAPHY

1. Altman, M., A generalization of Newton's Method. Bull. Acad. Polon. Sci. Cl. III 3 (1955), 189-193, MR 17, 176.

2. Altman, M., On the approximate solution of non-linear functional equations. Bull. Acad. Polon. Sci. Cl. III 5 (1957), 457-460, XXXIX. MR 19, 984 (1958).

3. __________, Concerning approximate solutions of non-linear functional equations. Ibid. 461-465. MR 19, 984 (1958).

4. __________, On the generalisation of Newton's method. Ibid. 789-795, LXVIII. MR 19, 983(1957).

5. __________, On the approximate solutions of operator equations in Hilbert space. Ibid. 605-609, LII. MR 19, 984.

6. __________, Concerning the approximate solutions of operator equations in Hilbert space. Ibid. 711-715, LXII-LXIII. MR 19, 984.

7. __________, A note on the approximate solutions of non-linear operator equations in Hilbert space. Ibid. 783-787, LXVII-LXVIII. MR 19, 984.

8. __________, Connection between the method of steepest descent and Newton's method. Ibid. 1031-1036, LXXXVI. MR 19, 984.

9. __________, On the approximate solutions of operator equations in L^p spaces. Ibid. 1099-1103, XCI. MR 19, 1068.

10. __________, On the approximate solutions of non-linear functional equations in Banach spaces. Bull. Acad. Polon. Sci. Ser. Sci. Math. Astr. Phys. 6, 19-24 (1958). MR 20, 5440 (1959).

11. __________, On the approximate solutions of functional equations in L^p spaces. Colloq. Math. 6, 127-134 (1958), MR 20, 7232 (1959).

12. __________, Approximate methods in functional analysis. Lecture notes, Calif. Inst. Tech., 1959.

13. __________, Functional equations involving a parameter. Proc. Amer. Math. Soc. 11 (1960), 54-61.

14. __________, An iterative method of solving functional equations Bull. Acad. Polon. Sci. Ser. Sci. Math. Astr. Phys. 9(1961), 57-62. MR 24, A 2263 (1962).

15. Altman, M., Iterative methods of higher order. Bull. Acad. Polon. Sci. Ser. Sci. Math. Astr. Phys. 9 (1961), 63-68. MR 24, A 2263 (1962).

16. __________, Concerning Tchebyshev's generalized method of solving non-linear functional equations. Ibid., 261-265. MR 24, A 2263 (1962).

17. __________, Extension and stability of certain iterative methods for solving non-linear functional equations in Banach spaces. Ibid. MR 24, A 2263 (1962).

18. Anselone, P. M., and Moore R. H., Approximate Solutions of Integral and Operator Equations. J. Math. Anal. Appl. (to appear).

19. Antosiewicz, H. A., and Rheinbolt, W. C., Numerical Analysis and Functional Analysis. Survey of Numerical Analysis, Chap.14, J. Todd (editor).

20. Baluev, A. N., Application of semi-ordered norms in approximate solution of non-linear equations. Leningrad. Gos. Univ. Uc. Zap. Ser. Mat. Nauk 33 (1958), 18-27. MR 22 (1961) 3958.

21. __________, Approximate solutions of non-linear integral equations, Ibid. 28-31. MR 22 (1961) 3959.

22. Bartle, R. G., Newton's Method in Banach spaces. Proc. Amer. Math. Soc. 6, 827-831 (1955). MR 17, 176 (1956).

23. Bennett, Albert A., Newton's Method in General Analysis, Proc. Nat. Acad. Sci. 2 (1916) 592 - 598.

24. Block, H. D., and Rosenbloom, P. C., Perturbation of non-linear eigenvalue problems. Arch. Math. 7, 172-183 (1956). MR 18, 235 (1957).

25. Borisovič, Yu. G., On the influence of error on the convergence of Newton's process for nonlinear functional operations. Kazan. Gos. Univ. Uc. Zap. 113 no. 10 (1953) 189-192. MR 17, (1956) 879.

26. Chandresekhar, and Breen, On the radiative equilibrium of a stellar atmosphere. Astrophys. J. 106 (1947) 143. (Table of results also given in Chandresekhar, Radiative Transfer, Dover, 1960, p. 125).

27. Chen, Wen-Yuan, Iterative processes for solving non-linear functional equations. Advancement in Math. 3 (1957) 434-444. (Chinese) MR 20 (1959) 3467, p. 574.

28. Fenyö, I., Über die Lösung der in Banachschen Raum definierten nichtlinearen Gleichungen. Acta Math. Acad. Sci. Hungar. 5, 85-93 (1954). MR 15, 964 (1954).

29. Ficken, F. A., The continuation method for functional equations. Comm. Pure, Appl. Math. 4, 435-456 (1951). MR 13, 562(1952).

30. Fine, Harry B., On Newton's Method of Approximation. Proc. Nat'l. Acad. Sci. 2 (1916) 546-552.

31. Graves, L. M., Riemann integration and Taylor's theorem in general analysis. Trans. Amer. Math. Soc. 29 (1927) 163-177.

32. Hart, W. and Motzkin, T., A Composite Newton-Raphson Gradient Method for the Solution of Systems of Equations. Pacif. J. Math. 6, 691-707 (1956).

33. Hildebrandt, T. H., and Graves, L. M., Implicit functions and their differentials in general analysis. Trans. Amer. Math. Soc. 29 (1927) 127-153.

34. Hirasawa, Y., Newton's Method in Convex Linear Topological Spaces. Comment. Math. Univ. St. Paul 3 (1954) 15-27. MR 16, 487.

35. Kaazik, Yu. J., On a class of iteration processes for the solution of the operator equations. Dokl. Akad. Nauk. SSSR (N. S.) 112 (1957) 579-582 (Russian). MR 20 (1959) 234.

36. __________, On approximate solution of non-linear operator equations by iterative methods. Uspehi. Mat. Nauk. (N. S.) 12 (1957) no. 1(73) 195-199 (Russian). MR 19 (1958) 687, Rzh. (1957) 8022, 10. AMS Transl. (2) 16(1960) 410-413. (MR (22) (1961) 8378: no review.)

37. __________, Über die Konvergenz von Iterationsmethoden. Tartu Rickl. Ül. Toimetised 62 (1958) 80-98. MR 22 (1961) 912.

38. Kaazik, Yu. Ya, and Tamme, È. È., Über eine Methode zur angenäherten Lösung nichtlinearen Operatorgleichungen. Tartu. Rickl. Ül. Toimetised 62 (1958) 99-116. MR 22(1961) 913.

39. Kantorovič , L. V., Lineare halbgeordnete Raume. Matem. Sbornik. 2 (44) 1, 121-165, (1937).

40. __________, The method of successive approximations for functional equations. Acta. Math. 71 (1939) 63-77. MR 1 p. 18.

41. __________, On Newton's Method for Functional Equations. Dokl. Acad. Nauk. SSSR (N. S.) 59 (1948) 1237-1240. MR 9, 537 (1949).

42. __________, On the general theory of the approximate methods of analysis. Dokl. Akad. Nauk. SSSR(N. S.) 60 (1948), 957-960; (Russian). MR 10, 717.

43. __________, Functional Analysis and Applied Mathematics. Uspehi. Mat. Nauk., (N. S.) 3 (1948) 89-185; (Russian). Transl. C. D. Benster, Nat'l. Bur. Stand., 1948. MR 10, 380.

44. __________, On Newton's Method. Trudy Mat. Inst. Steklov 28 (1949) 104-144. MR 12 (1951) 419.

45. __________, Functional analysis in partially ordered spaces. Gos. Izdat. Then-Teor. Lit. Moskow 1950, 548pp. (Russian). MR 12, 340 (1951).

46. __________, The Majorant Principle and Newton's Method. Dokl. Acad. Nauk. SSSR, (N. S.), 76 (1951) 17-20. MR 12, 835.

47. __________, Some further applications of the majorant principle. Dokl. Acad. Nauk. SSSR, (N. S.) 80, 849-852, (1951). MR 13,

48. __________, Approximate solution of functional equations, [with bibliography]. Uspehi. Mat. Nauk. (N. S.) 11 (1956), No. 6 (72) 99-116. MR 18, 747 (1957).

49. __________, On some further applications of the Newton approximation method. Vestnik. Leningrad. Univ. Ser. Mat. Meh. Astr. 12, no. 7, 68-103 (1957), (Russian; English summary). MR 19, 883 (1958).

50. Kwan, C. C., Une remarque sur le procédé de Newton pour la résolution des équations fonctionnelles non-linéaires. Advancement in Math. 2(1956) 290-295 (Chinese). MR 20(1959) 3639.

51. Kwan, Chao-chih, and Lin, Chün, Sur la méthode d'equations approximatives pour résoudre des équations fonctionelles non-lineaires. Sci. Record (N.S.) 1 (1957) 385-389. MR 21, 3786 (1960).

52. Masaitis, C., "Applications of Functional Analysis", in Recent Soviet Contributions to Mathematics, edited by Joseph LaSalle and Solomon Lefschetz; pp 102-113, Macmillan, New York, 1962.

53. Mertvetsova, M. A., An analog of the process of tangent hyperbolas for general functional equations. Dokl. Acad. Nauk. SSSR, (N.S.) 88, 611-614 (1953). (Russian). MR 15, 39 (1954).

54. Mysovskih, I. P., On convergence of Newton's Method. Trudy Mat. Inst. Steklov. 28, 145-147 (1949). MR 12, 419 (1951).

55. ____________, On the convergence of L. V. Kantorovič's mehtod of solution of functional equations and its applications. Dokl. Akad. Nauk. SSSR (N.S.) 70, 565-568 (1950). MR 11, 601.

56. ____________, On the convergence of the method of L. V. Kantorovič for the solution of nonlinear functional equations and its applications. (Russian). Vestnik Leningrad Univ. 1953, no. 11, 25-48, MR 17, 879 (1956).

57. Nečepurenko, M. I., On Čebyšev's method for functional equations. Uspehi. Matem. Nauk (N.S.) 9, No. 2(60), 163-170(1954). MR 15, 801-802 (1954).

58. Ostrowski, A., Konvergenzdiskussion und Fehlerabschätzung für die Newtonsche Method bei Gleichungsystemen. Comment. Math. Helv. 9 (1936/37) 79-103.

59. ____________, Über die Konvergenz und die Abrundungsfestigkeit des Newtonschen Vergahrens. Mat. Sbornik 2, 1073-1094 (1937).

60. ____________, Mat. Sbornik N.S. 3 (45) (1938) 253-258.

61. ____________, Solutions of equations and systems of equations. Academic Press, N. Y. (1960) ix + 202 pp.

62. Rall. L. B., Newton's Method for the Characteristic Value Problem $Ax = \lambda Bx$. J. Soc. Indust. Appl. Math. 9, (1961) 288-293.

63. Schröder, Johann, Über das Newtonsche Verfahren. Arch. Rat. Mech. Anal. 1 (1957) 154-180. MR 20 (1959) 342, 2072.

64. Slugin, S. N., On the theory of Newton's method and Chaplygin's method. Dokl. Akad. Nauk. SSSR 120 (1958), 472-474. (Russian). MR 20 (1959), 6046.

65. Stein, Marvin L., Sufficient conditions for the convergence of Newton's method in complex Banach spaces. Proc. Amer. Math. Soc. 3, 858-863 (1952). MR 14, 1094 (1953).

66. ____________, Erratum to "Sufficient conditions for the convergence of Newton's Method in complex Banach spaces". Proc. Amer. Math. Soc. 13, 1000(1962).

67. Stibbs, D. W. N., and Weir, R. E., On the H-functions for istoropic scattering. Monthly Notices of Royal Astronomical Society 119 (1959) 512-525.

68. Szeptycki, P., A remark on the method of Altman of solving operator equations in L^p spaces. Bull. Acad. Polon. Sci. Cl. III 5, (1957) 1109. MR 19, 1068.

69. Tamme, È. È., On approximate solution of functional equations by the method of expression in a series of an inverse operator. Dokl. Akad. Nauk. SSSR 103 (1955), 769-772. (Russian).

70. ____________, A class of convergent iteration methods. Izv. Vysš. Učebn. Zaved. Matematika 1958, no. 5(6), 115-121. MR 24, A 1042 (1962). (Russian).

71. Tricomi, F. G., "Integral Equations". Interscience, New York, 1957.

72. Ulm, S., On convergence of certain iterational processes in Banach space. Uc. Zap. Tartu. Gos. Univ. 42 (1956), 135-142. (Russian). MR 19 (1958) 687.

73. Vainberg, M. M., Variational methods for the investigation of nonlinear operators. Gostehkizdat, Moscow, 1956.

74. Vertgeim, B. A., On conditions of applicability of Newton's method. Dokl. Akad. Nauk. SSSR 110 no. 5, 719-722 (1956). MR 18, 734; Rzh (1957), 3536, 4.

75. ______________, On some conditions of convergence of the Newton method and on application of the method to solving systems of equations. Nauch. Tr. Molotov. Gor. Inst. 1956, no. 1, 142-153.

76. Vyhandu, L. K., On the iterative methods of solving equations. Dissertation, Tartu, 1955. (Russian).

77. Zagadskii, D. M., Dokl. Akad. Nauk., SSSR (N. S.) 59 no. 6 (1948) 1041-1044. MR 9, 443.

SUPPLEMENTARY REFERENCES ON NEWTON'S METHOD APPLIED TO DIFFERENTIAL EQUATIONS

1. Adachi, Ryuzo, A method of numerical solution of some differential equations. Kumamoto J. Sci. Ser. A 2 (1954) no. 1, 40-46. MR 17, 538 (1956).

2. Bellman, R, Juncosa, M. L., and Kalaba, R., Some numerical experiments using Newton's method for non-linear parabolic and elliptic boundary value problems. Comm. ACM 4 (1961) 187-191. MR 22 (1961) 10191.

3. Collatz, L., Das vereinfachte Newtonsche Verfahren bei nichtlinearen Randwertaufgaben. Arch. Math. 5, 233-240 (1954).

4. ____________, Monotonic und extremal-prinzipien beim Newtonschen verfahren. Numer. Math. 3, 99-106(1961). MR 23, B 2590 (1962).

5. Ljubčenko, I. S., Newton's method as a basis for solving approxmately the boundary-value problem for a non-linear second-order ordinary differential equation involving a small parameter in the higher derivative term. (Russian). Dokl. Akad. Nauk. SSSR 138, 39-42(1961), MR 24, A 3371.

6. Moser, Jurgen, A new technique for the construction of solutions of nonlinear differential euqations. Proc. Nat. Acad. Sci. USA 47, 1824-1831 (1961). MR 24 (1962) A 2695.

7. Stein, M. L., On methods for obtaining solutions of fixed end point problems in the calculus of variations. J. Res. NBS 50, 277-297 (1953).

C. L. DOLPH and G. J. MINTY

On Nonlinear Integral Equations of the Hammerstein Type

E. H. Rothe, unseren Freund, Kollegen und Lehren gewidmet

Contents

0. Introduction

The subject of non-linear integral equations originated naturally after Fredholm succeeded in generalizing the algebraic theory of linear systems to linear integral equations from an attempt to carry through the analogous problem for non-linear algebraic systems in n unknowns. As such, it was initially a theory "in the small". The beginning of the theory can be traced to the pioneering work of A. M. Liapunov (D-7) and its subsequent generalizations by E. Schmidt (D-8) and L. Lichtenstein (B-8) all of whom were concerned with non-linear integral equations expressible as integral power series and to the investigations of P. Urysohn (D-9) concerning the very general type of non-linear integral operator

$$Ay(s) = \int_G k(s, t, y(t))\, dt \tag{0.1}$$

which now bears his name. (Reference may be made to Hellinger and Toeplitz (B-4) for an account of the early non-Russian development of the subject.)[1] (In equation 0.1, G is usually a closed and bounded subset of E^n; s and t are elements of G).

After these initial investigations, the next large step forward was taken by A. Hammerstein (D-5) in 1930 who systematically developed a theory in the large for equations, subsequently named after him, of the form

$$y(s) = \int_G k(s, t)\, f[t, y(t)]\, dt \tag{0.2}$$

under a wide variety of conditions. Since then equations of this form have been the most extensively studied of all non-linear integral equations and here we shall be almost exclusively concerned with equations of this type.

While it is difficult to know precisely Hammerstein's motivation for considering this class of equations, it seems fair to conjecture that he was influenced by two classical problems dating from the turn of the century. The first of these concerns the non-linear elliptic boundary value problem $\Delta u = \exp u$, $u = f$ on the boundary of a finite domain G in two or three dimensions. This problem arises in the theory of automorphic functions, the theory of surfaces of constant negative curvature, the theory of gas discharges as discussed, for example, by von Laue (cf. B-2) in 1918 and in the Debye-Hückel theory of what is now called plasma physics. It was converted into an integral equation of what is now called the Hammerstein type by

[1] For an account of the Russian history, see Vainberg, M. and Trenogin, V., "The methods of Liapunov and Schmidt in the theory of non-linear equations and their further development." Russian Math. Surveys 17, 2, 1962, pp. 1-60.

L. Bieberbach (D-1) in 1912 and discussed at length by him (D-2) in 1916 and again in his article of Vol. I, page 286 of Frank-von Mises (B-2). To obtain an integral equation, Bieberbach let w be a solution of the problem: $\Delta w = 0$, $w = f$ on the boundary, thereby obtaining the boundary value problem $\Delta y = \exp(w)\exp(y)$, $y = 0$ on the boundary for the function $y = u - w$. Rewriting this as

$$\Delta y - (\exp w)\, y = (\exp w)\, [\exp y - y]$$

and introducing the positive semi-definite Green's function $k(s, t)$ for the corresponding homogeneous linear problem yields the nonlinear integral equation

$$y(s) = \int_G k(s, t)(\exp w)[\exp y - y]\, dt \quad . \tag{0.3}$$

A solution to this in the large was then established by a successive approximation method which would also yield a solution in the large for the more general problem $\Delta u = F(u, s, t)$ when $F(u, s, t) > 0$, $F(u_1) > F(u_2)$ when $u_1 > u_2$. Without these last restrictions, the existence and uniqueness can only be established in a sufficient small domain. Details of Bieberbach's treatment can be found in Frank-von Mises (B-2) or in the German edition of Vol. II of Courant-Hilbert (B-1), page 286. As we will see, equations of the type (0.3) have had a profound influence on modern developments.

The second problem conjectured to have influenced Hammerstein is that of the forced oscillation of finite amplitude of a pendulum as first treated by G. Duffing (D-3) in 1918 and then by G. Hamel (D-4) in 1922. The differential problem

$$d^2 y(t)/dt^2 + \alpha^2 \sin y(t) = f(t)$$

for an odd driving function $f(t)$ is readily converted to the Hammerstein integral equation

$$y(s) = -\int_0^1 T(s, t)\, [f(t) - \alpha^2 \sin y(t)]\, dt$$

where $T(s, t)$ is the triangular Green's function for $y''(t) = 0$, $y(0) = y(1) = 0$. Further details can be found in F. Tricomi (B-9), page 213.

In developing the theory of equations of the form (0.2) Hammerstein considered a theory involving a bounded domain of integration and a Hilbert-Schmidt kernel $k(s, t)$ that was symmetric, positive definite and "brauchbar unstetig" - i.e. sufficiently regular so that the usual Fredholm theory applies to the corresponding linear equation as is the case for so-called weak singularities (e.g. completely continuous kernel). In particular, it is implicit in his assumptions that the first iterated kernel is continuous. The assumptions made on $f(t, u)$ were of essentially two types: any one of three involving essentially linear behavior at infinity or a type of bounded monotonicity in the event that the kernel $k(s, t)$ itself was never negative. More specifically, in the first class he demonstrated existence of a solution if either

(i) $$|f(t, u)| < k|u| + A$$

where $k < \lambda_1$, the first and smallest eigenvalue of the kernel $k(s, t)$, or

(ii) $$2\int_0^u f(s, t)\,dq < k u^2 + B$$

where k is as in (i), if in addition $k(s, t)$ is continuous and hence bounded. Uniqueness in this class was established under the condition that

(iii) $$|f(t, u_1) - f(t, u_2)| < k|u_1 - u_2|$$

for k as before.

Typical results for the second type when $k(s, t) \geq 0$ required $f(t, u) \geq 0$ for $u \leq 0$ for both existence and uniqueness. More detail can be found in the last chapter of Tricomi's book (B-9) which in particular contains a table reproduced from Hammerstein's original paper which illustrates the various possibilities. Hammerstein's method for the most part consisted of using an approximating set of equations for the Fourier coefficients from which he obtained a convergent subsequence with the aid of the Arzelà-Ascoli theorem and hence a continuous solution. In addition, Hammerstein applied the bifurcation theory of Schmidt and made applications to Duffing's problem and to a non-linear elliptic boundary value problem involving a linear elliptic partial differential operator. In analogy to the theory of linear integral equations, Hammerstein's results can be mostly summarized by saying that they furnish a generalization of that part of the linear existence and uniqueness theory obtainable from Liouville-Neumann (or Born) series for symmetric kernels.

This analogy, while admittedly not perfect, does make it possible to interpret the subsequent developments in a natural way, at least in the cases where the non-linear function is asymptotically linear. The first part of this paper will mainly be concerned with these, interpreted historically according to the subject. Other developments of course include cone methods which can be viewed as a natural generalization of the second class of conditions of Hammerstein, and the post-war theory involving essentially non-linear behavior at infinity. This latter theory is the theory of Orlicz spaces and convex functions developed by the Russian school primarily under the leadership of M. Krasnosel'skii and Y. Rutičkii. The origin of this theory stems from A. Zaanen's (B-11) extension of the theory of non-singular linear integral equations to Orlicz spaces. Of this, he wrote in the introduction to (B-xi), "the Fredholm theory is lifted out of the L_2 space wherein it was imprisoned until rather recently and placed in more natural surroundings; the Lebesgue spaces L_p and the Orlicz spaces L_ϕ." In spite of the success achieved by Zaanen in this extension of the linear theory, the authors, while admittedly not experts in Orlicz space, have not found it possible to organize the existing non-linear Orlicz space theory so that the analogy with linear theory holds for the generalization, as in the case with linear asymptotic behavior. As a result, we have accepted the viewpoint of Krasnosel'skii and Rutičkii as expressed in either (I-2) or (I-3) and consider the decomposition of the problem into various pieces concerning questions of boundedness, complete continuity, etc. for the linear operator and the Nemytskii operator defined by $f(t, y)$ in various Orlicz spaces. This subject will be discussed in more detail in section 3. Time and space do not permit an inclusion of results obtained by the cone method originally due to Krein and Rutman (H-18). For these reference can be made to the bibliography, to the recent book (B-6) by Krasnosel'skii, to the survey article (C-2) by him available in translation, and to the companion paper in this volume by H. F. Bueckner.

1. Hammerstein Operators in L_2 Asymptotically Linear at Infinity

Several natural questions are suggested as a result of the interpretation of Hammerstein's result as a generalization of the symmetric Liouville-Neumann theory. Can the theory be extended to systems? Is the hypothesis of symmetry essential or does an analogue to the linear Schmidt theory exist in any sense? Can the hypothesis of positive-definiteness be relaxed? Can the hypothesis that $k < \lambda_1$, common to all three of Hammerstein's conditions, be relaxed? What is the general relation between the non-linear operator and the associated linear operator determining the bifurcation points of the non-linear operator? Can the bifurcation theory be extended to completely continuous operators, possibly in more general spaces? Is the hypothesis of complete continuity really essential? Can other methods be used to guarantee existence and uniqueness?

As will be seen, the subsequent developments of the theory have provided many answers to questions of this type.

Five years after the appearance of Hammerstein's paper, M. Golomb (H-5), (H-6) removed the symmetry restriction and extended the Liouville-Neumann type theory to systems of non-linear integral equations by use of the Caccioppoli fixed point theorem and functional analysis concepts. A typical and yet relatively early stated result of this -- Theorem II of (H-6) -- is the following: Let the kernels $k_i(s, t)$ be unsymmetric and "brauchbar unstetig" and assume (without loss of generality) that

$$[f_i(t, u_1, \dots, u_n)]_{u_i = 0,\ i = 1, \dots, n} = 0 .$$

Let

$$\int_0^1 \int_0^1 k_i^2(s, t)\, ds\, dt = k_i^2 .$$

Then the system

$$y_1(s) + \int_0^1 k_i(s, t)\, f_i(t, y_1(t) \dots y_n(t))\, dt = g_1(s)$$

$$i = 1, 2, \dots n$$

has exactly one solution, if for $0 \leq s \leq 1$, and for all values $u_1, u_2, \dots, u_n$ the condition

$$\sum_{k,\ j=1}^{n} k_i^2 \left[\frac{\partial f_i}{\partial u_j}(s, u_1 \dots u_n)\right]^2 \leq k^2 < 1$$

is satisfied, where k is smaller than the smallest eigenvalue of the kernels $k_1 \dots k_n$.

To Golomb we also owe the notion of a gradient of a non-linear functional which has played a significant role in many subsequent developments as well as the concept of the "decomposition" or "splitting" of a linear operator $K = \int k(s, t)\, dt$. The decomposition introduced originally by Golomb for the positive-definite symmetric case made it possible for him to obtain a non-linear integral equation equivalent to the Hammerstein equation in the sense that they were either solvable or not solvable together, with a simple relation between their solutions. This equivalent equation had the advantage of being more directly interpretable as the gradient of a non-linear functional than was possible for the original Hammerstein equation. As this "decomposition" plays a vital role even in the Orlicz spaces, it will be briefly sketched in the slightly more general form necessary for this theory.

Let F denote the non-linear operator f(x, u), now called the Nemyčkii operator in the Russian literature and let K be as above so that the Hammerstein equation can be written symbolically as

(1.1) $$y = KFy \ .$$

If K can be decomposed according to the relation $K = H\,H^*$ then the equation

(1.2) $$v = H * F\,H\,v$$

is equivalent to (2.1) in the sense that if y_0 is a solution to (1.1) then v_0 is a solution to (1.2), then $y_0 = H\,v_0$ is solution to (1.2), then $y_0 = H\,v_0$ is a solution to (1.1). The proof is by computation. Given $v_0 = H * F\,y_0$ where y_0 satisfies (1.1), one has $y_0 = H\,H * F(y_0) = H\,v_0$ so that (1.2) implies that

$$v_0 = H * H\,F\,v_0 \ .$$

Conversely, given $y_0 = H\,v_0$ where v_0 is a solution to (1.2) one has $y_0 = H\,v_0 = H\,H * F\,H\,v_0 = H\,H * F\,y_0 = K\,F\,y_0$. Moreover, it is readily verified that (1.2) is the gradient of the functional

(1.3) $$I(v) = 1/2 \ \langle v, v\rangle - G(v)$$

where $\langle v, v\rangle$ denotes the usual inner product in Hilbert space and

(1.4) $$G(v) = \int_G \int_0^{Hv} f(t, u)\,du\,dt \ .$$

A generalization of the Schmidt theory for a system of non-linear coupled dual integral equations was achieved by E. H. Rothe (A-3) who in this same paper used the theory of weak topology to establish a general theory of maximum and minimum for scalars in a Banach space of the form

$$i(x) = \|x\|^2/2 + I(x)$$

where I(x) had a completely continuous Fréchet differential. Rothe was the first to note the relationship between the weak continuity of a scalar, first in Hilbert space and then in Banach spaces and the complete continuity of its gradient map. This particular result, which closely parallels a more general discussion in (A-14) and which is too complicated to state here, represents only an isolated example of the many contributions E. H. Rothe has made to the use of topological methods in non-linear problems of functional analysis. Since this paper is dedicated to him, his contributions to this area are listed separately in the bibliography. While many of the abstract theorems proved by Rothe involving such quantities as vector fields, are valid more generally, to the best of our knowledge and his, the application of his results to Hammerstein integral operators have been limited to the case when the behavior at infinity is essentially linear. For example, in the case of treatment by means of the characteristic of a vector field, the vectors on a sufficiently large sphere are all required to point either outward or inward. As previously noted by Krasnosel'skii in (C-2), the concept of mapping degree and the characteristic of a completely continuous vector field are entirely equivalent. It also seems to be the case that most results obtainable in this direction have made essential use of a requirement equivalent to one of Hammerstein's condition relating to the smallest eigenvalue. Two additional comments are in order here. E. S. Čitlanadze in (J-2) and subsequent papers noted the same connection between weakly continuous scalars and completely continuous gradients for Hilbert spaces and reflexive Banach spaces with basis and this led him to undertake a program similar in many respects to the variational aspects of Rothe's contributions. E. H. Rothe in applying his theory to Hammerstein integral equations did not directly use the variational principle of Golomb but proceeded in an abstract manner analogous to that of Hammerstein's original treatment. In fact, Rothe found it convenient to introduce an auxiliary larger Hilbert space, completed by the addition of ideal elements as a tool even though he was able to prove in the end that the solution is, in reality, in the original space. Closely related procedures appear in the sequel in connection with a new existence theorem obtained by the method of monotonicity being developed by G. Minty in a series of papers (K-3), (K-4), (K-5) . As observed by F. Browder in (K-1), Minty's main theorem can be interpreted as a non-linear generalization of the Lax-Milgram lemma and in fact Theorem (4.6) can be restated simply by saying that if the linear operator satisfies the Lax-Milgram hypothesis guaranteeing the existence of a bounded inverse, and if the non-linear operator satisfies the strong monotonicity requirement of Minty, then the full non-linear operator has a bounded inverse.

C. L. Dolph(H-1), (H-2) appears to have made the first extension of the results of Hammerstein on existence and uniqueness beyond the interval below the smallest eigenvalue of the associated linear integral equation and to have been the first to obtain results which were natural generalizations of conditions (i) and (iii) of the introduction. The results parallel those theorems of Schmidt for linear symmetric integral equations for an arbitrary λ, not an eigenvalue. Since then these results have been slightly generalized by

M. Krasnosel'skii (H-12) and others and are perhaps most conveniently stated in terms of the concept, due to him, of a non-linear operator asymptotically close to a linear operator. Specifically, a non-linear operator A acting in a Banach space E is said to be asymptotically close to the linear operator B if, in terms of the norm of this space, the relation

$$\lim_{\|y\| \to \infty} \frac{\|Ay - By\|}{\|y\|} = 0 \quad \text{holds.}$$

In particular, if the operator A is completely continuous, then so is B. For the case of L_2, if $k(s, t)$ determines a completely continuous operator and if $f(t, u)$ satisfies the condition

$$|f(t, u) - \alpha u| \leq g(t)\,|u|^{1-\beta} + g_1(t) \tag{1.5}$$

for $g(t) \in L_{2/\beta}$, $0 < \beta < 1$, $g_1(t) \in L_2$, then the Hammerstein operator (0.2) is asymptotically close in L_2 to the linear operator B given by

$$By(s) = \alpha \int_G k(s, t)\, y(t)\, dt \ . \tag{1.6}$$

This condition, if α is not a characteristic value of the linear operator defined by (1.6), guarantees that Hammerstein's equation (0.2) has at least one L_2 solution. The proof as in Dolph (H-2) follows from the Leray-Schauder fixed point principle or the fixed point principle which says that if A, B are respectively non-linear, and linear completely continuous operators acting in a Banach space B and if for $\|y\| = \rho_0$

$$\|Ay - By\| < (1/\|(I - B)^{-1}\|)\ \|y\|$$

then the equation $Ay = y$ has at least one solution in this sphere.

While unquestionably the corresponding uniqueness result has also been established under a condition similar to (1.5), a specific reference for it is not known to us so that it will be stated here in the original form due to Dolph (H-2) corresponding to $g(t)$, $g_1(t)$ constant, with $\beta = 0$ in (1.5).

If in addition to the above hypotheses on $k(s, t)$, it is assumed to be symmetric (but not positive-definite) and if $f(t, u)$ satisfies the inequality

$$\lambda_N < \mu_N \leq \frac{f(t, u_2) - f(t, u_1)}{u_2 - u_1} \leq \mu_{N+1} < \lambda_{N+1} \tag{1.7}$$

where λ_N, λ_{N+1} are any two consecutive eigenvalues of the associated linear operator B given by (1.6), then the Hammerstein equation (0.2) has a unique solution which can be constructed by successive approximations.

The generalizations of Hammerstein's variational condition (ii) have not achieved the same generality to date. Those which are in the spirit of condition (ii) are due to Krasnosel'skii (G-8) and Vainberg (J-18) and depend on the following theorem:

Let $F(y)$ be a functional defined on the entire Hilbert space with the property that $\lim_{\|y\| \to \infty} F(y) = +\infty$ and let $F(y)$ be differentiable in a Fréchet sense with a bounded remainder in every sphere with $G = G_1 + G_2$ its gradient, where G_1 and G_2 are respectively a linear continuous operator and a completely continuous operator. Then there exists a point y_0 in the Hilbert space where $F(y)$ takes on its minimum value and $Gy_0 = 0$.

For the case of positive definite symmetric kernels these conditions will be fulfilled if $f(t, u)$ satisfies the condition analogous to (ii):

$$\int_0^u f(t, u)\, dt \leq \frac{\alpha}{2} u^2 + g(t)|u|^{2-\gamma} + g_1(t)$$

for $0 < \gamma < 2$, $g(t) \in L_{2/\gamma}$ and $\alpha < \lambda_1$, the smallest eigenvalue of the associated linear integral operator (1.6).

If the kernel $k(s, t)$ admits a finite number of negative characteristic values, a similar result can be obtained by the use of a unitary operator equal to the identity on the eigenfunctions associated with the positive eigenvalues and minus the identity on the others. These considerations depend on the same general principle given above but require that the unit sphere be replaced by a "hyperboloid". For further details and the corresponding L_p theory, reference may be made to Krasnosel'skii (G-8) or Vainberg (J-28), or to the companion paper by L. B. Rall in this volume.

A partial generalization more in the spirit of (1.5) or (1.7) is due to Dolph (H-2) but does not seem to have been subsequently pursued. If M_N^O denotes the N-dimensional linear manifold in Hilbert space spanning the origin and the first N eigenfunctions of the positive-definite completely continuous linear operator (1.6) and if Golomb's functional (1.4) satisfies the condition (with positive constants C_N, C_{N+1})

$$\mu_N \langle y, y\rangle - C_N \leq 2\, G(y) \leq \mu_{N+1} \langle y, y\rangle + C_{N+1} \tag{1.8}$$

where $\lambda_N < \mu_N < \mu_{N+1} < \lambda_{N+1}$; λ_N, λ_{N+1} have the same meaning as in (1.7), and if the functional $I(y)$ given by (1.3) has at most one maximum on each linear manifold parallel to M_N^o then the Hammerstein integral equation (0.2) has at least one solution.

The conditions are not strong enough to permit the establishment of an a priori bound, but are strong enough to yield such a bound in a sphere orthogonal to the space spanned by the first N eigenfunctions. (A simple three dimensional example shows that there is no topological reason for an a priori bound to exist under condition (1.8) . Nevertheless, once the existence of the solution has been established, it was possible to deduce a bound for it with respect to the space spanned by the first N eigenfunctions and hence a bound for the total solution. The first author is still of the opinion that use of more general topological cycles and displacements than those considered by him in (H-2) are in principle capable of yielding more general results for variational problems of this type through use of this concept of a posteriori estimation than have so far been obtained by methods depending upon a priori estimation.

If a parameter is introduced in equation (0.2) so that it takes the form

$$y(s) = \lambda \int_G k(s, t)\, f[t, y(t)]\, dt \tag{1.9}$$

it is natural to ask "for what values of the parameter do non-trivial solutions exist?" One of the first results in this direction is also due to Hammerstein (D-6) who demonstrated the existence of a denumerably infinite set of eigenvalues and characteristic solutions for the case of an elastic column in which the displacement was proportional to the curvature. Reference may be made to Krasnosel'skii (F-6) for more recent results in this direction. The beginning of a general theory is due to L. Lyusternik (I-10) who demonstrated a similar result for completely continuous homogeneous odd operators in Hilbert space. This was later generalized by I. Sobolev to non-homogeneous operators in Hilbert space and to Banach spaces with bases by E. S. Čitlanadze (J-6) and M. Vainberg (J-24). Here the basic concepts derive from and are related to those familiar from the Lyusternik-Shnirel'man category theory.

A closely related problem concerns the bifurcation points of the operator (1.9) . An earlier contributor to this theory is R. Iglisch who, beginning at about the time Hammerstein's basic paper appeared, wrote a series of papers ((G-4, G-8) of the bibliography) thoroughly treating this subject for the non-linear elliptic boundary value problem $\Delta u = f(u)$ and for the equation of Duffing (F-1, F-4) . While much of his work was based on Schmidt's bifurcation theory he did introduce and apply ideas now familiar from the Leray-Schauder degree and fixed point theory including those associated with the homotopy of the continuation method.

The most far reaching generalization of the Schmidt theory of bifurcation is due to a student of Rothe, namely Jane Cronin, who obtained an equivalent theory for branch points in Banach spaces in (G-1) and who subsequently made many applications in (G-2) and (G-3) including those to systems of ordinary non-linear differential equations. In view of the early publication of a book by her on this subject, we will not enter further into details here.

Again the bifurcation theory most pertinent to the equations of the Hammerstein type is due to the Russian school. In particular, Krasnosel'skii in (G-8) proved the following general result:

Let G, with $(G\theta = \theta)$ be a non-linear completely continuous operator which is the gradient of a weakly continuous functional $F(\phi)$, with $(F\theta = \theta)$ that is differentiable with a bounded remainder in some neighborhood of the origin θ of a Hilbert space H. Let the operator G possess a Fréchet derivative B (at the point θ) which is completely continuous and self-adjoint. Then every characteristic number of the linear operator B is a bifurcation point of the non-linear operator G.

For more general operators, while it is always true that bifurcation points of the non-linear completely continuous operator A, with $(A\theta = \theta)$ having a Fréchet derivative B at θ are always characteristic values of the linear operator B; the converse in general has only been established so far for eigenvalues of B of odd multiplicity. This result is again due to Krasnosel'skii (J-8) and a brief discussion of some of its simplifications can be found in (F-6) and (C-2).

While the above survey of the L_2 theory involving non-linear operators essentially linear at infinity is far from complete, it does amply illustrate that for this class a reasonably complete generalization of the existence, uniqueness, and characteristic value problems of the linear theory has indeed been achieved. This theory in almost all respect parallels that of the corresponding linear theory apart from such things as expansion theorems. This, of course, cannot be expected in a non-linear theory. In contrast, the interesting phenomena of bifurcation cannot hold in a linear theory.

2. Remarks on Various Methods of Solution

Non-linear integral equations of the Hammerstein type appear to have played a role for non-linear elliptic type problems similar to that played by Van der Pol's equation for the theory of periodic solutions of non-linear ordinary differential equations. As in the case of the latter, Hammerstein equations have frequently been used as the testing ground for a "new" method and in many cases they appear to furnish the only known general type of equation to which a given method can easily be applied. In addition to the methods indicated in the previous section, many other methods have been employed. In the broad general category of analytic methods, integral and fractional power series have been used and extensively developed by A. I. Nekrasov (C-6) and N. N. Nazarov (E-1)[2]. Many details of this method are sketched in Vlasov's book (F-16) which is more accessible than the original papers. In addition, Galerkin's and generalized Ritz methods have been applied. Besides the topological methods already mentioned, theorems have been obtained by use of contractive mappings, index theory, order theory and other fixed point theorems such as that of Tychonoff (cf. Schaefer (H-29)). The variational theory has now been highly developed and in particular Rothe has established quite generally relations between the alternating sum of the Morse numbers and the Leray-Schauder degree theory. It would be impossible to enter deeply into all of these here, but fortunately there are a number of excellent survey articles already in existence which treat these. The article (C-2) by Krasnosel'skii has already been mentioned several times and attention should be called to that by Rothe (A-18) as well as to the many others listed in this section of the bibliography.

In the subsequent sections only two other methods will be treated in detail. The first of these is that based on the use of Orlicz spaces. The second method is that of monotonicity which also has already been briefly commented upon.

The motivation for introducing Orlicz spaces has been given independently by Krasnosel'skii (C-2) and Rutičkii (I-29) by means of the example

$$Ay = \int k(s,t)\, e^{y(t)}\, dt \quad . \tag{2.1}$$

For this if $k(s,t) > m > 0$, it is always possible to find a function $y(t)$ in any given L_p space such that the integrand in (2.1) will be non-integrable with respect to t. Thus it is clear that a new framework is necessary for the treatment of non-linearities in Hammerstein equations if exponential non-linearities are to be allowed. The Orlicz space theory provides one such framework.

Since we have conjectured that the desire to treat problems leading to non-linear operators similar to (2.1) also motivated Hammerstein, it is at least historically interesting to note that Goursat (B-3) outlined an indirect method for constructing explicit solutions for one class of problems involving exponential non-linearities. Specifically, Goursat noted that any solution of a two-dimensional harmonic problem $\Delta u = 0$ will lead to an explicit solution of the equation

---

2 Many details are also in the reference of footnote 1.

(2.2) $$\Delta\phi = \exp(k\phi)$$

via the locally invertible transformation

$$k\phi = \log[2(u_x^2 + u_y^2)/u^2) \quad .$$

As an example, the harmonic function $u = r^n \cos n\theta$ gives a solution to (2.2) as $\exp\phi = 2\, n^2/(r^2 \cos^2 n\theta)$.

In contrast to this, the motivation for the monotonicity method stemmed from the desire of G. Minty (K-3-5) to develop a method in Hilbert space capable of yielding existence and uniqueness theorems similar to those obtainable from variational principles when such principles do not exist. As will be illustrated in theorem (4.7) this has proved to be possible for non-linear Hammerstein operators under monotonicity requirements in the presence of continuity and boundedness hypotheses instead of the usual symmetry and complete continuity requirements of the variational method.

3. Application of the Theory of Orlicz Spaces

These remarks do not pretend to be an adequate outline of the Orlicz space method. For such an outline, the reader is referred to the expositions in (C-2) and (B-vii), and to the detailed survey article (I-17) or (C-3) (not yet available in English translation). We confine ourselves here to the essential definitions, an outline of the philosophy of the approach, and statements of theorems which show the points of direct contact of the theory with the Hammerstein equation. We concentrate on theorems stating the existence of a solution.

Consider the equation

(3.1) $$y(s) = \int_G k(s,t)\, f(t, y(t))\, dt$$

where G is a closed, bounded region of E^n, the variables s and t take on (vector) values in G, and all functions appearing are real-valued. Considering k and f as "known functions", it is desired to know sufficient conditions for the existence of a solution y of (3.1) .

A "solution" is defined as a function $y(\cdot)$ such that (1°) the integral appearing in (3.1) exists (as a Lebesgue-integral), and (2°) the equation is satisfied as an identity in s, except possibly for a set of measure zero in G. We do <u>not</u> specify that the solution be an L_2-function, or even an L_p-function (for some p), but we <u>do</u> insist that it be a function, and not, say, a "distribution".

The problem can be phrased as follows. If we define F as the operator (on the space of all real-valued functions on G) $[F(y)](t) = f(t, y(t))$, and K as the linear operator

$$[K(y)](s) = \int_G k(s,t)\, y(t)\, dt \quad , \tag{3.2}$$

we wish to find a fixpoint of the operator KF. Note that F must map the solution y into the domain of definition of K.

An attack is to construct two Banach spaces of functions on G, which we shall call X and Y, such that (i) F carries every function in X into a function in Y, (ii) K is everywhere defined on Y, and maps Y back into X, and (iii) KF maps a sphere in X into itself, and is completely continuous. Under these hypotheses, a fixpoint of KF is guaranteed by Schauder's principle --"a completely continuous function from a closed, convex, bounded subset of a Banach space into the same subset, has always a fixpoint". In order to find suitable Banach spaces X and Y, we shall look farther than the L_p-spaces, since we are interested in functions $f(t, u)$ and kernels $k(s, t)$ whose associated operators do not map any L_p-space into another L_p-space.

It will be assumed throughout the discussion that k is a measurable function, and that a measurable solution y is sought; we shall also assume throughout that f satisfies the Carathéodory conditions: $f(t, u)$ is continuous in u for all $t \in G$, and measurable in t for all real u.

We shall search for the two spaces X and Y in the large class of Banach spaces called "Orlicz spaces". It is in the philosophy of this approach that there is no reason to incorporate any particular Banach-space into the definition of "solution", so that the Orlicz-spaces to be used appear merely as tools in the solution of the problem. This being the case, it would be permissible to give even nonconstructive proofs of the existence of two such spaces, and the only loss would be that we could no longer assert that the solution "in addition" satisfies an integral inequality (like $\int_G |y(t)|^p dt < \infty$).

In order to simplify and systematize the search for X and Y, we shall restrict attention to such cases where F is continuous and K is completely continuous, and where F maps some ball S_1 in X into a ball S_2 in Y, and K maps S_2 back into S_1. These assumptions are sufficient to guarantee the satisfaction of condition (iii) above, and reduce the study of KF to separate studies of K and F with respect to pairs of Orlicz spaces.

The two functions $(|x|^p)/p$ and $(|x|^q)/q$ which appear in the definition of the L_p-spaces are essentially a pair of convex functions whose derivatives are inverses of one another. The main idea of the theory of Orlicz spaces is to allow a larger class of such pairs than merely power-functions; in particular, we wish to permit exponential-functions, etc. The definitions will be set up in such a way that only the properties of the functions "for large values of the argument" enter in in an essential way.

In the first quadrant of the plane, we consider a curve which begins at the origin and proceeds at first upward and to the right, and (after leaving the origin) is permitted to travel upward, or to the right, or both; eventually the distance from the curve to either axis is to become infinite. (See Fig. 1.) It is easy to associate with such a curve two functions $M(u)$ and $N(v)$, shown by the areas of Fig. 1; we shall take both M and N as even functions, so that they are defined for all real arguments (in analogy with $|x|^p$). The pair M, N are called complementary N'-functions and are convex functions, since they are integrals of monotonic nondecreasing functions.

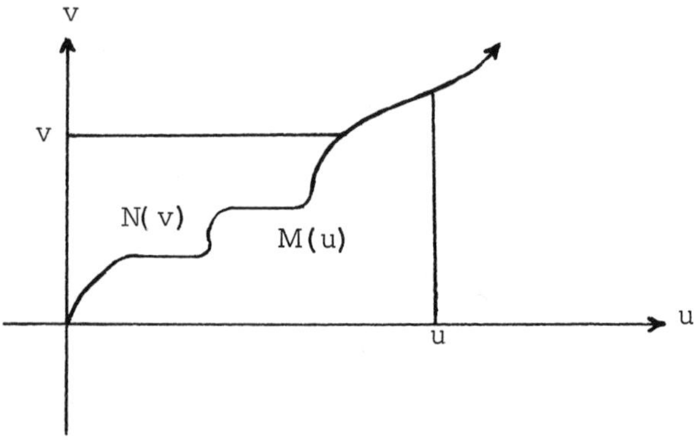

Figure 1

We denote by $L_M(G)$ the class of all real-valued functions, defined on G, such that

$$\int_G M[u(t)]\,dt < \infty , \tag{3.3}$$

and call (3.3) the "pseudo-norm" of u; the class $L_N(G)$ and corresponding pseudo-norm are defined analogously. It is easily seen that L_M and L_N are not in general linear spaces, and that the pseudo-norms have few of the virtues of norms. But now we define $L_M^*(G)$ as the set of all functions u satisfying

(3.4)
$$\left|\int_G u(x)\, v(x)\, dx\right| < \infty$$

for all $v \in L_N(G)$, and $L_N^*(G)$ analogously. These sets turn out to be linear spaces, and in fact it is possible to provide them with norms so that they are a conjugate pair of reflexive Banach spaces; the norm is namely

(3.5)
$$\|u\|_M = \sup \left|\int_G u(x)\, v(x)\, dx\right|$$

where the sup is taken over all $v \in L_N$ with pseudo-norm less than or equal to unity; the norm $\|v\|_N$ is defined analogously.

We shall say that an N'-function satisfies the Δ^2-condition provided there exists a positive constant k such that, for sufficiently large u, $[M(u)]^2 \leq M(ku)$. The exponential-function $e^{\alpha u}$ (modified so as to make it an N'-function) is an example, since $[e^{\alpha u}]^2 \leq e^{\alpha(2u)}$.

We state an existence-theorem [B-vii, p. 211] for a solution of the Uryson equation

$$u(s) = \lambda \int_G k[s, t, u(t)]\, dt + g(s)$$

Theorem 3.1.

Suppose there exist (i) a function $k(s, t)$, (ii) a continuous non-negative function $R(u)$, defined for $u \geq 0$, which is monotonic increasing, (iii) and N'-function $M(u)$ and (iv) a non-negative function $a(s)$, such that

1°) $|k(s, t, u)| \leq k(s, t)\,[a(s) + R(|u|)]$

2°) $\int_G \int_G M[k(s, t)]\, ds\, dt < \infty$ and $\int_G N[a(s)]\, ds < \infty$

3°) the N'-function $N(v)$ complementary to $M(u)$ satisfies the Δ^2-condition

4°) for some $c > 0$, $Ru < c\,\dfrac{M(u)}{u}$ for sufficiently large u .

Then (3.6) possesses a solution for any λ and any $g \in L_1(G)$.

The Orlicz-space which enables the proof of this theorem is constructed as follows: an N'-function $\Phi(u)$ is chosen such that

(a) $\Phi(uv) \leq C\, \Phi(u)\, \Phi(v)$ for some C, and sufficiently large u, v;

(b) $g \in L^*_\Phi$; and

(c) $$\int_G \int_G \Phi\{M[K(s, t)]\}\, ds\, dt < \infty .$$

The operator of the right-hand side of (3.6) then acts in the Orlicz space L^*_Φ, is completely continuous, and maps a certain (sufficiently large) ball in L^*_Φ into itself.

It will be noticed that $\Phi(u) = |u|$ almost, but not quite, satisfies the conditions imposed on Φ. Thus the Orlicz space which "works" is almost, but not quite, the space $L_1(G)$ (which is not an Orlicz space, since $\Phi(u) = |u|$ is not an N'-function).

We now state an existence-theorem for a solution of the Hammerstein equation

(3.7) $$u(s) = \mu \int_G k(s, t)\, f(t, u(t))\, dt$$

Theorem 3.2. (I-17 or C-3, p. 115)

Suppose the following conditions are satisfied:

(a) the kernel $k(s, t)$ satisfies the inequality

$$\int_G \int_G M[k(d, y)]\, ds\, dt < \infty$$

where the N'-function $N(v)$ complementary to $M(u)$ satisfies the Δ^2-condition;

(b) the function $f(t, u)$ satisfies the inequality

$$|f(t, u)| \leq b(t) + R(|u|) \quad (t G, \; -\infty < u < +\infty)$$

where $b(t) \in L_N$, and $R(u)$ is a positive, continuous, monotonically increasing function for $u \geq 0$;

(c) for large values of u, the inequality

$$uR(u) < CM(u) ,$$

where $C > 1$, holds.

Then equation (3.7) has a solution for every value of μ.

This theorem contains a typical "tradeoff" between the "good" properties of k and those of f; namely, in order for (c) to be satisfied, the function M(u) must be large for large u; but in order for (a) to hold, M(u) must be small for large u. Thus if the kernel k possesses "bad" singularities, then the function must not grow to infinity too fast with large u, but if k is (say) bounded, then the restriction on f is much weaker.

It is thus rather to be expected that in case the function f has an exponential nonlinearity, the existence-theorem will contain very strong restrictions on the singularities of the kernel. The greatest success with this case seems to have been achieved with variational methods rather than with the Schauder principle, and involves the use of the space $L_2(G)$ and the assumption of a positive definite symmetric kernel.

Theorem 3.3. (I-17 or C-3, p. 117)

Suppose the symmetric, positive definite kernel $k(s, t)$ satisfies the condition

$$\int_G \int_G \exp |K(s, t)|^{1+\epsilon} \, ds \, dt < \infty .$$

Let

$$|f(t, u)| \leq b + e^{\alpha|u|} \quad (t \in G, \; -\infty < u < \infty ; \; b > 0) .$$

Then if the constant μ satisfies

$$(3.8) \qquad \mu \int_0^u f(t, v) \, dv \leq \frac{a}{2} u^2 + b$$

where $a < 1/\lambda_0$ and λ_0 is the largest eigenvalue of the self-adjoint linear integral operator, then the equation

$$u(s) = \mu \int_G K(s, t) f[t, u(t)] \, dt$$

has at least one solution $\phi_0(t)$, satisfying the condition

$$\int_G \exp|\phi_0(t)|\, dt < \infty \ .$$

(Notice that if f is positive, all $\mu < 0$ will satisfy (3.8) .

It is not meant to suggest here that a large part of the existing theory can be summed up in theorems of this nature. It is well known to those who have tried to apply fundamental principles, such as the Schauder theorem, the variational method, etc. to concrete equations, that there is a large gap between these general principles and a proof that the concrete equation really has a solution. The Orlicz-space theory, as it is presently constituted, is a large collection of tools which can be used in various combinations to facilitate the application of these general principles, or, seen from another point of view, to develop information about the behavior of the operators involved in the concrete equation.

4. "Monotonicity" Methods

In this section, we present a new method for proving the existence of a solution of Hammerstein's equation in Hilbert space. To the best of the authors' knowledge, these theorems are original and appear here for the first time. We are interested, on the one hand, in eliminating the assumptions of symmetry and complete continuity of the linear integral operator associated with the kernel, and on the other hand, in making the theorems operator-theoretic, so that their usefulness is not confined to proving existence-theorems for concrete Hammerstein equations.

Let H be a Hilbert space, with real or complex scalars. If the scalars are complex, $\langle x, y\rangle$ will stand for the real part of the inner product of x and y; if the scalars are real, it is simply the inner product. Now, $\langle x, y\rangle$ obeys essentially the same law as the inner product, and also $\langle x, y\rangle = \langle y, x\rangle$. (In fact, it is well known that in the complex case $\langle x, y\rangle$ is simply the inner product in another Hilbert space, having the same vectors as H but only real scalars.)

Let $K : H \to H$ be a linear operator, and $F : H \to H$ a not-necessarily-linear operator. The equation $y + KFy = u$ will be called "the Hammerstein equation", and we are interested in whether, for given u, the equation has a solution for y .

An operator $G : H \to H$ will be called monotonic provided that, for all $x_1, x_2 \in H$,

$$\langle x_1 - x_2, Gx_1 - Gx_2\rangle \geq 0 \ . \tag{4.1}$$

It will be called strictly monotonic provided that, for $x_1 = x_2$, (>) replaces ($\geq$) in (4.1), and will be called strongly monotonic provided

$c\|x_1 - x_2\|^2$ replaces 0 in (4.1), with a positive constant c.

(A linear monotonic operator A satisfies $\langle x, Ax\rangle \geq 0$, and is known variously as "accretive", "negative dissipative", "nonnegative definite", etc. The notion of monotonicity was introduced[3] by Zarantonello in (K-5), and used by him to show existence of solutions of non-linear integral equations of cavity flows.)

We state first a uniqueness-theorem. (In this theorem, K need not be linear, and the operators K and F need not be everywhere-defined or continuous.)

Theorem 4.1.

A sufficient condition for the uniqueness of a solution of $y + KFy = u$, with K and F both monotonic, is that either of K, F be strictly monotonic.

Proof

Assume that

(4.2) $$y_1 + KF\,y_1 = u, \quad \text{and} \quad y_2 + KF\,y_2 = u \quad .$$

Subtract these two equations and form the real part of the inner product with $(F\,y_1 - F\,y_2)$:

(4.3) $$\langle F y_1 - F y_2, y_1 - y_2\rangle + \langle F y_1 - F y_2, KF y_1 - KF y_2\rangle = 0 \quad .$$

By the monotonicity of K and F, both terms of (4.3) are nonnegative. If F is strictly monotonic, there is a contradiction unless $y_1 = y_2$; if K is strictly monotonic, there is a contradiction unless $F y_1 = F y_2$, but in this case, from (4.2), we have $y_1 = y_2$.

Q.E.D.

Before passing on to existence theorems, we state some tool theorems which are already available in the literature.

Theorem 4.2. ((K-2), Theorem 4).

If $G: H \to H$ is continuous and monotonic, and if $(x, y) \in H\times H$ has the property that, for any (x_0, Gx_0) in the graph of G, $\langle x_0 - x, Gx_0 - y\rangle \geq 0$, then (x, y) is in the graph of G.

Theorem 4.3. ((K-2), Corollary to Theorem 4).

If $G: H \to H$ is continuous and monotonic, then for any $u \in H$, the equation $x + Gx = u$ has a unique solution for x; this solution depends continuously on u.

3 L. B. Rall has called our attention to an earlier use of the concept in Vainberg and Kachurovskiĭ (J-37).

The next theorem was stated by F. E. Browder in (K-1), and is a variant of Theorem 4.3; it appears to have the same general usefulness as the Lax-Milgram lemma.

Theorem 4.4.

If $G : H \to H$ is continuous and strongly monotonic, then the equation $Gx = u$ has, for any $u \in H$, a unique solution for x; this solution depends continuously on u.

(These theorems were essentially already known in the case where F is the Fréchet differential of a scalar functional, at least in the real case, and appear in various papers of E. H. Rothe in connection with the "variational method" of solving nonlinear integral equations, especially the Hammerstein equation. Essentially, the monotonicity of F guarantees the convexity, and hence weak lower semicontinuity, of the scalar; the monotonicity of F is also a necessary condition for the convexity of the scalar. Rothe uses monotonicity in the form of positive definiteness of the second Fréchet differential of the scalar).

Theorem 4.5.

If $\phi : H \to R$ is convex and strongly lower-semicontinuous, then it is sequentially weakly lower-semicontinuous. (See also (A-19), Theorem 4.2).

Remarks. The proof is almost trivial. Suppose $x_u \to x$ weakly and $\liminf \phi(x_n) < \phi(x)$. Then a subsequence x_{n_i} and a $b > 0$ can be found so that $\lim \phi(x_{n_i})$ exists and $\phi(x_{n_i}) < \phi(x) - b$. By a famous theorem of Banach, a sequence y_n of convex combinations of the x_{n_i} can be found, approaching x strongly; by the convexity of ϕ, $\phi(y_n) < \phi(x) - b$ and thus $\liminf \phi(y_n) < \phi(x)$, contradicting the strong lower-semicontinuity of ϕ.

(Much more is known about the relationships between the strong, weak, and weak sequential upper and lower semicontinuities for convex functions; see standard works on topological vector spaces, e.g. Bourbaki, Vol. XV, p. 92, and Vainberg (B - x).)

Lemma 4.1.

If $K : H \to H$ is linear and monotonic, then $\phi(x) = \langle Kx, x\rangle$ is a convex function.

Proof.

Let $s \geq 0$, $t \geq 0$, $s + t = 1$. The conclusion follows immediately from the identity

$$<sx_1 + tx_2, K(sx_1 + tx_2)> = [s(s+t)<x_1, Kx_1> + t(s+t)<x_2, Kx_2>]$$

$$- st <x_1 - x_2, Kx_1 - Kx_2> ,$$

by dropping the last term and changing (=) to ($\leq$) .

We are now ready to prove existence-theorems.

Theorem 4.6.

Suppose $K : H \to H$ is linear, continuous, and strongly monotonic, and $F : H \to H$ is continuous and monotonic. Then the equation $y + KFy = u$ has, for any $u \in H$, a solution for y; moreover, the solution depends continously on u .

Proof.

Assume these conditions are satisfied. Let $G = K + KFK^*$. Then G is continous; also, for any $x_1, x_2 \in H$, we have

$$<x_1 - x_2, Gx_1 - Gx_2>$$

(4.4)
$$= <Kx_1 - Kx_2, x_1 - x_2> + <K^*x_1 - K^*x_2, FK^*x_1 - FK^*x_2> .$$

The first term exceeds $c\|x_1 - x_2\|^2$, by the strong monotonicity of K, and the second is nonnegative by the monotonicity of F . Hence, by Theorem 4.4, the equation $Gx = u$ has a unique solution, and the solution depends continuously on u . In other words, the equation $K^*x + KFK^*x = u$ has a solution; but then $y = K^*x$ is a solution of $y + KFy = u$, and this solution depends continuously on u .

Another--equally good--proof is as follows. Since K is strongly monotonic, by Theorem 4.4, it has a continuous (i.e. bounded) inverse. (Recall that the linear special case of Theorem 4.4 is essentially a form of the Lax-Milgram Lemma). It is easily shown that K^{-1} is strongly monotonic, and from this that $(K^{-1} + F)x = K^{-1}u$ has a solution depending continuously on $K^{-1}u$, and hence on u . Apply K to both sides of this relation, and the conclusion follows.

We now state the main theorem of this section, and emphasize that the operator K need not be completely continuous or self-adjoint. A (nonlinear) operator is called bounded if it maps bounded sets into bounded sets; its range need not be bounded.

Theorem 4.7.

Let $K : H \to H$ be linear, continuous, and monotonic; let $F : H \to H$ be continuous, bounded, and monotonic, and also satisfy

(4.5) $$\|x\| > M \text{ implies } \langle x, Fx\rangle \geq 0$$

for some positive constant M. Then the equation

$$y + KFy = \theta$$

has a solution for y.

Proof.

Equation (4.4) is shown as before, but this time we can conclude only that $(K^* + KFK^*)$ is monotonic. Thus, for any positive integer n, the operator $n(K^* + KFK^*)$ is monotonic, and by Theorem 4.3, the equation $x + n(K^*x + KFK^*x) = \theta$ has a solution for x. Denoting this solution by x_n to emphasize its dependence on n, we write

(4.6) $$x_n/n + K^*x_n + KFK^*x_n = \theta \ .$$

Form the real part of the inner product of (4.6) with x_n, obtaining

(4.7) $$\|x_n\|^2/n + \langle x_n, Kx_n\rangle + \langle K^*x_n, FK^*x_n\rangle = 0 \ .$$

In this equation, the second term is non-negative; the first term is strictly positive (unless $x_n = \theta$), so the third term must be negative. But then by the hypothesis (4.5) on F, we have $\|K^*x_n\| \leq M$. By the boundedness of the operator F, we now see that $\{FK^*x_n\}$ is a bounded sequence. By the Schwarz inequality applied to the third term of (4.7), we see that this term is bounded (below); and hence the first term is bounded above, from which it follows that the sequence $\{x_n/n\}$ converges strongly to the zero-vector θ.

In the sum-space $H \dot{+} H$, consider the sequence $\{(K^*x_n, FK^*x_n)\}$. This is a bounded sequence, so (even if H is not separable) there is a weakly convergent subsequence, and its two parts $\{K^*x_{n_i}\}$ and $\{FK^*x_{n_i}\}$ are weakly convergent in the original space H. Replace n by n_i in (4.6) and (4.7) and call the resulting equations (4.6i) and (4.7i). (Note: alternatively, one can extract two successive subsequences, etc.).

(If the operator K is completely continuous, the proof can be finished in a few words. Since $\{FK^*x_{n_i}\}$ is weakly convergent, and K maps a weakly convergent sequence into a strongly convergent sequence, we see that $\{KFK^*x_{n_i}\}$ is a strongly convergent sequence. Thus from (6i), $\{K^*x_{n_i}\}$ is the sum of strongly convergent sequences, and hence is strongly convergent. Letting y denote the strong limit, and going to the strong limit in (6 i), we obtain $y + KFy = \theta$, and the proof is complete.)

We return to the assumption that the operator K is continuous, but not necessarily completely continuous. Let y denote the weak limit of $\{K^* x_{n_i}\}$ and z denote the weak limit of $\{FK^* x_{n_i}\}$. Going to the weak limit in (6 i), we obtain

$$y + Kz = \theta \ . \tag{4.8}$$

We shall show that (y, z) is a point of the graph of F. Consider any arbitrary $x_0 \in H$.

Since F is monotonic,

$$< x_0 - K^* x_{n_i}, Fx_0 - FK^* x_{n_i} > \ \geq 0 \ .$$

Making a substitution for $K^* x_{n_i}$ from (4.6), we have

$$< x_0 + (x_{n_i}/n_i) + KFK^* x_{n_i}, Fx_0 - FK^* x_{n_i} > \ \geq 0$$

and with rearrangement this becomes

$$\begin{aligned} &< x_0 - K^* x_{n_i}, Fx_0 > - < x_0, FK^* x_{n_i} > \\ &\geq \ < (x_{n_i}/n_i), FK^* x_{n_i} > + < KFK^* x_{n_i}, FK^* x_{n_i} > . \end{aligned} \tag{4.9}$$

Take the limit inferior of both sides of (4.9). By the weak convergence of $\{K^* x_{n_i}\}$, the left-hand side actually has a limit. The first term on the right-hand side goes to zero because it is (in absolute value, by the Schwarz inequality) less than or equal to $\|x_{n_i}/n_i\| \cdot \|FK^* x_{n_i}\|$, and the first factor goes to zero while the second factor remains bounded. The limit inferior of the second term on the right-hand side is greater than or equal to $<Kz, z>$ because $\phi(x) = <Kx, x>$ is a (strongly) continuous, convex function (by Lemma 4.1) and is hence weakly lower-semicontinuous (by Theorem 4.5). Thus we have finally

$$< x_0 - y, Fx_0 > - < x_0, z > \ \geq \ < Kz, z >$$

which on rearrangement and substitution for Kz from (4.8) becomes

$$< x_0 - y, Fx_0 - z > \ \geq \ 0 \ .$$

Since x_0 was arbitrary, by Theorem 4.2 we have that (y, z) is an element of the graph of F; in other words, z = Fy .

Substituting this into (4.8), we obtain the conclusion: $y + KFy = \theta$. Q.E.D.

We remark that if K or F is strictly monotonic and K is completely continuous, this proof is more constructive than it appears to be. For then the solution is unique, and it follows that the sequence $\{K^*x_n\}$ has precisely one weak limit point, hence precisely one strong limit point, and thus that the solution y can be obtained as the ordinary (strong) limit of the sequence $\{K^*x_n\}$.

We follow up with a few remarks on the application to the concrete Hammerstein equation

$$y(s) = \int_G k(s, t)\, f(t, y(t))\, dt = 0 \quad ,$$

using only the case where the scalars of the Hilbert space are real.

The theorems just proved can be applied to Hammerstein equations in which the domain G is infinite, the functions y and u are vector-valued and k is matrix-valued, etc. We shall, however, restrict attention to the case where G is closed and bounded, and y, k, u are real-valued.

In order for the operator F associated with the function f to be everywhere-defined in $L_2(G)$, it is sufficient that $f(t, u)$ be everywhere defined in $G \times R$ and satisfy the Carathéodory conditions (measurable in t for each fixed u and continuous in u for almost all t), and that there exist a function $b(t) \in L_2(G)$ and a $C > 0$ such that $|f(t, u)| \leq |b(t)| + C|u|$. In particular, $b(t)$ might be a positive constant.

In this concrete case, the continuity and boundedness of F follow from the fact that F maps $L_2(G)$ into $L_2(G)$; thus they can be dropped from the hypotheses of the existence-theorem. (See (B-v)).

Sufficient for F to be monotonic (resp. strictly monotonic) is that for each fixed t (except possibly for a set of measure zero in G) the function $f(t, u)$ be monotonic (resp. strictly monotonic) non-decreasing in the variable u . Sufficient for F to satisfy the hypothesis: $\|x\|$ sufficiently large implies $\langle x, Fx\rangle \geq 0$, is that there exist positive constants M, b, and c such that, for all t, $u > M$ implies $f(t, u) > b + cu$, and $u < -M$ implies

$$f(t, u) < -b + cu \quad .$$

The tool theorems, 4.2 and 4.3, were originally proved, in (K-2), under less restrictive assumptions, and there is some hope for the extension of the existence theorem to cases where the operator F is not everywhere-defined in the Hilbert space H . This project has not been carried out at the date of this writing.

A. Publications of E. H. Rothe On Non-linear Problems

1. Ueber asymptotische Entwicklungen bei gewissen nicht-linearen Randwertaufgaben, Compositio Mathematica 3, (1936) 310-327.

2. Ueber Abbildungsklassen von Kugeln des Hilbertschen Raumes, Compositio Mathematica 4 (1937), 294-307. Zb. 17, P. 39.

3. Ueber den Abbildungsgrad bei Abbildungen von Kugeln des Hilbertschen Raumes, Compositio Mathematica 5 (1937), 166-176. Zb. 17, P. 360.

4. Zur Theorie der topologischen Ordnung und der Vektorfelder in Banachschen Raeumen, Compositio Mathematic 5 (1937), 177-197. Zb. 18, P. 133.

5. Topological proofs of uniqueness theorems in the theory of differential and integral equations, Bulletin of the American Mathematical Society 45 (1939), 606-613. MR 1, P. 18.

6. Theory of the topological order in some linear topological spaces, Iowa State College Journal of Science 13 (1939), 373-390.

7. Asymptotic solution of a boundary value problem. Iowa State College Journal of Science 13 (1939), 373-390. MR 1, P. 54.

8. On topology in function spaces. Lectures in Topology, The University of Michigan Press (1941), 303-305. MR 3, P. 135.

9. On non-negative functional transformations, Am. J. of Math. 66 (1944), 245-254. MR 6, P. 71.

10. Gradient mappings in Hilbert space, Ann. of Math. 47 (1946), 580-592. MR 8, P. 158.

11. Completely continuous scalars and variational methods, Ann. of Math. 49 (1948), 265-279. MR 10, P. 461.

12. Gradient mappings and extrema in Banach spaces, Duke J. of Math. 15 (1948), 421-431. MR 10, P. 548.

13. Weak topology and non-linear integral equations, Trans. Am. Math. Soc. 66 (1949), 75-92. MR 11, P. 184.

14. Critical points and gradient fields of scalars in Hilbert space, Acta Matematica 85 (1951), 73-98. MR 13, P. 254.

15. A relation between the type numbers of a critical point and the index of the corresponding field of gradient vectors, Math. Nachrichten 4 (1950/51), 12-27. MR 12, P. 720.

16. A remark on isolated critical points, Am. J. of Math. 74 (1952), 253-263. MR 13, P. 755.

17. Leray-Schauder index and Morse type numbers in Hilbert space, Ann. of Math. 55 (1952), 433-467. MR 14, P. 185.

18. Gradient mappings (Address delivered before the Norman meeting of the Am. Math. Soc. 11/23/51), Bull. AMS 59 (1953), 5-19. MR 14, p. 657.

19. A note on the Banach spaces of Calkin and Morrey, Pacific J. of Math. 3 (1953), 493-499. MR 15, P. 39.

20. Correction to the paper "Leray-Schauder index and Morse type numbers in Hilbert space," Ann. of Math. 58 (1953), 593-594. MR 15, P. 236.

21. Mapping degree in Banach spaces and spectral theory, Math. Zeitschrift 63 (1955), 195-218. MR 17, P. 646.

22. Remarks on the application of gradient mappings to the calculus of variations and the connected boundary value problems, Communications of Pure and Applied Mathematics, IX (1956), 551-568. Appeared also in Trans. Symp. on Partial Diff. Equations held at the U. of Calif. at Berkeley, June 20-July 1, 1955, Interscience Publishers, Inc. pp. 253-270. MR 18, P. 808.

23. Some applications of functional analysis to the calculus of variations (Lecture delivered at the Symposium on Calculus of variations and its applications at the University of Chicago, 4/13/56). Published in Proc. of Symposia in Applied Math., Vol. 8, McGraw-Hill, 1958, p. 143-151. MR 20, p. 1244.

24. A note on gradient mappings, Proc. AMS 10 (1959), 931-935.

25. Some remarks on critical point theory in Hilbert space, Proc. of a symposium conducted by the Math. Research Center, U. S. Army, at the U. of Wisconsin, April 30-May 2, 1962. U. of Wisconsin Press, 1963, pp. 233-256.

B. Books

i) R. Courant and D. Hilbert, "Methoden der Mathematischen Physik," II, Springer, Berlin, 1937.

ii) P. Frank and R. von Mises, "Die Differential und Integralgleichungen der Mechanik und Physik," I. M. Rosenberg, New York, 1937.

iii) E. Goursat, "Leçons sur l'intégration des equations derivées partielles du premier ordre," Herman, Paris, 1921, p. 197.

iv) E. Hellinger and O. Toeplitz, "Integralgleichungen und Gleichungen mit unendlichvielen Unbekannten," Chelsea, New York, 1953.

v) M. Krasnosel'skii, "Topological methods in the theory of non-linear integral equations," Gos. Izdat. Fiz. Mat., Moscow, 1956.

vi) ______________, "Positive solutions of operator equations," Gos. Izdat. Fiz. Mat., Moscow, 1962.

vii) M. Krasnosel'skii and Ya. B. Rutičkii, "Convex functions and Orlicz spaces," Noordhoff, Groningen, 1961.

viii) L. Lichtenstein, "Vorlesungen uber einige Klassen nichtlinearer Integralgleichungen und Integro-Differentialgleichungen nebst Anwendungen," Springer, Berlin, 1931.

ix) F. Tricomi, "Integral Equations," Interscience, New York, 1957.

x) M. Vainberg, "Variational methods in the study of non-linear operators," Gos. Izdat. Tekh-Teoret. Lit., Moscow, 1956; English translation by A. Feinstein, Holden-Day, San Francisco, 1963.

xi) A. Zaanen, "Linear Analysis," Interscience, New York, 1957.

C. Survey Articles

1. V. Achmedov, "The analytic methods of Nekrazov-Nazarov in non-linear analysis," Uspehi Mat. Nauk. 12, No. 4 (76), 1957, p. 135; Zb. 93, p. 130 (Fractional power series).

2. M. Krasnosel'skii, "Some problems of non-linear analysis," Am. Math. Soc. Trans. Ser 2, Vol. 10, 1958, p. 354; MR 17, p. 769.

3. M. Krasnosel'skii and Ya. Rutičkii, "Orličz spaces and non-linear integral equations," Trudy Moskov, Mat. Obšč. 7, 1958, p. 63; MR 21, No. 7433 (A self-contained presentation which the authors feel is near final form).

4. L. Lyusternik, "Some questions of non-linear functional analysis," Uspehi Mat. Nauk. 11, No. 6 (72) 1956, p. 10; MR 18, p. 911 (Series of Nekrazov-Nazarov, implicit function theory, and bifurcation theory).

5. B. Navarro, "Lectures on the theory of integral equations," Consejo Superior de Invetigacionias Cientifices Madrid, 1942, 188 pages; MR 7, p. 451.

6. N. Nazarov, "Non-linear integral equations of the Hammerstein type," Trudy Univ. Asiae Mediae Ser. Va Fas 33, 1941, 79 pages; MR 3, p. 150.

7. V. Nemyčkii, "Fixed point methods in analysis," Uspehi Mat. Nauk. 1, 1936, p. 141.

8. N. Nazarov, "Methods for the solution of integral equations of Hammerstein type," Acta Trudy Univ. Asiae Mediae N.S. Fasc 6, 14 pp. 1949; MR 8, p. 518 (Analysis methods and fixed points of Caccioppoli and Schauder).

9. N. Nazarov and M. Vainberg, "The present status of the theory of non-linear integral equations," Trudy Tretego Vseojuzn Mat. S'ezda, Moscow, 1956, 3, 1958, p. 10; Zb. 87, p. 103 (existence theory, uniqueness theory, eigenvalue theory, continuation methods, and bifurcation theory).

10. M. Vainberg, "Some problems of functional analysis and variational methods," Am. Math. Soc. Trans. ser 2, vol. 16, 1960, p. 375; MR 22, No. 8390.

11. M. Vainberg, R. Vinograd, and B. Demidovič, "V. V. Nemyčkii on his 60th birthday," Uspehi Mat. Nauk. 1 (97), 1961, p. 201-213; MR 23, A 1506.

D. General Historical References

Memoirs

1. L. Bieberbach, " $u = \exp u$ und die automorphen Funktionen," Gött. Nachr., 1912, p. 599.

2. ________________, Math. Annalen, 77, 1916, p. 173.

3. G. Duffing, "Erzwungene Schwingungen bei veranderlicher Eigenfrequenz une ihre technische Bedeutung," Sammlung Vieweg, 41-42, Braunschwieg, 1918.

4. G. Hamel, "Uber erzwungene Schwingungen bei endlichen Amplituden," Math. Ann. 86, 1922, p. 2.

5. A. Hammerstein, "Nichtlineare Integralgleichungen nebst Anwendungen," (Ivar Fredholm in memoriam) Acta. Math. 54, 1930, p. 117.

6. ________________, "Uber die Eigenwerte gewisser nichtlinearer Differentialgleichungen," Crelle's Journal, 168-69, 1932-33, p. 37.

7. A. Liapunov, "Sur les figures d'equilibre peu différentes des ellipsoides d'une masse liquide homogène douée d'un mouvement de rotation, I, étude générale du problème," Acad. Imp. Sci., St. Petersbourg, 1906.

8. E. Schmidt, "Uber die Auflösung der nichtlinearen Integralgleichung und die Verzweigung ihrer Lösungen," Math. Ann. 65, 1906, p. 370.

9. P. Urysohn, "On a type of non-linear integral equation," Mat. Sb. 31, 1924, p. 236.

E. Analytical Methods and Approximations

1. A. Baluev, "Application of semi-ordered norms in approximate solutions of non-linear integral equations," Leningrad Gos. Univ. Uč. Zap. Ser. Mat. Nauk 37, 1958, p. 18; MR 21A, No. 3958, (Urysohn equations treated by the methods of Kantorovich.)

2. ________________, "Approximate solutions of non-linear integral equations," Leningrad Gos. Univ. Uč. Zap. Ser. Mat. Nauk 37, 1958, p. 28; MR 21A, No. 3959 (The algebraic approach of Fredholm applied to Urysohn's equation).

3. M. Krasnosel'skii and Ya. Rutičkii, "Some approximate methods of solutions for non-linear operators based on linearization," Sov. Math. 2, 1961, p. 1542.

4. M. Lotkin, "On mixed non-linear integral equations," Kiel Dissertation, 1937, p. 23; Zb. 18, p. 66 (Systems of Hammerstein type with infinitely many variables.)

5. ________________, "The solution by iteration of non-linear integral equations," J. Math. and Phys. 33, 1955, p. 346; Zb. 64, p. 101 (Lichtenstein type).

6. D. Maravall, "The uniqueness theory of non-linear integral equations," Rev. Mat. Hisp. Amer. iv S 8, 1948, p. 143; Zb. 38, p. 63. (Spanish) (Picard approximation method).

7. N. Nazarov, "On one class of homogeneous non-linear integral equations," Acta Univ. Asiae Med. Taschkent, Ser. Va Fasc 28, 1939, p. 1; Zb. 23, p. 393; 8, p. 518 (Power series expansions in a parameter).

8. ________________, "On the boundary value problem for non-linear differential equations of the second order," Trudy Sredneaziat Gos. Univ. Ser. V-a, No. 13, 1934.

9. ________________, "On the theory of non-linear integral equations," Trudy Sredneaziat Gos. Univ. Ser. V-a, No. 28, 1939.

10. ________________, "Non-linear integral equations of Hammerstein type," Trudy Sredneaziat Gos. Univ. Ser. V-a, No. 33, 1941.

11. S. Pohožaev, "Analogue of Schmidt method for non-linear integral equations," Doklady Akad. Nauk SSSR 136, 1961, p. 541 or Sov. Math. 2, 1961, p. 103; MR 22A, 5859 (Degenerate Kernels).

12. V. Pokornyi, "Two analytic methods in the theory of small solutions of non-linear integral equations," Doklady Akad Nauk SSSR 133, 1960, p. 1027-1030 (Soviet Math 1, 1961, p. 938; MR 23A, 406)(Proof of the equivalence of the bifurcation theories of Liapunov and Schmidt).

13. V. Pokornyi and P. Rybin, "Stabilization of a process for determining formal implicit functions," Usphei Mat. Nauk 15, 1960, p. 169; MR 22A 12209 (The method of Nekrasov-Nazarov as stabilized by Krasnosel'skii).

14. P. Rybin, "A formula in the Nekrasov-Nazarov method," Izv Vysš Učebn. Zaved Matematica,1959, 6 (13), p. 131; MR 23A 3980.

15. M. Siddiqi, "On an infinite system of non-linear integral equations," Bull. Calcutta Math. Soc. 24, 1932, p. 37; Zb. 4, p. 398 (Lichtenstein type).

16. ________________, "On the theory of non-linear integral equations," Proc. Ind. Acad. Sci. Sec. A 6, 1937, p. 83; Zb. 17, 168.

17. S. Sundaran, "On an infinite system of non-linear integral equations," Proc. Ind. Acad. Sci. Sec. A 8, 1938, p. 288; Zb. 19, p. 413 (Volterra type).

18. A. Temliakow, "On the non-linear integral equations of type $\int_a^b F(x, s, \phi)\,ds = f(x)$, Mitt. Forsch. Inst. Math u. Mech. Univ. Tomsk 2, 1938, p. 83; Zb. 20, p. 30. (Polynomial approximation to Urysohn type).

19. D. Zagadsii, "An analogue of Newton's method for non-linear integral equations," Doklady Akad. Nauk. SSSR 59, 1948, p. 1041; MR 9, p. 443.

F. Applications

1. R. Iglisch, "Zur Theorie der Schwingungen," I, Monatschefte 37, 1930, p. 325; II, Monat. 39, 1932, p. 173; III, Monat. 42, 1935, p. 7. (Bifurcation theory applied to Duffing's equation).

2. ________________, "Über die Lösungen des Duffingschen Schwingungsproblems bei grossen Parameterwerten," Math. Ann. 11, 1935, p. 568.

3. ________________, "Die erste Resonantkurve beim Duffingschen Schwingungsproblem," Math. Ann. 112, 1935, p. 112.

4. ________________, "Verzweigung Periodischer Lösungen nichtlinearer Schwingungsgleichungen," Math. Ann. 114, 1937, p. 194.

5. M. Krasnosel'skii, "On Nekrasov's equation in the theory of waves at the surface of a heavy liquid," Doklady Akad. Nauk. SSSR 109, 1956, p. 456; Zb. 74, p. 101; MR 20, No. 3692.

6. ________________, "Investigation of the spectrum of a non-linear operator in the neighborhood of a branch point and application to the problem of longitudinal bending of a compressed rod," Am. Math. Soc. Translations 2, Vol. 16, 1960, p. 418; MR 22A, No. 8379.

7. R. Kulikowski, "On the theory of non-linear oscillations," Polska Acad. Nauk. Bull. Sci. 6, 1958, p. 353 (Here thru 10, the topological methods of Krasnosel'skii are used).

8. ________________, "On the theory of non-linear servomechanisms," Polska Acad. Nauk. Bull. Sci. 6, 1958, p. 271.

9. ________________, "General aspects of transmission system theory," Polska Acad. Nauk. Bull. Sci. 6, 1958, p. 265.

10. ________________, "On the theory of non-linear AM receivers," Polska Acad. Nauk. Bull. Sci. 6, 1958, p. 235.

11. A. I. Nekrasov, "The exact theory of steady waves on the surface of a heavy fluid," Izdat Akad. Nauk. SSSR, Moscow, 1951.

12. A. Pohožaev, "Dirichlet's problem for $\Delta u = u^2$, Soviet Math 1, No. 5, 1960, p. 1143.

13. ________________, "On the boundary value problem $\Delta u = u^2$, Soviet Math. 2, No. 3, 1961, p. 609.

14. M. Schiffer and N. Hawley, "Connections and conformal mapping," Acta Math. 107, 1962, p. 175.

15. W. Thimm, "On a class of integral equations which play a role in probability theory," Veröfflichung Math. Inst. Tech. Hochschule Braunschweig, 1947, No. 2, p. 22; MR 11, p. 183.

16. A. A. Vlasov, "Many particle theory and its application to plasma," Gordon and Breach Sci. Pub., Inc., 1961.

G. Bifurcation Theory

1. J. Cronin, "Branch points of solutions of equations in Banach spaces," Trans. Am. Math. Soc. 69, 1950, p. 208; MR 12, p. 716.

2. ________________, "The existence of multiple solutions of elliptic differential equations," Trans. Am. Math. Soc. 68, 1950, p. 105.

3. ________________, "Analytic functional mappings," Ann. of Math. 11, 1953, p. 175; Zb. 50, p. 343.

4. R. Iglisch, "Reele Losungenfelden der elliptischen Differential Gleichung $\Delta u = F(u)$, Math. Ann. 101, 1929, p. 98.

5. ________________, "Zur Theorie der reelen Verzweigungen von Lösungen nichtlinearer Integralgleichungen," Journ. fur Reine und Ang. Math. 164, 1931, p. 151; Zb. 1, p. 338.

6. ________________, "Über die Vielfachheit einer Lösung in der Theorie der nichtlinearen Integralgleichungen von E. Schmidt." Jahres. d. Math. Verein 39, 1930, p. 65.

7. ________________, "Zur Topologie der verzweigung Lösungen einer nichtlinearen Integralgleichung," Jahres. Math. Verein, 41, 1931, p. 245.

8. M. Krasnosel'skii, "Application of variational methods in problems of bifurcation theory," Mat. Sbornik 33 (75), 1953, p. 199; Zb. 50, p. 343; MR 15, p. 439.

9. M. Krasnosel'skii and A. Povoločkij, "On the variational method in problems of bifurcation points," Doklady Akad. Nauk. SSSR 91, 1953, p. 19; Zb. 52, p. 345; MR 15, p. 440.

10. J. Leray, "On certain classes of non-linear integral equations," Compte Rendu, Paris, 194, 1932, p. 1627; Zb. 4, p. 215.

11. ________________, "Study of diverse non-linear integral equations and some problems posed by hydrodynamics," J. Math. Purs and App. IX, S. 12, 1933, p. 1; Zb. 6, p. 167.

H. Degree, Fixed Point and Related Topological Methods

1. C. L. Dolph, "Non-linear equations of the Hammerstein type," Proc. Nat. Acad. Sci. U.S.A. 31, 1945, p. 60.

2. ________________, "Non-linear integral equations of the Hammerstein type," Trans. Am. Math. Soc. 66, 1949, p. 289; Zb. 36, p. 203; MR 11, p. 367.

3. D. W. Doubrovsky, "On certain non-linear integral equations," Uchenye Zab. Moskow Gos. Univ. Matematika 30, 1939, p. 49; Zb. 1941, p. 97 (Hammerstein type treated by fixed point theories of Schauder and Caccioppoli).

4. T. Ebanoidze, "On infinite systems of certain non-linear and singular integral equations," Soobšč. Akad. Nauk. Gruzin SSSR 22, 1959, p. 649; MR 1961, No. 6958 (Tychonow fixed point theory).

5. M. Golomb, "On the theory of non-linear integral equations, integral systems and general functional equations," Math. Zeit. 39, 1935, p. 45; Zb. 9, p. 312. (Fixed point theorem of Caccioppoli, successive approximations and variational methods).

6. ________________, "On systems of non-linear integral equations," Pub. Univ. Belgrade 5, 1936, p. 52; Zb. 17, p. 404.

7. R. Iglisch, "Existence and uniqueness of non-linear integral equations," Math. Ann. 108, 1932, p. 161; Zb. 6, p. 313 (Hammerstein type treated by Schauder fixed point theory coupled with the continuation method).

8. M. Krasnosel'skii, "Fixed points of cone compressing or cone extending operators," Sov. Math. 1, 1961, p. 1285; MR 1962, A 1012.

9. ________________, "Regular and perfectly regular cones," Sov. Math. 1, 1961, p. 1249.

10. ________________, "On a fixed point principle for completely continuous operators in function spaces," Doklady Akad. Nauk. SSSR 73, 1950, p. 13.

11. ________________, "On a topological method in the problem of eigenfunctions of non-linear operators," Doklady Akad. Nauk. SSSR 74, 1950, p. 5.

12. ________________, "Eigenfunctions of non-linear operators asymptotically near to linear operators," Doklady Akad. Nauk. SSSR 74, 1950, p. 177.

13. ________________, "Investigations in non-linear functional analysis," Dissertation, Inst. Mat. Kiev, 1950.

26. G. Salehov, "Eigenvalue problems for non-linear integral equations," Bull. Soc. Phy. Math. Kazan (30 - 12), 1949, p. 75; MR 19, p. 123.

27. N. Smirnow, "Existence theorem of non-linear integral equations," Doklady Akad. Nauk. SSSR 3, 1936, p. 203; Zb. 15, p. 162 (Fixed point theory).

28. H. Schaefer, "On the theory of non-linear integral equations," Math. Nach. 11, 1954, p. 13.

29. _______________, "New existence theorem in the theory of non-linear integral equations," Akad. der Wiss. Leipzig, 110, 1955, p. 3. (Tychonoff fixed point theory).

30. _______________, "Positive transformations in locally convex partially ordered vector spaces," Math. Ann. 129, 1955, p. 323.

31. _______________, "On non-linear positive operators," Pac. J. Math. 9, 1959, p. 847.

32. _______________, "Some non-linear eigenvalue problems," in "Nonlinear problems", Univ. of Wisconsin Press, 1963, p. 117.

33. K. Stepaniuk, "Some generalizations of the fixed point principle," Ukrain. Math. Z. 9, 1957, p. 105; MR 19, p. 155 (A generalization of the Schauder fixed point principle).

34. M. Vainberg, "Topological methods of investigations of a problem of eigenfunctions of non-linear integral equations," Moskov. Oblas. Pedagog. Inst. Uč. Zap. Trudy Kaefeder Math. 20, 1954, p. 33; MR 17, p. 751.

35. Shen Wang, "On the solutions of the Hammerstein Integral equations," Bull. Acad. Polon. Sci. Ser. Math. 8, 1960, p. 339; Zb. 93, p. 111 (this review indicated errors; MR 1962, No. 2727).

36. S. Yamamuno, "On the theory of non-linear operators," Proc. Jacp. Acad. 36, 1960, p. 305-309; MR 22A, No. 8361. (Application of Schaefer's method to Hammerstein equations).

I. Orlicz and L^p spaces

1. T. Andô, "Linear functionals on Orlicz spaces," Nieuw Arch. Wisk. 13-8, 1960, p. 1960; MR 23A, 1228.

14. ________________, "Vector fields symmetric relative to a subspace," Dopovidi Akad. Nauk. Ukrain. RSR 1951, p. 8, Ukrainian.

15. ________________, "Continuity of the operator $\underline{F}u = f(x, u(x))$," Doklady Akad. Nauk. 76, 1951, p. 481.

16. ________________, "On the theory of completely continuous vector fields," Ukrainian Mat. Z. 3, 1951, p. 174.

17. M. Krasnosel'skii and P. Zabreiko, "Calculation of the index of an isolated stationary point of a completely continuous vector field," Sov. Math. 2, 1961, p. 1436.

18. M. Krein and M. Rutman, "Linear operators leaving invariant a cone in a Banach space," Am. Math. Soc. Trans. 326, 1950.

19. N. Marčenko, "The existence of solutions of a certain class of non-linear integral equations," Sov. Math. 2, 1961, p. 305 (Urysohn type treated by Leray-Schauder degree theorie).

20. V. Niemytski, "On non-linear integral equations," Comptes Rendus. Paris, 196, 1933, p. 838; Zb. 6, p. 209 (Fixed point theory for Hammerstein type).

21. ________________, "Some non-linear integral equations comparable with linear," Doklady Akad. Nauk. SSSR 15, 1937, p. 13; Zb. 16, p. 360.

22. ________________, "Theorem of existence and uniqueness of solutions of some non-linear integral equations," Math. Sbornik 41, 1934, p. 421; Zb. 11, p. 26 (Hammerstein type in Hilbert space).

23. ________________, "On a class of non-linear integral equations," Math. Sbornik 41, 1935, p. 655; Zb. 11, p. 404. (Fixed point theory of Banach and Caccioppoli).

24. A. Povolčkij, "Non-local existence theorems for solutions of systems of non-linear integral equations," Doklady Akad. Nauk. 99, 1954, p. 901; Zb. 58, p. 93 (Krasnosel'skii's topological methods).

25. B. Nikitin, "On the existence of solutions of an infinite system of non-linear integral equations," Trudy Mos. Oblas Pedagog. Inst. Oč. Zap, 5, 1957, p. 81; Zb. 90, p. 321; MR 20, No. 4751.

2. F. Bachtin, "Non-linear equations with concave and uniformly concave operators," Doklady Akad. Nauk. SSSR 126, 1959, p. 9-12.

3. F. Bachtin and M. Krasnosel'skii, "On the theory of equations with concave operators," Doklady Akad. Nauk. SSSR 123, 1958, p. 17; Zb. 92, p. 322 (Cone methods and successive approximation).

4. Y. Engelson, "Some questions in the variational theory of non-linear equations in locally convex spaces," Latvijas Valsts Univ. Zinātn Raksti, 28, 1959, No. 4, p. 45; MR 22, A 9834.

5. M. Krasnosel'skii, "The decomposition of operators acting on a space L_q to a space L_p," Doklady Akad. Nauk. SSSR 82, 1952, p. 333.

6. ________________, "Some properties of a root of a linear integral operator," Doklady Akad. Nauk. SSSR 88, 1953, p. 749.

7. ________________, "New existence theorems on the solutions for non-linear integral equations," Doklady Akad. Nauk. SSSR 88, 1953, p. 949.

8. ________________, "Decomposition of linear integral operators acting from one Orlicz space to another," Doklady Akad. Nauk SSSR 97, 1954, p. 777.

9. M. Krasnosel'skii and L. Ladyženskii, "Conditions for complete continuity of P. S. Urysohn's operator acting in the space L_p," Trudy Moskov Mat. Obšč. - va (1954) p. 307; MR 15, p. 966.

10. M. Krasnosel'skii and Ya. Rutičkii, "On the theory of Orlicz spaces," Doklady Akad. Nauk SSSR 81, 1951, p. 497; MR 13, p. 357; Zb. 45, p. 61.

11. ____ and ____, "Linear integral operators in Orlicz spaces," Doklady Akad. Nauk. SSSR 85, 1952, p. 33; Zb. 48, p. 94; MR 14, p. 57.

12. ____ and ____, "Differentiability of non-linear integral operators in Orlicz spaces," Doklady Akad. Nauk. SSSR 89, 1953, p. 601; MR 15, p. 137 (Exponential growth).

13. ____ and ____, "On a method of constructing N'-functions equivalent to the complementary ones to given N'-functions," Trudy fiz.-mat f-ta Voronez, Goz. Univ. 33, 1954, p. 3; MR 17, p. 768.

14. ______ and ______, "On linear functionals in Orlicz spaces," Doklady Akad. Nauk. SSSR 97, 1954, p. 581; MR 16, p. 263.

15. ______ and ______, "General theory of Orlicz spaces," Trudy Seminara po funkcional'nomu analizu, Voronez. Gos. Univ. No. 1, 1956, p. 3; MR 18, p. 912.

16. ______ and ______, "Linear integral operators operating in Orlicz spaces," Trudy Seminara po funkcional'nomu analizu, Voronez. Gos. Univ. No. 2, 1956, p. 55; MR 18, p. 811.

17. ______ and ______, "Orlicz spaces and non-linear integral equations," Trudy Mosk. matem ob-va. 7, 1958, p. 63; MR 21, p. 1379.

18. ______ and ______, "On a class of convex functions," Trudy Seminara po funkcional'nomu analizu, Voronez. Gos. Univ. No. 5, 1957.

19. ______ and ______, "On some non-linear operators in Orlicz spaces," Doklady Akad. Nauk. SSSR, 117, 1957, p. 363; Zb. 79, p. 333; MR 20, No. 1933 (Differentiability of Nemyčkii operators).

20. M. Krasnosel'skii and V. Sobolev, "Conditions for separability of Orlicz spaces," Izvestiya Akad. Nauk. SSSR seriya matem. 19, 1955, p. 59; MR 16, p. 718.

21. ______ and ______, "On the decomposition of linear operators," Uspehi Matem. Nauk. 12, 1957, p. 313; MR 19, p. 666.

22. M. Krasnosel'skii, V. Sobolev, and E. Pustylmik, "Test for the complete continuity of linear and non-linear operators, Doklady Akad. Nauk. SSSR 142, 1962, p. 25; MR 23A, 1915.

23. W. Luxemberg and A. Zaanen, "Conjugate spaces of Orlicz spaces," Neder. Akad. Wet. Proc. Ser. A., 59, 1956, p. 217; Zb. 72, p. 123; MR 17, p. 1113.

24. W. Orlicz, "On a certain class of spaces of type B," Bull. Intern. Acad. Polon. Sci. Lett. Cl. Sci. Math. Nat. Ser. A, 1932, p. 207.

25. ______________, "On spaces of type L^M," Bull. de l'Acad. Pol. Ser. A. Krakhow, 1937.

26. Ya. Rutičkii, "Concerning a linear operator operating in an Orlicz space," Dopovidi Akad. Nauk. USSR, Kiev 3, 1952, p. 161, (Ukrainian), MR 19, p. 45 (Complete continuity and boundedness).

27. ________________, "Application of Orlicz spaces for the investigation of certain functionals in L_2," Doklady Akad. Nauk. SSSR 105, 1955, p. 1147; MR 17, p. 768.

28. ________________, "On a property of completely continuous linear integral operators operating in Orlicz spaces," Uspehi Matem. Nauk. 11, 1956, p. 201; MR 17, p. 1113.

29. ________________, "On a class of Banach spaces," Am. Math. Soc. Trans. Ser. 2, Vol. 16, 1960, p. 445.

30. J. Simohenko, "Boundedness of singular integrals in Orlicz spaces," Doklady Akad. Nauk., SSSR 130, 1960, p. 984, Sov. Math. 1, p. 124; MR 23, A 2724.

31. S. I. Šragin, "On certain operators in generalized Orlicz spaces," Doklady Akad. Nauk. SSSR 117, 1959, p. 4043; Zb. 87, p. 112 (Investigation of weak continuity).

32. ________________, "The continuity of a Nemyčkii operator in Orlicz spaces," Sov. Math. 2, 1961, p. 1246.

33. M. Vainberg, "The operator of V. V. Nemyčkii," Ukrain. Mat. Z. 7, 1955, p. 363; MR 17, p. 977 (L_p theory).

34. ________________, "On a non-linear operator in Orlicz spaces," Studia Math. 17, 1958, p. 58; Zb. 84, p. 335.

35. M. Vainberg and I. Šragin, "Non-linear operators and Hammerstein's equation in Orlicz spaces," Doklady Akad. Nauk. SSSR 128, 1959, p. 9; MR 21, No. 7414; Zb. 92, p. 322.

36. ______and______, "Nemyčkii operator and its potential in Orlicz spaces," Doklady Akad. Nauk. SSSR 120, 1958, p. 941; Zb. 88, p. 91; MR 20, No. 6048.

J. Variational Methods

1. E. Čitlanadze, "On the question of eigenvalues of non-linear compact operators in Hilbert space," Doklady Akad. Nauk SSSR 57, 1947, p. 879; Zb. 29, p. 54 (Projective sphere and Fréchet differential).

2. ________________, "On integral equations of the Lichtenstein type," Soobščenija Akad. Nauk. Grunzinskoj SSSR 8, 1947, p. 357; Zb. 54, p. 45; MR 13, p. 951 (eigenvalues and weak continuity in Hilbert space).

3. ________________, "On variational methods of a class of non-linear operators in L_p," Doklady Akad. Nauk. 71, 1950, p. 441; Zb. 36, p. 361 (use of Haar orthogonal systems).

4. ________________, "On a class of non-linear functional equations," Soobščenija Akad. Nauk. Gruzinskoj SSSR 11, 1950, p. 73; Zb. 41, p. 441 (The method of Lusternik-Sobolev in L_p, $1 < p < \infty$).

5. ________________, "On extrema of functionals in linear spaces," Doklady Akad. Nauk. SSSR 76, 1951, p. 797; Zb. 42, p. 120 (Min-max procedures in Banach spaces for eigenfunctions).

6. ________________, "Certain extremal problems relative to the theory of characteristic values," Doklady Akad. Nauk. SSSR 56, 1947, No. 1, p. 15; MR 9, p. 95.

7. ________________, "Some problems of non-linear operators and the calculus of variations in spaces of Banach type," Uspehi Mat. Nauk. 5, 1950, p. 141; MR 12, p. 110.

8. ________________, "Existence theorem for minimax points in Banach space and applications," Trudy Mos. Mat. Obšč 2, 1953, p. 235; Zb. 52, p. 348 (Lusternik-Shnirelman category methods surveyed).

9. ________________, "The method of orthogonal trajectories for non-linear operators of variational type in L_p." Trudy Tbilisk Mat. Inst. Razmadze 20, 1954, p. 245; Zb. 57, p. 344 (Lusternik-Schnirelman category theory).

10. ________________, "Investigation of a class of non-linear integral equations through a topological analogue of direct methods," Trudy Tbilisk Mat. Inst. Razmadze 21, 1955, p. 125; Zb. 66, p. 90 (infinitely many solutions on a unit sphere in L_p).

11. I. Gelman, "Integrals of potential type in Orlicz spaces," Izv. Vysš. Učebn, Zaved. Matematika, 1960, 2 (15), p. 44; MR 23, A 1019.

12. Z. Nehri, "On a class of non-linear integral equations," Math. Zeit. 72, 1959, p. 175; MR 1961, No. 3960.

13. A. Povoločkij, "Applications of variational methods to investigate the spectrum of non-linear operators," Mat. Sbornik, 42 (84), 1957, p. 287; Zb. 80, p. 330 (Operators near Hermitian and bifurcation).

14. W. Schmeidler, "Variational methods in integral equations," J. Reine u. Angew. Math. 200, 1958, p. 182; MR 20, p. 6017. (Lichtenstein type).

15. V. Sobolev, "On the characteristic values of certain operators," Doklady Akad. Nauk. SSSR 31, 1941, p. 735; MR 3, p. 208.

16. ________________, "On a non-linear integral equation," Doklady Akad. Nauk. SSSR 71, 1950, p. 831; MR 11, p. 728. (Lusternik's method).

17. M. Vainberg, "On the existence of an eigenfunction for a class of non-linear integral equations," Doklady Akad. Nauk. SSSR 46, 1945, p. 42; MR 6, p. 272.

18. ________________, "On Hammerstein's theorem of non-linear integral equations," Ucenie Zapiski Moskov, Gos. Univ. 100 Matematika 1, 1946, p. 93; MR 12, p. 107.

19. ________________, "Existence of eigenfunctions for a class of non-linear integral equations," Ucenie Zapiski Moskov. Gos. Univ. Matematika, 100, 1, 1946, p. 85; MR 12, p. 107.

20. ________________, "The existence of solutions of non-linear integral equations," Doklady Akad. Nauk. SSSR 63, 1948, p. 605; MR 10, p. 460 (Hammerstein type).

21. ________________, "On characteristic values of some systems of non-linear integral equations," Uspehi Mat. Nauk. 4, 1949, p. 130, MR 11, p. 366 (Hammerstein type).

22. ________________, "Existence theorems for characteristic values of a class of non-linear integral equations," Mat. Sbornik NS 20 (68) 1950, p. 364; MR 12, p. 340.

23. ________________, "The existence of characteristic functions for a certain class system of non-linear integral equations," Doklady Akad. Nauk. SSSR 61, 1948, p. 965; MR 10, p. 304 (Nemyčkii's methods).

24. ________________, "The existence of characteristic functions for non-linear integral equations with non-positive kernels," Doklady Akad. Nauk. SSSR 78, 1951, p. 1077; MR 13, p. 248.

25. ________________, "On the variational theory of characteristic values of non-linear integral equations," Mat. Sbornik N, 30, 1952, p. 3; MR 13, p. 658.

26. ________________, "On variational theory of eigenfunctions of non-linear integral equations," Doklady Akad. Nauk. SSSR 80, 1951, p. 309; MR 1952, p. 353 (Hammerstein type).

27. ________________, "On a variational problem in the theory of operators," Uspehi Mat. Nauk. No. 2 (48), 1952, p. 197; Zb. 46, p. 338. (Golomb theory via sphere methods of Lusternik and Rothe).

28. ________________, "The existence of eigenfunctions of non-linear integral operators with non-positive kernels which are products of self-adjoint operators and a potential operator," Mat. Sbornik 32 (74) 1953, p. 665; Zb. 51, p. 93 (Use of hyperboloids in place of a unit sphere); MR 14, p. 1014.

29. ________________, "On the solvability of certain operator equations," Doklady Akad. Nauk. SSSR 92, 1953, p. 457; Zb. 52, p. 1344; MR 15, p. 536 (A generalization of a theorem of Golomb).

30. ________________, "Non-linear integral equations," Doklady Akad. Nauk. SSSR 58, 1953, p. 953.

31. ________________, "Variational theory of eigenfunctions of non-linear integral and other operators," Trudy Moskov, Mat. Obšč. 3, 1954, p. 375; Zb. 57, p. 345; MR 16, p. 374 (Hammerstein type).

32. ________________, "On hyperboloids and the conditions for extrema of certain functionals in Hilbert space," Uspehi Mat. Nauk. N. S. 9, No. 2 (60), 1954, p. 105; MR 15, p. 967.

33. ________________, "Potential operators and variational theory of non-linear operator equations," Uspehi Mat. Nauk 10, N 23 (65), 1957, p. 227; Zb. 65, p. 119 (Dissertation).

34. ________________,"On the positive solutions of non-linear integral equations," Moskov. Oblast. Ped Inst. Ucenye Zapiski Trudy Kafedr Mat. 4, 1957, p. 61; Zb. 90, p. 321; MR 20, p. 4750 (Urysohn type plus an iteration process).

35. ________________, "The operators of V. V. Niemyčkii," Ukrain. Mat. Žurn. 7, 1958, p. 363; Zb. 66, p. 363; MR 17, p. 977 (Lipschitz conditions and Gâteaux differentials).

36. ________________, "On the convergence of the process of steepest descent for non-linear equations," Sibirsk Mat. Zeit., 1961, p. 201; MR 1962, A 4026.

37. M. Vainberg and R. I. Kachurovskiĭ, "On the variational theory of non-linear operators," Doklady Akad. Nauk. SSSR 129, 1959, p. 1199; Zb. 94, p. 108; MR June 22A - 4930, 1961 (Potential operators monotonic in the sense of "monotonicity methods".

K. Monotonicity Methods

1. Browder, F. E., "On the solvability of Nonlinear Functional Equations", to appear in Duke Math. J. See also three papers of F. E. Browder, "Variational Boundary Problems for Quasi-Linear Elliptic Equations, I, II, III" to appear in Proc. Nat. Acad. Sci.

2. Minty, G. J., "Monotone (Non-linear) Operators in Hilbert Space," Duke Math. J., 29, pp. 341-346 (1962).

3. ________________, "On the Maximal Domain of a 'Monotone' Function," Mich. Math. J., 8, pp. 135-137 (1961).

4. ________________, "On the Monotonicity of the Gradient of a Convex Function," submitted to Pacific J. Math.

5. Zarantonello, E. H., Solving Functional Equations by Contractive Averaging, U. S. Army Math. Res. Ctr. T.S.R. 160 (1960).

L. Additional Miscellaneous References

1. S. Asinov, "Conditions for complete continuity of the operator Azerbaidžan. Gos. Univ. Uč. Zap. 1958, p. 13; MR 21, No. 3741 (Systems of Urysohn type).

2. Ya. Bykov, "On problems of eigenfunctions of non-linear integral equations," Doklady Akad. Nauk. SSSR 72, 1950, p. 449; Zb. 40, p. 350 (the existence of infinitely many eigenfunctions).

3. D. Davidenko, "On an application of the method of variation of parameters in the theory of non-linear functional equations," Ukrain. Mat. Žurn. 7, 1955, p. 18; Zb. 64, p. 373.

4. N. Dzavadov, "On an integral equation," Akad. Nauk. Azerbajaz SSSR Doklady 13, 1957, p. 597; Zb. 77, p. 305 (Urysohn type with Bochner integrals).

5. A. Granas, "On a class of non-linear mappings in Banach spaces," Bull. Acad. Poln. Sci. Cl. III-5, 1957, p. 867; Zb. 78, p. 117; MR 19, p. 968 (Mappings which are asymptotically linear).

6. A. Gremjacenski, "On eigenvalues of systems of non-linear integral equations," Doklady Akad. Nauk. SSSR 60, 1948, p. 337; Zb. 30, p. 124 (Hammerstein type treated via degenerate kernels).

7. M. Gurvic, "Continuation of solutions of non-linear integral equations of Hammerstein type," Izv. Vyšš Ucebn Zaved Matematika, 1959, 1 (18) p. 45; MR 23 A 405 (Use of the implicit function theorem of W. Hart).

8. L. Kalnibolackaja, "On the complete continuity of

$$Au = \int k(x, y) f(y, u(y)) dy$$

Vestnik Leningrad Univ. 9, 1954, p. 37; MR 17, p. 751.

9. M. Krasnosel'skii, "The eigenvalues of non-linear operators which are asymptotically linear," Doklady Akad. Nauk. SSSR 74, 1950, p. 177; Zb. 8, 279; MR 12, p. 187 (Hammerstein type).

10. ________________, "The convergence of Galerkin's method for non-linear integral equations," Doklady Akad. Nauk. SSSR 73, 1950, p. 1121; Zb. 41, p. 71.

11. ________________, "New existence theorem for solutions of non-linear integral equations," Doklady Akad. Nauk. SSSR 88, 1953, p. 949; Zb. 50, p. 102 (Close to Hammerstein's result for L_p, $p < 2$).

12. M. Krasnosel'skii and L. Ladyženskaja, "Conditions for the compactness of L_p of operators of P. S. Urysohn, Trudy Moskow, Mat. Obšč. 3, 1954, p. 307; Zb. 56, p. 340; MR 15, p. 966.

13. ______ and ______, "The structure of the spectrum of positive inhomogeneous operators," Trudy Moskow Mat. Obšč. 3, 1954, p. 321; Zb. 56, p. 340; MR 15, p. 966 (The cone method of Krein-Rutman).

14. ______ and ______, "The scope of the concept of a non-concave operator," Izv. Vyšš Ucebn Zved. Matematika, 1959, No. 5(12), p. 112; MR 1962, 1043 (Urysohn type).

15. L. Ladyženskaja, "On a class of non-linear equations," Trudy Semi. Funk. Analiza, 56, No. 2, 1956, p. 31; Zb. 73, p. 104; MR 18, p. 914 (Positive operators and the non-linear analogue of Fredholm equations of the second kind).

16. ______________, "On non-linear equations with positive non-linearity," Uspehi Mat. Nauk. 12, 1 (73), 1957, p. 211; Zb. 78, p. 119 (A short survey).

17. L. Lusternik, "On a class of non-linear operators in Hilbert space," Bull. Akad. Sci. SSSR Ser. Mat. No. 3, 1939, p. 257; Zb. 24, p. 213 (homogeneous operators).

18. Ya. Mamedov, "On the positive non-linear integral equations of Urysohn type," Akad. Nauk. Azerbajdžan SSSR Doklady 11, 1955, p. 591; Zb. 67, p. 335 (Comparison with an auxiliary linear system).

19. ______________, "On the positive solutions of Urysohn's non-linear integral equation when the kernels depend non-linearly on a parameter," Akad. Nauk. Azerbajdžan SSSR Doklady 12, 1956, p. 311; Zb. 70, p. 103; MR 18, p. 390 (Comparison with an auxiliary linear system).

20. ______________, "On the solution of non-linear integral equations in Banach spaces," Akad. Nauk. Azerbajdžan SSSR Doklady 16, 1960, p. 327; Zb. 94, p. 108 (Use of Tonnelli's theory for Urysohn and Volterra equations).

21. S. Mihlin, "The Ritz method in non-linear problems," Sov. Mat. 3, 1962, p. 170.

22. V. V. Neymčkii, "On the structure of the spectrum of non-linear compact operators," Mat. Sbornik, No. 33, 1953, p. 544; Zb. 52, p. 348 (Existence of continuous spectrum).

23. ______________, "A method for finding all solutions of non-linear operator equations," Sov. Mat. 1, 1960, p. 330; Zb. 94, p. 107.

24. H. Pachale, "On the Urysohn integral operator," Arch der Math. 10, 1959, p. 134; Zb. 88, p. 83; MR 21, No. 6537 (Compactness in spaces of Hölder continuous functions).

25. U. Pirl, "Positive solutions of a non-linear integral equation," Ber. Veh. Sachs. Akad. Wiss. Leipzig, Math. Natur Kl 100, H8, 1953, 44 pages; Zb. 51, p. 81 (Lichtenstein equations treated by Schmeidler's algebraic method).

26. N. Polskij, "A generalization of the method of B. G. Galerkin," Koklady Akad. Nauk. SSSR 86, 1952, p. 469; Zb. 47, p. 113; MR 12, p. 187.

27. A. Povoločkij, "On the existence of disconnected spectra for non-linear compact operators," Doklady Akad. Nauk. SSSR 99, 1954, p. 345; Zb. 57, p. 345 (Asymptotically linear operators).

28. D. Scorza, "A remark on a theorem of Golomb's on non-linear equations," Atti Acad. Naz Lincei Rend. VI, S 22, 1935, p. 385; Zb. 13, p. 168 (Use of the continuation method).

29. M. Semenov, "On the question of the structure of the spectrum of non-linear operators," Trudy Semi. Funk Analiza 56, 1956, p. 71; Zb. 73, p. 104 (A counter example to a theorem of Nemyčkii on eigenvalues).

30. G. Tautz, "Non-linear integral equations in an infinite domain and application to boundary value problems," Jahr. d. Deut. Math. Ver. 48, 1939, p. 175; Zb. 20, p. 132 (Hammerstein type).

31. A. Temljakow, "On singular solutions of non-linear integral equation of type

$$\phi(x) = \int_a^b k(x, s)\, f(s, \phi(s))\, ds$$

Mitt. Forsch Inst. Math and Mech. Univ. Tomsk 1, 1935, p. 39; Zb. 12, p. 21.

32. M. Vainberg, "An integral equation of Urysohn," Moskow Oblast Pedagog, Inst. Uč.Zap.Trudy Kafeder Mat. 21, 1954, p. 49; MR 17, p. 751.

33. E. Voskresenskii, "On non-linear integral equations of Hammerstein type," Voronež Gos. Univ. Trudy Fiz. Mat. Sb. 27, 1954, p. 75; MR 17, p. 751.

34. E. Voskresenskii and V. Sobolev, "On a class of non-linear integral equations," Doklady Akad. Nauk. SSSR 79, 1951, p. 717; Zb. 43, p. 318 (The existence of at least a denumerable number of eigenfunctions for Hammerstein type).

Appendix I

Translation of Table of Contents of Topological Methods in the Theory of Non-linear Integral Equations, by M. A. Krasnosel'skii Moscow: Gos. Izdat. Tekh-Teoret. Lit. (1956).

3. Completely continuous vector fields. Finite-dimensional lemma. Rotation of a completely continuous vector field. Homotopic fields. Algebraic number of fixed points of a completely continuous vector field. Classification-theorem. Correctness of posure of problems. Extension of a completely continuous vector field. Possibility of extension of a vector field without null-vector. Rotation of field on boundary of a bounded region.

4. Leray-Schauder Principle. General principle of existence of fixed point. Schauder principle. Odd field on the sphere. Vector fields which are nearly linear. Vector fields symmetrical with respect to subspaces. Multiplication of rotations of completely continuous vector fields. Linear fields. Computation of the index of a fixed point.

III. EXISTENCE THEOREMS FOR SOLUTIONS.

1. Contractive mapping principle. Contractive mapping principle. Resolvent of a non-linear operator and its properties. Existence-theorems for solutions. Approximate computation of characteristic numbers and functions of a perturbed linear operator.

2. Application of topological fixed-point principles to the proof of existence-theorems. General posure of problems. Vector fields not completely continuous. Odd integral power series. Close-to-linear equations: local theorems. Close-to-linear equations: non-local theorems.

3. Convergence of the B. G. Galerkin method, with approximate solution of a non-linear equation. Convergence of the process. Speed of convergence. Method of B. G. Galerkin. The generalization of G. I. Petrov. Computation of characteristic numbers of linear operators.

IV. PROBLEMS ON CHARACTERISTIC FUNCTIONS.

1. Topological principles of existence of an eigenvector. Approximate eigenvectors. Principle of equality for two completely continuous vector fields. Characteristic functions of nonzero index. Small eigenfunctions. Method of small perturbations.

2. Legitimacy of linearization in the problem of bifurcation points. Bifurcation points. Continuous branches of eigenvectors. The case of a completely continuous operator. Examples. The structure of the spectrum. General case. The operator of A. M. Liapunov.

3. Asymptotically linear operators. Asymptotic bifurcation-points. Indications of compactness of the spectrum.

4. Theorems of the Liapunov type. Index of a fixed point. Case of a real space. The case of a complex space. Branching points.

5. Distribution of the spectrum in the neighborhood of a bifurcation point. The sets N- and N+ . Theorem on bifurcation points. Differentiable operators. Examples.

V. CHARACTERISTIC FUNCTIONS OF POSITIVE OPERATORS

1. Theorem on characteristic vector. A cone in a Banach space. Positive operators. Branches of characteristic vectors. The cone $K_{u_0, k}$.

2. Operators with monotonic minorants. Distribution of operators close to the ones we investigated. Monotonic operators. Homogeneous operators. Linear operators. Linear u_0-bounded operators. Monotonic minorants.

3. Urysohn-theorems on the spectrum. Closedness of the set of characteristic vectors. Completion of the positive spectrum of an interval. Boundary of the positive spectrum. Non-linear u_0-involuted operators. u_0-monotonic operators. Continuous dependence on a parameter. Theorems of P. S. Urysohn.

VI. VARIATIONAL METHODS

1. Existence-theorems for solutions. General principle. Theorems of existence for solutions of Hammerstein equation with positive definite kernel. Theorems of existence of solutions for Hammerstein equation with symmetrical kernels, in which a finite number of negative characteristic values appear. Topological principle.

2. Principle of linearization in problems on bifurcation points. Nearly-quadratic functionals. Lemma of L. A. Lyusternik. Existence of one bifurcation-point. Hilfssätze. Non-contractible sets. Basic theorems. Example.

3. Theorems of existence of characteristic functions. Variational principle. Theorem of M. Golomb. Generalization of the theorem of Golomb. Kernels with finite number of negative characteristic numbers.

4. Stable critical points of even functionals. Theorem of L. A. Lyusternik. Genus of a set. The M_k classes. Trace of a deformation. Even functionals. Separability of the space. Critical number of a functional. The set R_a. Existence of various values of $d(a)$. Norm of a functional. Stability of a given critical point. Basic theorem. Remark. Odd operators of Hammerstein. Critical points on the hyperboloid. Connection with problem on bifurcation points.

LITERATURE

INDEX

Appendix II

Another Monotonicity Theorem. See also: G. J. Minty, "Two Theorems on Nonlinear Functional Equations", to appear in Bull. A. M. S.

(This note appears as an appendix because, although we make no connection between the theorem and the Hammerstein equation, it is an interesting generalization of Theorem 4.4 and may find future applications.)

F. E. Browder, in (K-1), has shown the following generalization of Theorem 4.4. (As before, $\langle x, y\rangle$ is the real part of the inner product.)

Let G *be a continuous mapping of the Hilbert space* H *into itself such that for all* x_1 *and* x_2 *in* H,

$$\langle Gx_1 - Gx_2, x_1 - x_2\rangle \geq c(\max \|x_1\|, \|x_2\|)\, \|x_1 - x_2\|^2 ,$$

where $c(r)$ *is a positive non-increasing function of* r *such that*

$$\int_1^\infty c(r)\, dr = +\infty .$$

Then G *is one-to-one and onto, and its inverse is continuous.*

The theorem we are about to state is a partial generalization.

THEOREM

Suppose $G : H \to H$ is a continuous monotonic function, and that there is a positive number M such that

$$\|x\| > M \text{ implies } <x, Gx> \geq 0 .$$

Then the equation $Gx = \theta$ has a solution.

PROOF. Just as in the proof of Theorem 4.7, we can find $\{x_n\}$ $(n = 1, 2, 3, \ldots)$ such that

$$\frac{x_n}{n} + Gx_n = \theta .$$

Form the inner product with x_n :

$$\frac{\|x_n\|^2}{n} + <x_n, Gx_n> = 0 .$$

We now see that $\|x_n\| \leq M$ for all n, and extract a weakly convergent subsequence, $\{x_{n_i}\}$. Let (x_0, Gx_0) be any point of the graph of G. By monotonicity of G,

$$<x_0 - x_{n_i}, Gx_0 - Gx_{n_i}> \geq 0 .$$

By a simple substitution,

$$<x_0 - x_{n_i}, Gx_0> + \frac{x_0, x_{n_i}}{n_i} - \frac{\|x_{n_i}\|^2}{n_i} \geq 0 .$$

Taking the limit, we obtain

$$<x_0 - x, Gx_0 - \theta> = 0$$

where x is the weak limit of x_{n_i}; hence, as in the proof of Theorem 4.7, the pair (x, θ) is an element of the graph of G, and $Gx = \theta$.

REMARK 1. It appears possible to relax the assumption that G is everywhere defined in H .

REMARK 2. A sufficient condition for the existence of a number M such that

$$\|x\| > M \text{ implies } \langle x, Gx\rangle \geq 0$$

is that there exist N such that

$$\|x\| = N \text{ implies } \langle x, Gx\rangle \geq 0 .$$

The proof (based on the monotonicity of G) is left to the reader.

Thus the hypotheses of the above theorem and of Theorem 4.7 can be weakened. This fact seems interesting in connection with Remark 1 and the notion of the "topological degree" of G on the surface of the ball of radius N .

Appendix III[4]

Contractive Methods for Hammerstein Equations by I. I. Kolodner.

In this Appendix we use the definitions and notations of Section 4, except that it is convenient now to write $-F$ in place of F. We shall also write $T \geq S$ whenever $T - S$ is monotonic. It should be noted that in this context, $\geq$ is not a symbol for a partial order, and that in the case of a linear operator T the assertion $T \geq 0$ means that T is monotonic but not necessarily a positive operator. On the other hand, if T is positive, then $T \geq 0$.

Consider again the 'Hammerstein' equation for y,

$$y = KFy + u \quad , \tag{1}$$

in which we assume that the domain of K and F is the Hilbert space H, that K is linear and $K \geq aI$ for some $a \geq 0$, and that F is not merely continuous as in Section 4, but Lipshitzian. As in the case of linear operators, the norm $\|F\|$ of a non-linear operator F is the infimum of its Lipshitz constants. Without loss of generality one may assume that $F(\theta) = \theta$. The assumptions on K imply already that it is, as one may show, continuous.

We shall obtain the solution of (1) in several important cases by eventually applying the Banach-Caccioppoli contractive mapping theorem. Our deductions are based on the following idea. If $m \geq 0$, then $I + mK$ has a continuous inverse (defined on H) and $\|(I + mK)^{-1}\| \leq 1$. If $a > 0$ and $m < -1/a$, then $(I + mK)^{-1}$ exists again and $\|(I + mK)^{-1}\| \leq 1/(a|m| - 1)$. With such m's, we add mKy to both sides of (1) and apply $(I + mK)^{-1}$, thus obtaining the equivalent equation

$$y = K_m F_m y + u_m \quad , \tag{2}$$

[4] This appendix was kindly furnished to the authors by Professor Kolodner, University of New Mexico, Albuquerque, New Mexico.

where $K_m = (I + mK)^{-1}K$, $F_m = F + mI$, $u_m = (I + mK)^{-1}u$. If $\|KF\| < 1$ then the contractive mapping theorem yields $(I - KF)^{-1}$ by successive iterations. If KF is not contractive, we still have at our disposal the equation (2) and by varying m one may put the norms of K_m and F_m in competition. If for some m, $\|K_mF_m\| < 1$, then the contractive mapping theorem yields $(I - K_mF_m)^{-1}$ and one easily verifies that

$$(3) \qquad (I - KF)^{-1} = (1 - K_mF_m)^{-1}(I + mK)^{-1}$$

$$\|(I - KF)^{-1}\| \leq \|(I + mK)^{-1}\|/(1 - \|K_mF_m\|) .$$

We shall now indicate how this reduction works in special cases. Note that the basic idea may be used if H is merely a linear complete metric space with translation invariant metric. K must be a linear operator since in the process of establishing (2) one has to commute K with a scalar multiple of identity. In the case $K = I$ equation (2) is identical with that of Zarantonello, (K-5), p. 6.

Lemma 1. a) If $m \geq 0$ and $F \leq \mu I$ $(\mu \geq -\|F\|)$ then

$$\|F_m\|^2 \leq m^2 + 2m\mu + \|F\|^2 ;$$

b) if $m \leq 0$ and $F \geq \mu I$ $(\mu \leq \|F\|)$ then

$$\|F_m\|^2 \leq m^2 - 2|m|\mu + \|F\|^2 .$$

The proof of Lemma 1 is obtained by expanding $\|(Fx - Fy) + m(x - y)\|^2$. See also (K-5), Lemma 5.

Lemma 2. a) If $a \geq 0$, $m \geq 0$ and $K \geq aI$, then

$$\|K_m\| \leq (m + a/\|K\|^2)^{-1}$$

b) if $a > 0$, $m < -\|K\|/a^2$ and $K \geq aI$, then

$$\|K_m\| \leq (|m| - \|K\|/a^2)^{-1} .$$

Lemma 3. a) $m \geq 0$ and K is a positive operator, then

$$\|K_m\| = (m + 1/\|K\|)^{-1}$$

b) if K is a positive operator, $a = \inf\{(Kx, x) \mid x \in H, \|x\| = 1\} > 0$ and $m < -1/a$, then

$$\|K_m\| = (|m| - 1/a)^{-1} .$$

Proofs of Lemmas 2 and 3 will be found in I. I. Kolodner's 'Contractive Methods for the Hammerstein Equation in Hilbert Spaces,' University of New Mexico TR No. 35, July 1963. These proofs are based essentially on the study of numerical ranges of $(K+\epsilon I)^{-1}+mI$ where $\epsilon > 0$.[5] If K is compact, then Lemma 3a follows also by a simple application of the spectral theorem. However, the compactness of K is not needed in the proofs, nor does it simplify them.

Theorem. $(I-KF)^{-1}$ exists, is Lipshitzian, and is represented by (3) with suitable m in each of the following cases:

i) if $K \geq aI$, $a \geq 0$, $F \leq \mu I$, and $\mu < a/\|K\|^2$

ii) if K is positive, $F \leq \mu I$, and $\mu < 1/\|K\|$

iii) if $K \geq aI$, $a > 0$, $F \geq \mu I$, and $\mu > \|K\|/a^2$

iv) if K is positive, $K \geq aI$, $a > 0$, $F \geq \mu I$ and $\mu > 1/a$.

Proof. In each case one shows that for some m, $\|K_m F_m\| < 1$. We supply the proof in case i); the other proofs follow the same pattern. From Lemmas 1a and 2a, we get for $m \geq 0$,

$$\|K_m F_m\|^2 \leq \|K_m\|^2 \|F_m\|^2 \leq g(\sigma) = 1-2(\lambda-\mu)\sigma + (\|F\|^2 - 2\lambda\mu + \lambda^2)\sigma^2$$

where $\lambda = a/\|K\|^2$, $\sigma = 1/(m+\lambda)$. Since $\lambda > \mu$, $g(\sigma) < 1$ for $\sigma > 0$ sufficiently small, i.e. for m sufficiently large. Q.E.D.

Part i of the Theorem with $a > 0$ and $\mu = 0$ reproduces the result of Theorem 4.6, Section 4, in the case when F is Lipshitzian. Parts ii and iii with $K = I$ on a real Hilbert space, are identical with Theorem 1 in (K-5). Several extensions and applications of the theorem will be found in the report of Kolodner quoted above. It is worthwhile to note that the requirement on F may be relaxed: it suffices to assume that F is Lipshitzian on all balls in H (but not uniformly Lipshitzian) and that the norms of F restricted to these balls satisfy a certain growth condition.

Both authors were partially supported by an N.S.F. grant in the preparation of this paper.

[5] If H is a real space one will have to consider in this study the complexifications of H and K.

L. B. RALL

Variational Methods for Nonlinear Integral Equations

1. Introduction

The use of variational methods for the investigation of nonlinear integral equations goes back at least to a paper published by G. Fubini in 1913 [14]. Further developments were made before 1940 by L. Lichtenstein [42a, pp. 79-84; b], A. Hammerstein [23], and M. Golomb [20]. Since 1945, papers have appeared by E. Rothe [66] and a number of authors in the USSR, such as M. M. Vaĭnberg [68], M. A. Krasnosel'skiĭ [34], É. S. Tsitlanadze [67], A. P. Gremiachenskiĭ [22], Ia. V. Bykov [5], V. I. Kondrashev [33], and R. I. Kachurovskiĭ [29]. The work done to 1955 has been summarized in a book by M. M. Vaĭnberg. Since not many of the Soviet publications are available in English, one purpose of this paper is to give a survey of their results, based mainly on Vaĭnberg's book, with references to the original papers being included in the Bibliography.

The use of variational methods for the study of nonlinear equations is based on a familiar idea. If the nonlinear operator $F(x)$ with domain D in some real Banach space E is the derivative (in some sense) of a real functional $f(x)$ on D, then any point x_0 at which $f(x)$ has a relative maximum or minimum will be a solution of the nonlinear equation $F(x) = 0$. Conditions for $f(x)$ to have relative extremal points, or conditional relative extremal points, furnish theorems on the existence of solutions of operator equations, proper values and elements of nonlinear operators, and bifurcation points of solutions of nonlinear equations.

In general, the theorems obtained by variational methods are non-constructive in character. Here, they will be applied mainly to nonlinear integral equations of Hammerstein type.

2. Gradients and Potentials

In what follows, only real Banach spaces E will be considered, bounded linear operators and functionals on E being referred to simply as linear operators and functionals. The space conjugate to E will be denoted by E^*. If $y \in E^*$, it is a real linear functional on E, and we shall write

$$y(x) = (y, x) \quad . \tag{2.1}$$

In case E is a real Hilbert space H, the notation (y, x) will denote the inner product of the elements $x, y \in H$.

If $F(x)$ is an operator from a space E_x into a space E_y it is said to be G-differentiable at the point $x \in E_x$ if a linear operator L from E_x into E_y exists such that

$$\lim_{t \to 0} \left\| \frac{F(x + th) - F(x)}{t} - Lh \right\| = 0 \tag{2.2}$$

for all $h \in E_x$ [17]. If L exists, it is called the Gâteaux derivative (or G-derivative) of F at x, and is denoted by

$$L = \frac{\partial F(x)}{\partial h} \quad . \tag{2.3}$$

If L satisfies the more restrictive condition that

$$\lim_{\|\Delta x\| \to 0} \frac{\|F(x + \Delta x) - F(x) - L\Delta x\|}{\|\Delta x\|} = 0 \quad , \tag{2.4}$$

then $F(x)$ is said to be F-differentiable at x, and

$$L = \frac{dF(x)}{dx} \tag{2.5}$$

is called the Fréchet derivative (or F-derivative) of F at x [12]. If $F(x)$ is F-differentiable at x_0, then its G-derivative at x_0 exists and equals its F-derivative at x_0. On the other hand, if the G-derivative of $F(x)$ exists in some neighborhood of x_0 and is continuous at x_0, the F-derivative of $F(x)$ at x_0 exists and equals its G-derivative at x_0. In what follows, the notation $F'(x)$ will be used to denote either derivative of F at x, a distinction being made in the text only when significant.

If $f(x)$ is a differentiable real functional with domain D in E, the operator

$$F(x) = f'(x) \tag{2.6}$$

will be called the gradient of $f(x)$, and denoted on occasion by grad $f(x)$. The functional $f(x)$ will be called the potential of the operator $F(x)$. If $f(x)$ is only G-differentiable, $F(x) = f'(x)$ is called a weak gradient; otherwise, a strong gradient. The gradient $F(x) = \text{grad } f(x)$ will be a linear operator from E into the reals, and thus is an element of the space E^* for each value of x for which it is defined.

Given an operator $F(x)$ from E into E^*, the following results may be used to determine whether or not it is the gradient of some functional $f(x)$.

Theorem 2.1. If $f(x)$ is G-differentiable in the open ball $D = \{x: \|x - x_0\| < R\}$ and the functional $(F'(x)h_1, h_2)$ is continuous at every point $x \in D$ for arbitrary $h_1 h_2 \in E$, then $F(x)$ is the gradient of some functional $f(x)$ in the ball D if and only if

$$(F'(x)h_1, h_2) = (F'(x)h_2, h_1) \tag{2.7}$$

for all $h_1, h_2 \in E$ and $x \in D$ [68x, pp. 79-80].

In a Hilbert space H, condition (2.7) is satisfied if the linear operator $F'(x)$ in H is self-conjugate for all $x \in D$. The following theorem gives a necessary and sufficient condition for $F(x)$ to be a gradient without the requirement that $F'(x)$ exist.

Theorem 2.2. If $F(x)$ is continuous in the simply-connected region R in E, it is the gradient of some functional $f(x)$ on R if and only if the curvilinear Riemann-Stieltjes integral

$$I = \int_L (F(x), dx) \tag{2.8}$$

is independent of path in R [68x, pp. 87-88].

Since $F(x)$ is assumed to be continuous, it will be the strong gradient (F-derivative) of $f(x)$ in R.

Theorem 2.3. If $F(x)$ is a gradient, it has the unique potential

$$f(x) = f_0 + \int_0^1 (F\{x_0 + t(x - x_0)\}, x - x_0)\, dt \tag{2.9}$$

which takes on the value f_0 at the point x_0 [68x, p. 83].

Formula (2.9) provides a method for constructing the potential of an operator.

Two operators of importance in the theory of nonlinear integral equations will now be considered as examples of gradients. First, suppose that R is a set of finite measure in n-dimensional Euclidean space. A function

$$g(u_1, \ldots, u_n, x), \quad x \in R, \quad u_i \in (-\infty, +\infty) ,$$

will be called an (H)-function if it is continuous in $u = (u_1, \ldots, u_n)$ for almost every $x \in R$, and measurable in x for fixed u. For vector functions $u = (u_1(x), \ldots, u_n(x))$ and $v = (v_1(x), \ldots, v_n(x))$, a transformation $v = F(u)$ may be defined by

$$v_i(x) = g_i(u_1(x), \ldots, u_n(x), x), \quad x \in R, \ i = 1, \ldots, n , \tag{2.10}$$

where each g_i is an (H)-function. The operator F defined in this way is called a Nemytskii operator [52] by Vaĭnberg. A necessary and sufficient condition for F to be a continuous operator from $L_{p,n}(R)$ into $L_{q,n}(R)$ $(p \geq 2,\ p^{-1} + q^{-1} = 1)$ is that

$$|g_i(u_1, \ldots, u_n, x)| \leq a_i(x) + b \sum_{k=1}^{n} |u_k|^{p-1} , \tag{2.11}$$

almost everywhere, for some $a_i(x) \in L^q$ and $b > 0$ [68x, pp. 213-214]. If F is continuous, it is the gradient of a functional on $L_{p,n}$ if and only if a function $G(u_1, \ldots, u_n, x)$ exists such that

$$g_i(u_1, \ldots, u_n, x) = \frac{\partial}{\partial u_i} G(u_1, \ldots, u_n, x), \quad i = 1, \ldots, n . \tag{2.12}$$

Setting

$$f_0 = \int_R G(0, \ldots, 0, x)\, dx , \tag{2.13}$$

$F(u)$ is the gradient of the functional

$$f(u) = \int_R G(u_1(x), \ldots, u_n(x), x)\, dx \tag{2.14}$$

if (2.11) and (2.12) are satisfied [20b, 22, 66c]. The functional

$f(u)$ given by (2.14) has the useful property that it satisfies a Lipschitz condition in any ball in $L_{p,n}$ [68x, pp. 228-230].

As a second example, if $K_n(s_1, \ldots, s_{n+1})$ is real, symmetric with respect to all arguments, and square integrable on the unit cube $0 \leq s_i \leq 1$, then for $x(s) \in L^2$, the expression

$$\int_0^1 \cdots \int_0^1 K_n(s, t_1, \ldots, t_n) x(t_1) \ldots x(t_n) \, dt_1 \ldots dt_n$$

is a special case of the integral power forms considered by Erhard Schmidt [60]. Further, if

$$\sum_{n=1}^{\infty} \left(\int_0^1 \cdots \int_0^1 \{K_n(t_1, \ldots, t_{n+1})\}^2 \, dt_1 \ldots dt_{n+1} \right)^{\frac{1}{2}} < +\infty \ , \tag{2.15}$$

the operator

$$F(x) = \sum_{n=1}^{\infty} \int_0^1 \cdots \int_0^1 K_n(s, t_1, \ldots, t_n) \prod_{i=1}^{n} x(t_i) \, dt_i \tag{2.16}$$

may be defined on the unit ball of the space L^2. $F(x)$ is WS-continuous, that is; it transforms all weakly convergent sequences in its domain into strongly convergent ones. It is the gradient of the functional

$$f(x) = \sum_{n=2}^{\infty} \frac{1}{n} \int_0^1 \cdots \int_0^1 K_{n-1}(t_1, \ldots, t_n) \prod_{i=1}^{n} x(t_i) \, dt_i \ . \tag{2.17}$$

Vainberg calls $F(x)$ defined by (2.16) the Liapunov-Lichtenstein operator [68x, pp. 230-237, 64ab, 67ej].

3. Critical and Relative Extremal Points of Functionals

A point x_0 at which

$$\operatorname{grad} f(x_0) = f'(x_0) = 0 \tag{3.1}$$

is called a critical point of the functional $f(x)$. An interior point x_0 of a set S such that $f(x) \leq f(x_0)$ $\{f(x) \geq f(x_0)\}$ for all $x \in S$ is called a relative maximum {minimum} point of the functional $f(x)$. Relative maximum and minimum points of $f(x)$ are called relative extremal points of $f(x)$.

Theorem 3.1. A relative extremal point x_0 of a differentiable functional $f(x)$ is a critical point of $f(x)$.

This is proved simply by noting that for any $h \in E$, $t = 0$ is a relative extremal point of the real function

$$r(t) = f(x_0 + th) , \tag{3.2}$$

for which

$$\frac{dr}{dt} = f'(x_0 + th)h \tag{3.3}$$

by the chain rule for derivatives [30c]. As thus $f'(x_0)h = 0$ for arbitrary h, $f'(x_0) = 0$.

From this point on, only Banach spaces E with weakly compact spheres will be considered. A set S is said to be weakly compact if every infinite sequence of elements of S has a weakly convergent subsequence, the limit of which does not have to belong to S. All reflexive Banach spaces and thus all Hilbert spaces have weakly compact spheres [44]. Since weak continuity is too restrictive, use will be made of the idea of weak semicontinuity of functionals. The functional $f(x)$ is said to be weakly lower semicontinuous at x_0 if

$$f(x_0) \leq \liminf_{n\to\infty} f(x_n) \tag{3.4}$$

for all sequences $\{x_n\}$ which converge weakly to x_0. A theorem of Weierstrass type holds for such functionals.

Theorem 3.2. A weakly lower semicontinuous functional is bounded below and attains its lower bound on each bounded and weakly closed subset of the Banach space E [68x, p. 107].

Since E is assumed to have a weakly compact sphere, all bounded subsets of E are weakly compact. Theorem 3.2 and a maximum principle give a sufficient condition for a functional to have a critical point. A weakly lower semicontinuous functional $f(x)$ is said to have the m-property on a bounded, weakly closed, and hence closed, subset S of E if for some interior point x_0 of S,

$$f(x) > f(x_0) \tag{3.5}$$

for all x on the boundary ∂S of S.

Theorem 3.3. A G-differentiable functional with the m-property has at least one critical point.

By Theorem 3.2, $f(x)$ attains its lower bound on the set S for which (3.5) holds. The m-property insures that it is attained at an interior point x_0 of S, which is thus a relative minimum point.

Another sufficient condition may be obtained for functionals which have second G-derivatives. Since $F(x) = f'(x)$ is an operator from E into E^* as a function of x,

$$f''(x) = F'(x) \tag{3.6}$$

will be a linear operator from E into E^* for each x at which it exists, that is, for all $h \in E$, $f''(x)h \in E^*$. Thus, one may define a bi-linear functional $f''(x)hk$ for all $h, k \in E$ by

$$f''(x)hk = (f''(x)h, k) . \tag{3.7}$$

Theorem 3.4. Suppose that $f(x)$ is G-differentiable twice, and

$$f''(x)hh \geq \|h\| \zeta(\|h\|) , \tag{3.8}$$

where $\zeta(t)$ is continuous and non-negative for $t \geq 0$, and $\lim_{t\to\infty} \zeta(t) = \infty$.

It follows from inequality (3.8) that $f(x)$ is weakly lower semi-continuous in any ball $D_R = \{x: \|x\| \leq R\}$ [68x, p. 103]. Also, by (2.9),

$$(F(x), x) = (F(0), x) + \int_0^1 (F'(tx)x, x)\,dt \tag{3.9}$$

so that from (3.8),

$$(F(x), x) \geq (F(0), x) + \|x\| \zeta(\|x\|) . \tag{3.10}$$

Another application of (2.9) gives

$$f(x) = f(0) + \int_0^1 (F(tx), x)\,dt = f(0) + \int_0^1 (F(tx), tx)\frac{dt}{t} . \tag{3.11}$$

For $\|x\| = R$, (3.10) gives

$$f(x) \geq f(0) + \int_0^1 \{(F(0), tx) + \|tx\| \zeta(t\|x\|)\}\frac{dt}{t} \tag{3.12}$$

or

$$(3.13) \qquad f(x) \geq f(0) + (F(0), x) + R \int_0^1 \zeta(tR)\,dt \ .$$

Since $(F(0), x) \geq -\|F(0)\| R$ for $\|x\| = R$,

$$(3.14) \qquad f(x) \geq f(0) + R\{\int_0^1 \zeta(tR)\,dt - \|F(0)\|\} \ .$$

As the quantity in braces will be positive for R sufficiently large, $f(x) > f(0)$ for $\|x\| = R$, and thus $f(x)$ has the m-property, since D_R is bounded and weakly closed. Theorem 3.4 now follows from Theorem 3.3.

4. Solution of Equations in Hilbert Space

If $f(x)$ is a differentiable functional on a real Hilbert space H, $f'(x)$ may be considered to be an element of H, with $f'(x)h = (f'(x), h)$ for all $h \in H$. If A is a self-conjugate linear operator in H, $\{f(Ax)\}' = f'(Ax)A$ by the chain rule, so that for all $h \in H$,

$$(4.1) \qquad \{f(Ax)\}'h = (f'(Ax), Ah) = (Af'(Ax), h) = \{Af'(Ax)\}h \ .$$

Thus, if $F(x) = \text{grad}\, f(x)$,

$$(4.2) \qquad \text{grad}\, f(Ax) = AF(Ax) \ .$$

In order to investigate the equation

$$(4.3) \qquad x = KF(x) \ ,$$

where K is a positive, self-conjugate, and bounded linear operator on H, and $F(x)$ is the gradient of a functional $f(x)$, the positive square root A of K $(A^2 = K)$ and the functional

$$(4.4) \qquad g(x) = \frac{1}{2}(x, x) - f(Ax)$$

are introduced. If z_0 is a critical point of $g(x)$,

$$(4.5) \qquad Az_0 = A^2F(Az_0) \ ,$$

so that $x_0 = Az_0$ is a solution of (4.3).

The functional $g(x)$ will be weakly lower semicontinuous if $f(x)$ is continuous and K (and hence A) is completely continuous, or if $f(x)$ is weakly upper semicontinuous. If now

(4.6) $$f(x) \leq \frac{1}{2} a_1 (x, x) + a_2 (x, x)^{\delta} + a_3 \ ,$$

or, if $(F(tx), x)$ is an integrable function of t on $0 \leq t \leq 1$,

(4.7) $$(F(x), x) \leq a_1(x, x) + c_1(x, x)^{\delta} \ ,$$

where $a_1 \|K\| < 1$ if $a_1 > 0$, $0 < \delta < 1$, and a_2, a_3, c_1 are positive, there will be a ball D_R which is sufficiently large so that $g(x) > g(0)$ for all $x \in \partial D_R$, and thus $g(x)$ will have the m-property. Therefore, by Theorem 3.3, a solution of equation (4.3) will exist if (4.6) or (4.7) holds. As

(4.8) $$g''(x) = I - AF'(Ax)A \ ,$$

where I is the identity operator, and

(4.9) $$g''(x)h = h - AF'(Ax)Ah \ ,$$

then

(4.10) $$g''(x)hh = (h, h) - (AF'(Ax)Ah, h) = (h, h) - (F'(Ax)Ah, Ah) \ .$$

If now

(4.11) $$(F'(x)h, h) \leq a_1(h, h) \ ,$$

where $a_1 \|K\| < 1$ if $a_1 > 0$, then

(4.12) $$g''(x)hh \geq \begin{cases} \|h\|^2 & \text{if } a_1 \leq 0 \ , \\ (1 - a_1 \|K\|) \|h\|^2 & \text{if } a_1 > 0 \ , \end{cases}$$

so that a solution of (4.3) exists by Theorem 3.4. It also follows that if (4.11) holds, the equation

(4.13) $$x = \lambda KF(x)$$

will have a solution for all λ such that

(4.14) $$0 < \lambda a_1 \|K\| < 1 \ .$$

It is possible to relax the condition that K be a positive operator slightly. A self-conjugate and bounded linear operator K will be said to be semi-negative if it has positive proper values, but only a finite number with finite multiplicities. It will be assumed that these proper values lie in the interval $m \leq \lambda \leq b$, where $m > 0$, and the finite-dimensional space spanned by the corresponding proper vectors will be denoted by H_1. P_1 will denote the projection operator from H into H_1, and P_2 the projection operator from H into the orthogonal complement H_2 of H_1. The operator K is regarded as the sum of a positive part K^+ with range H_1, and a negative part K^- with range H_2. If A^+ denotes the positive square root of K^+, and A^- is the positive square root of the absolute value of K^-, the operator

$$A = A^+ - A^- \tag{4.15}$$

will be called the principal square root of the operator K. Use will also be made of the positive square root C of the absolute value of the operator K. Some useful relationships involving these operators are

$$AC = CA = (A^+)^2 - (A^-)^2 = K \,, \tag{4.16}$$

and

$$A(P_1 - P_2) = C; \quad C(P_1 - P_2) = A \,. \tag{4.17}$$

Instead of (x, x), the functional

$$((x))^2 = \|P_1 x\|^2 - \|P_2 x\|^2 \tag{4.18}$$

will be employed, for which

$$\operatorname{grad} ((x))^2 = 2(P_1 x - P_2 x) \,. \tag{4.19}$$

If now z_0 is a critical point of the functional

$$g(x) = 2f(Ax) - ((x))^2 \,, \tag{4.20}$$

then, for $F(x) = f'(x)$,

$$AF(Az_0) - (P_1 - P_2) z_0 = 0 \,, \tag{4.21}$$

and operation by C yields

$$KF(Az_0) - Az_0 = 0 \tag{4.22}$$

by (4.16) and (4.17) . Hence, $x_0 = Az_0$ will be a solution of (4.3) in this case. A similar result is obtained if the functional $f(Ax)$ in (4.20) is replaced by $f(Cx)$.

The functional $g(x)$ will be weakly lower semicontinuous if $f(x)$ is continuous and K is completely continuous, or if $f(x)$ is weakly lower semicontinuous. If also

$$f(x) \geq \frac{1}{m}(x,x) + a_2(x,x)^{\delta} + a_3 , \tag{4.23}$$

where a_2, a_3 are negative and $0 < \delta < 1$, then $g(x)$ will have the m-property, as $g(x) > g(0)$ for all $x \in \partial D_R$ if R is sufficiently large. Thus, if (4.23) holds, equation (4.3) will have a solution by Theorem 3.3 . This also will apply in this case to equation (4.13) for all $\lambda \geq 1$. If

$$(F'(x)h, h) \geq \frac{2}{m}(h, h) , \tag{4.24}$$

the solvability of equation (4.3) follows from Theorem 3.4 .

If the operator $F(x)$ satisfies the Lipschitz condition

$$\|F(x_2) - F(x_1)\| \leq a_1 \|x_2 - x_1\| \quad (0 < a_1 \|K\| < 1) , \tag{4.25}$$

the solution of equation (4.3) will be unique.

An equation of the first kind

$$F(x) = y \tag{4.26}$$

may be investigated by using the functional

$$g(x) = f(x) - (x, y) . \tag{4.27}$$

For $F(x) = f'(x)$,

$$g'(x) = F(x) - y , \tag{4.28}$$

and

$$g''(x) = F'(x) , \tag{4.29}$$

so that if

$$(F'(x)h, h) \geq c(h, h) \tag{4.30}$$

for some $c > 0$, (4.26) has a solution by Theorem 3.4 [68x, pp. 111-120].

Equation (4.3) may be investigated in more general Banach spaces E if the (principal) square root A of K acts from E^* into H, and from H into E, where H is some Hilbert space. To illustrate this, consider the Hammerstein operator KF, where $v = Ku$ in $L_{2,n}$ is defined by

$$v_i(x) = \int_R K_i(x, y)\, u_i(y)\, dy, \quad i = 1, \ldots, n, \tag{4.31}$$

with symmetric kernels $K_i(x, y)$, and F is defined by (2.10), it being assumed that (2.12) holds. In this case, equation (4.3) takes the form

$$u_i(x) = \int_R K_i(x, y)\, g_i(u_1(y), \ldots, u_n(y), y)\, dy, \quad i = 1, \ldots, n, \tag{4.32}$$

which is called a Hammerstein equation. The Hammerstein operator (or equation) will be said to be positive or semi-negative according as K is positive or semi-negative, considered as an operator in the space $L_{2,n}$. If K is completely continuous from $L_{q,n}$ into $L_{p,n}$ ($p \geq 2$, $p^{-1} + q^{-1} = 1$), then its (principal) square root is completely continuous from $L_{2,n}$ into $L_{p,n}$, and from $L_{q,n}$ into $L_{p,n}$ [68x, pp. 260-262]. If (2.11) holds, the following theorems are valid.

Theorem 4.1. If the Hammerstein equation (4.32) is positive and

$$G(u_1, \ldots, u_n, x) \leq \frac{1}{2} \sum_{i=1}^{n} a_i u_i^2 + \sum_{i=1}^{n} b_i(x) |u_i|^\delta + c(x), \tag{4.33}$$

where $0 \leq a_i < \lambda_{i1}$, the smallest characteristic value of the kernel $K_i(x, y)$, $0 < \delta < 2$, $0 \leq b_i(x) \in L^\zeta$, $\zeta = 2/(2 - \delta)$, $0 \leq c_i(x) \in L$, then it has at least one solution $u(x) = (u_1(x), \ldots, u_n(x))$ in $L_{p,n}$.

If (4.33) is satisfied, $f(u)$ given by (2.14) will satisfy (4.6). In $L_{2,n}$, (4.33) will be satisfied if

$$|g_i(u_1, \ldots, u_n, x)| \leq a_i(x) + \sum_{k=1}^{n} b_{ik} |u_k| + \sum_{k=1}^{n} c_{ik}(x) |u_k|^{\delta - 1}, \tag{4.34}$$

and

$$\frac{1}{2} \sum_{k=1}^{n} (b_{ik} + b_{ki}) < \lambda_{i1}, \tag{4.35}$$

for $i = 1,\ldots,n$, where $0 \leq a_i(x) \in L^2$, $0 \leq c_{ik}(x) \in L^\zeta$, [68x, pp. 267-274].

Theorem 4.2. If the Hammerstein equation (4.32) is semi-negative and

$$G(u_1,\ldots,u_n,x) \geq \sum_{i=1}^{n} a_i u_i^2 + \sum_{i=1}^{n} b_i(x)|u_i|^\delta + c(x) \quad , \tag{4.36}$$

where $a_i = 1/\lambda_{i1}$, λ_{i1} being the largest positive characteristic value of $K_i(x, y)$, $0 < \delta < 2$, $0 \geq b_i(x) \in L^\zeta$, $\zeta = 2/(2-\delta)$, $0 \geq c(x) \in L$, then it has at least one solution $u(x) = (u_1(x),\ldots,u_n(x))$ in $L_{p,n}$.

If (4.36) is satisfied, $f(u)$ given by (2.14) satisfies (4.23).

The Hammerstein operator (or equation) is said to be bounded if $K_i(x, y)$ is essentially bounded for $(x, y) \in R^2$, $i = 1,\ldots,n$. In this case, the (principal) square root of K is completely continuous from $L_{2,n}$ into $L_{\infty,n}$, the space of essentially bounded vector functions, and from $L_{1,n}$ into $L_{2,n}$. If also

$$|g_i(u_1,\ldots,u_n,x)| \leq a_{ir}(x) \in L^q, \quad 1 < q < 2 \quad , \tag{4.37}$$

for $-r \leq u_i \leq r$, the positive Hammerstein equation (4.32) has an essentially bounded solution if (4.33) holds, and the semi-negative equation has an essentially bounded solution if (4.36) holds. [68x, pp. 280-286].

In the case $n = 1$, if $g(u, x)$ has the partial derivative $g_u(u, x)$ which is continuous in u and bounded for almost all $x \in R$, the operator F has the G-derivative

$$F'(u) = g_u(u(x), x) I \quad , \tag{4.38}$$

where I is the identity operator. In this case, the Hammerstein operator (or equation) in L^2 will be said to be of Carleman type if the symmetric kernel $K(x, y)$ is of Carleman type, that is, that $K(x_0, y) \in L^2$ for almost all $x_0 \in R$.

Theorem 4.3. If the Hammerstein equation of Carleman type

$$u(x) = \int_R K(x, y)\, g(u(y), y)\, dy \tag{4.39}$$

is positive and $g_u(u, x) \leq M$, where $M\|K\| < 1$ if $M > 0$, then it has a solution $u(x)$ in L_2. This solution will be unique if $|g_u(u, x)| < M$.

The hypotheses of this theorem guarantee satisfaction of (4.11). Uniqueness follows from (4.25).

Theorem 4.4. If the Hammerstein equation (4.39) of Carleman type is semi-negative, and $g_u(u, x) \geq 2\lambda_1$, where λ_1 is the largest positive characteristic value of the kernel $K(x, y)$, then it has at least one solution $u(x) \in L^2$.

The hypotheses of this theorem guarantee the satisfaction of condition (4.24).

5. Relative Conditional Extrema and Conditional Critical Points of Functionals

If $f(x)$ and $g(x)$ are two continuous real functionals, and $U_c = \{x: g(x) = c\}$, a point $x_0 \in U_c$ is called a relative conditional minimum {maximum} point of $f(x)$ with respect to U_c if there exists a neighborhood V of x_0 such that $f(x) \geq f(x_0)$ $\{f(x) \leq f(x_0)\}$ for all $x \in V \cap U_c$ is such that

$$\text{(5.1)} \qquad \operatorname{grad} f(x_0) = \lambda \operatorname{grad} g(x_0)$$

for some number λ, x_0 is called a conditional critical point of $f(x)$ with respect to U_c. The following theorem [43a, 39, 68ℓ] relates these concepts.

Theorem 5.1. If $f(x)$ and $g(x)$ are F-differentiable at x_0, where $g(x_0) = c$ and $\|\operatorname{grad} g(x_0)\| > 0$, and if x_0 is a relative extremal point of $f(x)$ with respect to U_c, then it is a conditional critical point of $f(x)$ with respect to U_c, so that (5.1) holds.

In a Hilbert space H, if one takes $g(x) = (x, x)$, so that for $c \neq 0$, $g(x) = c^2$ defines a sphere,

$$\text{(5.2)} \qquad \operatorname{grad} f(x_0) = \lambda x_0$$

if x_0 is a relative extremal point of $f(x)$ with respect to the sphere $S_c = \{x: (x, x) = c^2\}$.

Returning to the functional $g(x) = ((x))^2$ defined previously by (4.18), the set

$$\text{(5.3)} \qquad G_c = \{x: ((x))^2 = c^2\}$$

will be called the hyperboloid generated by the operator K if $c \neq 0$. If x_0 is a relative extremal point of $f(x)$ with respect to G_c, then

(5.4) $$\operatorname{grad} f(x_0) = \lambda (P_1 x_0 - P_2 x_0) \ .$$

The hyperboloidal regions $V_c = \{x: ((x)) \geq c > 0\}$ and the conical region $V_0 = \{x: ((x)) \geq 0\}$ are weakly closed [68x, p. 124].

If $\|\operatorname{grad} f(x)\| > 0$ in the interior of a weakly closed, and bounded region S, and if $f(x)$ is weakly lower {upper} semicontinuous, then $f(x)$ attains its lower {upper} bound on the boundary ∂S of S. This gives a sufficient condition for conditional extrema of a functional $f(x)$ with respect to a sphere S_c; the following similar result holds for hyperboloids.

Theorem 5.2. If $f(x)$ is a weakly lower semicontinuous functional such that

(5.5) $$\|\operatorname{grad} f(x)\| > 0 \ ,$$

and

(5.6) $$\lim_{\|x\| \to \infty} f(x) = +\infty$$

for all x in the interior of the conical region V_0, then $f(x)$ has at least one conditional minimum point on any hyperboloid G_c.

For a fixed $x_0 \in V_c$, a sphere $S = \{x: \|x\| = a > \|x_0\|\}$ exists by (5.6) for which $f(x) > f(x_0)$ for all $x \in S \cap V_c$. The intersection $U = V_c \cap D$, $D = \{x: \|x\| \leq a\}$ is weakly closed and bounded, so $f(x)$ attains its lower bound at some point $x_1 \in \partial U$. Since $f(x) > f(x_0) \geq f(x_1)$ on $S \cap V_c$, $x_1 \in G_c \cap (D \setminus S)$, so that $x_1 \in G_c$ and $\|x_1\| < a$.

The conclusion of Theorem 5.2 holds if $F(x) = \operatorname{grad} f(x)$ satisfies the following conditions:

(5.7) $$F(0) = 0 \ ,$$

(5.8) $$(F'(x)h, h) \geq 0$$

at each point $x \in H$, and

(5.9) $$(F'(x)h, h) \geq \zeta(\|h\|)$$

in the conical region V_0, where $h \in H$ is arbitrary, and $\zeta(t)$ is an increasing function for $t \geq 0$, with

(5.10) $$\lim_{t \to +\infty} \zeta(t) = +\infty \ ,$$

[68x, pp. 139-140].

Theorem 5.3. Suppose that the weakly lower semicontinuous functional $f(x)$ is continuous at $x = 0$ and has a positive monotone minorant on the intersection of the conical region V_0 and the ball $D_R = \{x: \|x\| \leq R\}$, that is,

$$f(x) \geq f(0) + \eta(\|x\|) , \tag{5.11}$$

for $x \in V_0 \cap D_R$, where $\eta(t)$ is a positive, monotone increasing function on the interval $0 \leq t \leq R$, and $\|\text{grad } f(x)\| > 0$ for interior points x of $V_0 \cap D_R$. Then, for some $r > 0$, there exists at least one conditional minimum point of $f(x)$ on all hyperboloids G_c for $c \leq r$.

Conditions (5.11) and (5.5) will be satisfied if

$$(\text{grad } f(x), x) > 0 \tag{5.12}$$

for all $x \neq 0$ in $V_0 \cap D_R$ [68x, pp. 137-138].

The conclusions of Theorem 5.3 will also hold if $F(x) = \text{grad } f(x)$ satisfies (5.7) and (5.8) in some ball D_R, and

$$(F'(x)h, h) > 0 \tag{5.13}$$

for $x \in V_0 \cap D_R$ [68x, pp. 140-141].

6. Proper Values and Elements of Nonlinear Operators

For a given operator T, an element $x_0 \neq 0$ such that for some number λ_0,

$$T(x_0) = \lambda_0 x_0 \tag{6.1}$$

is called an invariant direction of T if $\lambda_0 \neq 0$. If $T(0) = 0$ and (6.1) is satisfied for $x_0 \neq 0$, x_0 is called a proper element of T corresponding to the proper value λ_0. Here, $\lambda_0 = 0$ is permitted. Reciprocals of nonzero proper values of T are called characteristic values of T.

Invariant directions of nonlinear operators were investigated some time ago by Birkhoff and Kellogg [3], and applications of proper elements and values of nonlinear operators have appeared in papers by Liapunov [41], Nekrasov [51], Iglisch [26], Iasinskiĭ [25], and others, in areas such as fluid dynamics, nonlinear oscillations, and the stability of compressed objects. Investigation of proper functions of the Hammerstein operator goes back to Lichtenstein [42] and Golomb [20].

If $F(x)$ is the strong gradient of a functional $f(x)$ in a Hilbert space H, the following results hold.

Theorem 6.1. Suppose that $F(x) = \text{grad } f(x)$ is positive, that is

$$(F(x), x) > 0 \text{ if } x \neq 0 \tag{6.2}$$

and that K is a positive, self-conjugate, bounded linear operator. If K is completely continuous or if $f(x)$ is weakly continuous, there will exist an element z_r on any sphere $S_r = \{x: \|x\| = r > 0\}$ such that $x_r = Az_r$ is an invariant direction of the operator KF, where A is the positive square root of K.

The functional $f(x)$ is continuous, as it is F-differentiable, so that $f(Ax)$ will be weakly continuous if K is completely continuous. As

$$\frac{d}{dt} f(tAx) = (F(tAx), Ax) = \frac{1}{t}(F(tAx), tAx) > 0 \tag{6.3}$$

for any x such that $Ax \neq 0$, $f(Ax)$ will attain its upper bound at some point z_r of S_r. Since this will be a conditional critical point of $f(Ax)$ with respect to S_r,

$$AF(Az_r) = \lambda z_r \tag{6.4}$$

by (5.2), so that $KF(x_r) = \lambda x_r$ for $x_r = Az_r$. As

$$\lambda(z_r, z_r) = (AF(Az_r) = (F(Az_r), Az_r) > 0 \tag{6.5}$$

it follows that $\lambda > 0$, and thus x_r is an invariant direction of KF. In this proof, it is sufficient to consider $f(Ax)$ in the set $D_r \cap H_1$, where $D_r = \{x: \|x\| \leq r\}$, and H_1 is the orthogonal complement of the null space H_0 of K. It may thus be concluded that if x_r, x_s are invariant directions of KF, then $x_r \neq x_s$ if $r \neq s$, as otherwise $(z_r - z_s) \in H_0$. If $F(0) = 0$, theorem 6.1 guarantees the existence of proper elements of KF with arbitrarily small norms, as A is a bounded operator.

Theorem 6.2. Suppose that $F(x) = \text{grad } f(x)$ is positive, $F(0) = 0$, and that K is a semi-negative, self-conjugate, bounded linear operator. If $f(x)$ is continuous and K is completely continuous, or if $f(x)$ is weakly lower semicontinuous, and also

$$\lim_{\|x\| \to \infty} (F(x), x) = +\infty \tag{6.6}$$

for $x \in CV_0$ and $x \in AV_0$, then for $z_c^{(1)}, z_c^{(2)}$ belonging to any hyperboloid G_c generated by K for $c > 0$, there exist proper elements

(6.7) $$x_c^{(1)} = Az_c^{(1)}, \; x_c^{(2)} = C z_c^{(2)}$$

of the operator KF, which correspond to the positive proper values

(6.8) $$\lambda_c^{(i)} = c^{-2}(F(x_c^{(i)}), x_c^{(i)}) > 0 \quad (i = 1,2) .$$

A is the principal square root of K, and C is the positive square root of the absolute value of K . There exist proper elements of KF with norms larger than any given positive number a , and also ones with norms smaller than a . The proper elements found for different values of c are distinct.

For $g(x) = f(Ax)$ or $g(x) = f(Cx)$, condition (6.6) insures that for $x \in AV_0$ and $x \in CV_0$,

(6.9) $$\lim_{\|x\| \to \infty} f(x) = +\infty$$

from which it follows that

(6.10) $$\lim_{\|x\| \to \infty} g(x) = +\infty$$

for $x \in V_0$. Thus, (6.7) follows from (4.16), (4.17),(5.4), and Theorem 5.2. The existence of proper elements of KF with norms smaller than a given positive number follows from the proof of Theorem 5.2. For $z_c^{(1)}, z_c^{(2)} \in G_c$,

(6.11) $$\|Az_c^{(1)}\| \geq cm^{\frac{1}{2}}, \; \|Cz_c^{(2)}\| \geq cm^{\frac{1}{2}} ,$$

where m is the smallest positive proper value of K [68x, p. 176]. This shows that there are proper values of KF with norms larger than an arbitrary positive number. It also follows from (6.11) that $z_c^{(1)}$ is not an element of the null space of A, so that if $c \neq d$, then $x_c^{(1)} = Az_c^{(1)} \neq x_d^{(1)} = Az_d^{(1)}$, and, similarly, $x_c^{(2)} \neq x_d^{(2)}$.

The conclusions of this theorem also hold if $F(x) = \text{grad } f(x)$ satisfies (5.7)-(5.10).

Theorem 6.3. If $(F(x), x) > 0$ for all nonzero $x \in A(V_0 \cap D_R)$ and $x \in C(V_0 \cap D_R)$, $D_R = \{x: \|x\| \leq R\}$, there exists some $r > 0$ such that for all $c \leq r$, there are proper elements (6.7) and positive proper values (6.8) of the operator KF for semi-negative K . There exist proper elements of KF with norms smaller than an arbitrary positive number.

This is a direct consequence of Theorem 5.3, as (5.12) holds for $g(x) = f(Ax)$ and $g(x) = f(Cx)$. If $F(x)$ satisfies (5.7) in some ball D_R, and (5.13) holds for $x \in A(V_0 \cap D_R)$ and $x \in C(V_0 \cap D_R)$, the conclusions of this theorem also hold [68x, pp. 182-183].

These results may be applied to show the existence of proper values and proper elements (functions) in $L_{p,n}$ of Hammerstein operators KF in much the same way as before. If, in addition to (2.12) and (2.11) or (4.37),

$$g_i(0,\dots,0,x) = 0, \quad i = 1,\dots,n \tag{6.12}$$

holds for $x \in R$, then $F(0) = 0$, and the invariant directions of the Hammerstein operator KF will be proper elements.

If K is positive and

$$\operatorname{sgn} g_i(u_1,\dots,u_n,x) = \operatorname{sgn} u_i, \quad i = 1,\dots,n \ , \tag{6.13}$$

or for $\|u\| > 0$ in $L_{2,n}$,

$$\sum_{i=1}^{n} \int_R g_i(u_1(x),\dots,u_n(x), x)\, u_i(x)\, dx > 0 \ , \tag{6.14}$$

then Theorem 6.1 applies.

If K is semi-negative and (6.13) or (6.14) holds, then KF has proper functions with arbitrarily small norms by Theorem 6.3. If also

$$\lim_{\|u\| \to \infty} f(u) = \lim_{\|u\| \to \infty} \int_R G(u_1(x),\dots,u_n(x), x)\, dx = +\infty \ , \tag{6.15}$$

where $\|u\|$ is the $L_{2,n}$ norm of $u(x) = (u_1(x),\dots,u_n(x))$, proper functions of KF with arbitrarily large norms also exist by Theorem 6.2. In all these cases, the corresponding proper values are positive.

As before, these results carry over to bounded Hammerstein operators, and to Hammerstein operators of Carleman type in L^2 [68x, pp. 303-312].

The following theorems also relate to the problem of proper values and elements.

Theorem 6.4. If $f(x)$ is an F-differentiable and weakly lower semicontinuous functional which does not have a critical point on the sphere $S_R = \{x: \|x\| = R\}$, and if $f(0)$ is not the absolute minimum of $f(x)$ in the ball D_R, then the equation grad $f(x) = \lambda x$ has solutions with norms smaller than any arbitrary positive number [68x, pp. 142-143].

This theorem applies to the operator $a(s)F(x)$, where $F(x)$ is the Liapunov-Lichtenstein operator defined by (2.16), and $a(s) \geq 0$ is a measurable function on R for which ess sup $a(s) = M^2 > 0$ [68x, pp. 312-313].

Theorem 6.5. If the F-differentiable and weakly lower semi-continuous functional $f(x)$ does not have a conditional critical point with respect to the hyperboloid G_c, and (6.9) holds for $x \in V_0$, the equation grad $f(x) = \lambda(P_1 x - P_2 x)$ has solutions with norms larger than any given positive number [68x, pp. 143-148].

7. Branch and Bifurcation Points

For a general transformation $T(u, v)$ defined for $u \in E_1$, $v \in E_2$, with range in E_3, (u_0, v_0) is called a regular point of the equation

$$T(u, v) = 0 \tag{7.1}$$

if $T(u_0, v_0) = 0$ and there is a continuous function $u = f(v)$ from E_2 into E_1 such that $(f(v), v)$ is the unique solution of (7.1) in some neighborhood of (u_0, v_0). If $T(u_0, v_0) = 0$, but (u_0, v_0) is not a regular point of (7.1), it is called a branch point of the equation (7.1). If $T(0, v) = 0$ for all v, a branch point $(0, v_0)$ (or v_0 for brevity) is a bifurcation point of the equation $T(0, v) = 0$ if for every positive δ, η, $T(u, v) = 0$ for some u, v satisfying

$$0 < \|u\| < \delta, \quad \|v - v_0\| < \eta . \tag{7.2}$$

For $T(x, \lambda) = F(x) - \lambda x$, where $F(0) = 0$, bifurcation points of the equation $T(0, \lambda) = 0$, where λ is a numerical parameter, are called bifurcation points of the operator $F(x)$.

If $F(x)$ is differentiable,

$$\{F(x) - \lambda x\}' = F'(x) - \lambda I , \tag{7.3}$$

so that only proper values of the linear operator $F'(0)$ may be bifurcation points of $F(x)$ if it is completely continuous. Otherwise, $(0, \lambda)$ is a regular point by the Hildebrandt-Graves theorem [24]. If $F(x) =$ grad $f(x)$ has an F-derivative which is WS-continuous in some neighborhood of $x = 0$, and $F'(0)$ is self-conjugate in a Hilbert space H, every proper value of $F'(0)$ will be a bifurcation point of $F(x)$ [34g].

The existence of bifurcation points of operators KF, where $F(x)$ is a strong gradient, follows from the corresponding theorems on the existence of proper elements with arbitrarily small norms, and the inequality

(7.4) $$|(F(x), x| < M(x, x)$$

for x in some ball D_R and constant M if K is positive and F satisfies the hypotheses of Theorem 6.1. Similarly, for semi-negative K, if (7.4) holds in $A(V_0 \cap D_R)$ and $C(V_0 \cap D_R)$, and $F(x)$ satisfies the conditions of Theorem 6.3, or

(7.5) $$(F(x), x) \leq M(x, x)$$

in $A(V_0 \cap D_R)$ or $C(V_0 \cap D_R)$ and $F(x)$ satisfies the conditions of Theorem 6.2, the operator KF will have at least one bifurcation point. These statements follow from the fact that the infinite sets of proper values defined by (6.3) or (6.8) are bounded, and hence will contain subsequences converging to some bifurcation point λ_0.

Theorem 7.1. If K is positive and (6.13) or (6.14) is satisfied, and

(7.6) $$|g_i(u_1, \ldots, u_n, x)| \leq b\sum_{k=1}^{n} |u_k|^{p-1} ,$$

then the Hammerstein operator KF has positive proper values smaller than any given $\delta > 0$, so that $\lambda_0 = 0$ is a bifurcation point of this operator.

For $\|z_r\| = r$ in $L_{2,n}$, the estimate

(7.7) $$\lambda_r = r^{-2}(F(Az_r), Az_r) \leq Mr^{p-2}$$

may be obtained [68x, pp. 315-317]. Theorem 7.1 holds for bounded Hammerstein operators KF if

(7.8) $$|g_i(u_1, \ldots, u_n, x)| \leq \sum_{k=1}^{n} w_{ik}(|u_k|) ,$$

where the $w_{ik}(t)$ are monotone increasing, $w_{ik}(0) = 0$, and $w_{ik}(t) = o(t)$ as $t \to 0$ [68x, pp. 318-319].

The above results hold for semi-negative operators K in $L_{p,n}$ if (6.13) and (7.6) are satisfied, and for bounded Hammerstein operators if (4.37) and (7.8) hold.

It is possible to replace (7.6) by the condition

$$(7.9) \qquad |g_i(u_1,\ldots,u_n,x)| \le a_i(x) + b\sum_{k=1}^{n} |u_k|^{p-1} ,$$

for $a_i(x) \in L^2$, $1 < p < 2$.

Theorem 7.2. For the Hammerstein operator KF, if K is completely continuous from L^p into L^q ($p \ge 2$, $p^{-1} + q^{-1} = 1$), and is positive and self-conjugate in L^2, $g(0, x) = 0$ for $x \in R$, and

$$(7.10) \qquad \left|\frac{\partial}{\partial u} g(u, x)\right| \le a(x) + b|u|^{p-2} ,$$

where $a(x) \in L^\zeta$, $\zeta = p/(p-2)$, then every proper value of the linear integral operator with kernel $K(x, y)\frac{\partial}{\partial u}g(0, y) = L(x, y)$ is a bifurcation point of the operator KF in case $n = 1$.

This follows from a theorem of M. A. Krasnosel'skiĭ [67g], and will also hold if $\frac{\partial}{\partial u} g(u, x)$ and $\frac{\partial^2}{\partial u^2} g(u, x)$ are bounded and continuous for u in some interval $-r \le u \le r$, and

$$(7.11) \qquad |g(u, x)| \le a(x) \in L^q$$

for $1 < q < 2$ [68x, pp. 331-333].

8. Even Functionals

A variational theory for even functionals (odd operators) has been developed by L. A. Liusternik [43b], V. I. Sobolev [64ab], L. G. Shnirel'man [51, 71], and applied by M. M. Vaĭnberg [68] and É. S. Tsitlanadze [67] to Hammerstein and Liapunov-Lichtenstein operators. The principal theorem runs as follows.

Theorem 8.1. Suppose that an even functional $f(x)$ has a positive and WS-continuous gradient in the ball $D_R = \{x: \|x\| \le R\}$ of a real, separable Hilbert space H . Then, on any sphere $S = \{x: \|x\| = a \le R\}$, there exists a sequence $\{x_n\}$ of critical points of $f(x)$ which converges weakly to 0 [68x, pp. 148-159] .

The proof of this theorem uses the Liusternik-Shnirel'man category of sets, and shows that $f(x)$ has a critical point in the minimal set of a compact homotopy class in projective Hilbert space. Two applications of this theorem will be cited.

Theorem 8.2. If the positive Hammerstein operator KF satisfies (6.15) and

$$g_i(0,\ldots,0,-u_i,\ldots,-u_n,x) = -g_i(0,\ldots,0,u_i,\ldots,u_n,x) \tag{8.1}$$

or

$$g_i(-u_1,\ldots,-u_i,0,\ldots,0,x) = -g_i(u_1,\ldots,u_i,0,\ldots,0,x) \ , \tag{8.2}$$

then for any $c > 0$, there exists a sequence of pairwise linearly independent proper elements $x_n = Az_n$ of KF such that $\|z_n\| = c$, and $\{x_n\}$ converges weakly to 0. A denotes the positive square root of K [68x, pp. 289-292].

Theorem 8.3. If $a(s) \geq 0$ is measurable on $0 \leq s \leq 1$, and ess sup $a(s) = M^2 > 0$, and $F(x)$ is the Liapunov-Lichtenstein operator

$$F(x) = \sum_{n=1}^{\infty} \int_0^1 \ldots \int_0^1 K_{2n-1}(s, t_1,\ldots,t_{2n-1}) \prod_{i=1}^{2n-1} x(t_i)dt_i \ , \tag{8.3}$$

such that

$$\sum_{n=1}^{\infty} \int_0^1 \ldots \int_0^1 K_{2n-1}(t_1,\ldots,t_{2n}) \prod_{i=1}^{2n} x(t_i)dt_i > 0 \tag{8.4}$$

for all $x(s)$ in the unit ball of L_1^2, then there exists a sequence of proper functions $x_n(s) = \{a(s)\}^{1/2} z_n(s)$ of the operator $a(s)F(x)$ such that $\|z_n\| = c$, and $\{x_n\}$ converges weakly to 0.

BIBLIOGRAPHY

References marked with a * are in Russian.

1. Akhiezer, N. I., and Kreĭn, M. G.
*On certain problems of the theory of moments. Khar'kov, Gos. Nauch.-Tekhn. izd. Ukrainy, 1938.

2. Alexiewicz, A., and Orlicz, W.
On the differentials in Banach spaces. Ann. Soc. Polon. Math. 25 (1952), 95-99 (1953).

3. Birkhoff, G. D., and Kellogg, O. D.
Invariant points in function spaces. Trans. Amer. Math. Soc. 23 (1922), 96-115.

4. Borisovich, Iu. G.
a) *On the problem of estimation of the number of critical points of functionals. Dissertation, Kazanskiĭ State Univ., 1955.
b) *On an estimate for the number of critical points of functionals. Dokl. Akad. Nauk. USSR, 101, No. 2 (1955) 205-207.

5. Bykov, Ia. V.
*On the problem of proper functions of nonlinear integral equations. Dokl. Akad. Nauk. USSR, 72, No. 3 (1950), 449-452.

6. Carleman, T.
Sur les équations intégrales singulières à Noyali réel symétrique. Uppsala, 1923.

7. Dolph, C. L.
Nonlinear integral equations of the Hammerstein type. Trans. Amer. Math. Soc. 60 (1949), 289-307.

8. Dragioni, G. S.
Sur sistemi di equazioni integrali non lineari. Rendiconti del Sem. Matem. di Padova 7 (1936), 1-35.

9. Dubrovskiĭ, V. M.
a) *On some nonlinear integral equations. Uch. Zap. Mos. State Univ., 30 (1939), 49-60.
b) *Systems of nonlinear integral equations. Uspekhi Mat. Nauk, 4 vyp. 2(30) (1949), 176-177.

10. Eberlein, W. F.
Weak compactness in Banach spaces, I. Proc. Nat. Acad. Sci. 33 (1947), 51-53.

11. Ézrokhi, I. A.
*Certain types of linear homomorphisms of Banach spaces. Uch. Zap. Leningrad State Univ., ser. mat. 16 (1949), 54-119.

12. Fréchet, M.
a) La notion de differentielle dans l'analyse générale. Ann. Sc. de L'Ecole Norm. Supér. 42 (1925), 293-323.
b) Sur la notion differentielle. Journal de Math. 16 (1937), 233-250.

13. Friedrichs, K.
a) Spektraltheorie Halbbeschrankter Operatoren und Anwendung auf die Spekralzerlegung von Differential Operatoren. Math. Ann. 109 (1934), 465-487; 685-713.
b) On the boundary-value problems of the theory of elasticity and Korn's inequality. Ann. of Math. 48 (1947), 441-471.

14. Fubini, G.
Alcuni nuovi problemi di calcolo delle variazioni con applicazioni alla teoria delle equazioni integro-differenziali. Annali di Mat. 20 (1913), 217-244.

15. Gantmakher, V. R., and Shuml'ian, V. L.
a) On linear spaces with weakly compact unit spheres. Dokl. Akad. Nauk USSR 17 (1937), 91-94.
b) *On weak compactness in Banach spaces. Mat. sb. 8 (50) (1940), 489-492.

16. Gavurin, M. K.
a) Über die Stieltjessche Integration Abstrakter Funktionen. Fund. Math. 27 (1936), 254-268.
b) On k-multiple linear operators in Banach spaces. Dokl. Akad. Nauk USSR, 22 No. 9 (1939), 552-556.
c) On the construction of differential and integral calculus in Banach spaces. Dokl. Akad. Nauk USSR, 22 No. 9 (1939), 547-551.
d) *Analytic methods for the study of nonlinear functional transformations. Uch. Zap. Leningrad State Univ. ser. matem. 19 (1950), 59-154.

17. Gâteaux, R.
a) Sur les fonctionelles continues et les fonctionelles analytiques. Compt. Ren. 157 (1913), 325-327.
b) Sur les fonctionelles continues et les fonctionelles analytiques. Bull. de la Soc. Math. de France 50 (1922), 1-21.

18. Gel'fand, I. M.
Abstrakte Funktionen und Lineare Operationen. Matem. sb. 4 (46) (1938), 235-283.

19. Gerchinskiĭ, R.
a) *Certain topological properties of nonlinear mappings in functional spaces. Cand. dissertation, Moscow State Univ., 1955.
b) *Theorems on the existence of implicit functions in function spaces. Dokl. Akad. Nauk USSR, 105, No. 1 (1955) 7-10.

20. Golomb, M.
   a) Zur Theorie der nichtlinearen Integralgleichungen, Integralgleichungssysteme und algemeinen Funktionalgleichungen. Math. Zeitschrift 39 (1934), 45-75.
   b) Über Systeme von nichtlinearen Integralgleichungen. Publ. Math. Univ. Belgrade 5 (1936), 52-83.

21. Graves, L. M.
Riemann integration and Taylor's theorem in general analysis. Trans. Amer. Math. Soc. 29 (1927), 163-177.

22. Gremiachenskiǐ, A. P.
*On proper values of systems of nonlinear integral equations. Dokl. Akad. Nauk USSR, 60, No. 3 (1948), 337-340.

23. Hammerstein, A.
   a) Über nichtlineare Integralgleichungen und die damit zusammenhangenden Randwertaufgaben. Jahresser. der Deutschen Math.-ver. 38 (1929), 21-28.
   b) Nichtlineare Integralgleichungen nebst Anwendungen. Acta Math. 54 (1930), 117-176.

24. Hilderbrandt, T. H., and Graves, L. M.
Implicit functions and their differentials in general analysis. Trans. Amer. Math. Soc. 29 (1927), 127-153.

25. Iasinskiǐ, F. S.
*Selected works on the stability of compressed cores. Gostekhizdat, Moscow, 1952; application IV, 125-129.

26. Iglisch, R.
   a) Zur Theorie der Schwingungen. Monat. F. Math. und Physik 37 (1930), 325-342; 39 (1932), 173-220; 42 (1935), 7-36.
   b) Zur Theorie der reelen Verzweigungen von Lösungen nichtlinearer Integralgleichungen. Journal für die reine und angewandte Math. 164 (1931), 150-172.
   c) Reele Lösungsfelder der Elliptschen Differentialgleichung und nichtlinearer Integralgleichungen Math. Ann. 101 (1929), 98-119.

27. Iokhvidov I. S.
   a) *On the spectra of Hermitian and unitary operators in spaces with indefinite metrics. Dokl. Akad. Nauk USSR, 71, No. 2 (1950), 225-228.
   b) *Unitary and self-conjugate operators in spaces with invariant metrics. Cand. dissertation, Odessa, 1950.

28. Ivanov, N. A.
   *On Gâteaux and Fréchet differentials. Uspekhi Matem. Nauk, 10, vyp. 2(64) (1955), 161-166.

29. Kachurovskiĭ, R. I.
   *An example of an operator of class A . Uch. Zap. Moscow Ped. Inst. 77 (1959), 187.

30. Kantorovich, L. V.
   a) On functional equations. Uch. zap. Leningrad State Univ. 3 (17) (1937), 17-33.
   b) The method of successive approximation for functional equations. Acta Math. 71 (1939), 63-97.
   c) Functional analysis and applied mathematics. Tr. by C. D. Benster, NBS Report 1509, Los Angeles, 1952.

31. Kerner, M.
   a) Sur les variations faibles et fortes d'une fonctionelle. Annaly di Math. 4 (1932), 145-164.
   b) Die Differentiale in der algemeinen Analysis. Ann. of Math. 34 (1933), 546-572.

32. Kolmogorov, A. N.
   Über die Kompaktheit der Funktionenmengen bei der Konvergenz im Mittel. Nach. Ges. Wiss. Göttingen, 1931, 60-63.

33. Kondrashov, V. I.
   *Theory of boundary problems and the problem of proper values for variations and differential equations in regions with degenerate contours. Dissertation, Steklov Math. Inst., Leningrad, 1950.

34. Krasnosel'skiĭ, M. A.
   a) *Criteria for continuity of certain nonlinear operators. Ukr. Matem. Zhurnal 2, No. 3 (1950), 70-86.
   b) *Continuity of the operator fu . Dokl. Akad. Nauk USSR 77, No. 2 (1951), 185-188.

c) *Studies in nonlinear functional analysis. Dissertation, Math. Inst. Acad. Sci. USSR, Moscow, 1950.

d) *Decomposition of linear operators acting from L_p into L_q. Dokl. Akad. Nauk USSR, 82, No. 3 (1952), 333-336.

e) *Certain properties of roots of linear integral operators. Dokl. Akad. Nauk USSR 88, No. 5 (1953), 749-751.

f) *New theorems on the existence of solutions of nonlinear integral equations. Dokl. Akad. Nauk USSR 88, No. 6 (1953), 949-952.

g) *Application of variational methods to the problem of bifurcation points. Matem. sb. 33 (1953), 199-214.

h) *Certain problems in nonlinear analysis. Uspekhi Matem. Nauk 9, vyp. 3 (61) (1954), 57-114.

i) *On the problem of bifurcation points. Dokl. Akad. Nauk USSR 79, No. 3 (1951), 389-392.

j) *Topological methods in the theory of nonlinear integral equations. Gostekhizdat, Moscow, 1956.

35. Krasnosel'skiĭ, M. A., and Povolotskiĭ, A. I.
*On variational methods for the problem of bifurcation points. Dokl. Akad. Nauk USSR 91, No. 1 (1953), 19-22.

36. Kreĭn, M. G.

a) *Helices in Lobatchevskiĭ space of infinitely many dimensions and Lorentz transformations. Uspekhi Matem. Nauk 3, vyp. 3 (25) (1948), 158-160.

b) *On an application of the principle of fixed points to the theory of linear transformations in spaces with indefinite metrics. Uspekhi Matem. Nauk 5, vyp. 2 (36) (1950), 180-190.

37. Kreĭn, M. G., and Rutman, M. A.
*Linear operators in Banach spaces for which cones remain invariant. Uspekhi Matem. Nauk 3, vyp. 1 (23) (1948), 3-95.

38. Kulakov, N. G.
*Investigation of a system of nonlinear integral equations. Dissertation, Moscow Ped. Inst., 1955.

39. Lavrent'ev, M., and Liusternik, L.
*Fundamentals of the calculus of variations, v. 1. Moscow, 1935.

40. Leray, J., and Schauder, J.
*Topology and functional analysis. Uspekhi Matem. Nauk 1, vyp. 3-4 (13-14) (1946), 71-85.

41. Liapunov. A. M.
Sur les figures d'equilibre peu différentes des ellipsoides d'une masse liquide homogéne donée d'un mouvement de rotation, premiere partie. Etude général du probleme. Zap. Akad. Nauk, St. Pëterburg, 1906, 1-225.

42. Lichtenstein, L.
a) Über einige Existenzprobleme der Variationsrechnung. Journal für Math. 145 (1915), 24-85.
b) Vorlesungen über einige Klassen nichtlinearer Integralgleichungen und Integro-Differentialgleichungen. Berlin, 1931.

43. Liusternik, L. A.
a) On conditional extrema of functionals. Matem. sb. 41 (1934), 390-401.
b) On a class of nonlinear operators in Hilbert space. Izu. Akad. Nauk USSR, ser. matem., No. 5 (1939), 257-264.
c) *Topological function spaces and the calculus of variations in the large. Trudy. Steklov. Inst. 19 (1947), 1-60.
d) Grundlaben der allgemeinen Eigenwerttheorie. Monat. für Math. und Phys. 37 (1930), 125-130.

44. Liusternik, L. A., and Sobolev, V. I.
Elements of functional analysis. New York, 1961.

45. Liusternik, L. A., and Shnirel'man, L. G.
a) *Topological methods for variational problems. Trudy Inst. Mat. Mekh. Moscow State Univ. 1 (1930), 1-68.
b) *Applications of topology to extremal problems. Trudy 2nd. All-Soviet Math. Cong., v. 1 (1935), 224-237.
c) *Topological methods in variational problems and their application to the differential geometry of surfaces. Uspekhi Matem. Nauk 2, vyp. 1 (17) (1947), 166-217.
d) Sur un principe topologique d'analyse. Comp. Rend. 188 (1929), 295-297.

46. Marinescu, G.
A supra diferentialei si derivatei in spatiile normate. Bull. Stiint. Acad. R. P. Rômane, seet. mat. si fiz. 6 (1954), 213-219.

47. Mikhlin, S. G.
a) *Direct methods in mathematical physics. Gostekhizdat, Moscow, 1950.

b) *Variational methods for the solution of problems in mathematical physics. Uspekhi Matem. Nauk 5, vyp. 6(40) (1950), 3-51.
c) *On equations of elliptic type. Dokl. Akad. Nauk USSR 77, No. 3 (1951), 377-380.
d) *The problem of minima of quadratic functionals. Gostekhizdat, Moscow, 1952.
e) *On the application of variational methods to certain degenerate elliptic equations. Dokl. Akad. Nauk USSR 91, No. 4 (1953), 723-726.

48. Mil'man, D. P.
On some criteria for the regularity of Banach spaces. Dokl. Akad. Nauk USSR 20 (1938), 243-246.

49. Naĭmark, M. A.
*Linear differential operators. Gostekhizdat, Moscow, 1954.

50. Nazarov, N. N.
a) *Nonlinear integral equations of Hammerstein type. Trudy Sredne-aziatskogo Gos. in.-ta., seriia V-a, mat., vyp. 23 (1941), 79.
b) *Certain topics in the spectral theory of nonlinear integral equations. Trudy Instituta Matem. l Mekh. Akad. Nauk Uz. SSR, vyp. 4 (1948), Matem. Analiz l Mekh., 28-44.

51. Nekrasov, A. I.
*Pointwise theory of permanent waves on the surface of heavy fluids. Izd. Akad. Nauk USSR, Moscow, 1951.

52. Nemytskiĭ, V. V.
a) Theorems of existence and uniqueness for nonlinear integral equations. Matem. sb. 41 (1934), 438-452.
b) On a general class of nonlinear integral equations. Matem. sb. 41 (1934), 655-658.
c) *The method of fixed points in analysis. Uspekhi Matem. Nauk, 1 (1936), 141-174.
d) Solution des équations elliptiques pour les "petits" domains. Matem. sb. 1 (43) (1936), 485-500.
e) Comparison of nonlinear integral equations with linear ones. Dokl. Akad. Nauk USSR 15, No. 1 (1937), 17-20.
f) *Certain questions about the structure of the spectra of completely continuous nonlinear operators. Dokl. Akad. Nauk USSR 80, No. 2 (1951), 161-163.

g) *Structure of the spectra of completely continuous nonlinear operators. Matem. sb. 33 (75) (1953), 545-558.

53. Nikaido, H.
On a minimax theorem and its applications to functional analysis. J. Math. Soc. Japan 5 (1953), 86-94.

54. Pontriagin, L. S.
*Hermitian operators in spaces with indefinite metrics. Izv. Akad. Nauk USSR (ser. matem.) 8 (1944), 243-280.

55. Povolotskiĭ, A. I.
*Nonlocal theorems on the existence of solutions of nonlinear integral equations. Dokl. Akad. Nauk USSR 99, No. 6 (1954), 901-904.

56. Riesz, F.
Untersuchungen über Systeme integrierbarer Funktionen. Math. Ann. 69 (1910), 449-497.

57. Rothe, E.
a) Gradient mappings in Hilbert space. Ann. of Math. 47, (1946), 580-592.
b) Completely continuous scalars and variational methods. Ann. of Math. 49 (1948), 265-278.
c) Weak topology and nonlinear integral equations. Trans. Amer. Math. Soc. 66 (1949), 75-92.
d) Critical points and gradient fields of scalars in Hilbert space. Acta Math. 85 (1951), 73-98.
e) A note on the Banach spaces of Calkin and Morrey. Pacific J. Math. 3 (1953), 493-499.
f) Zur Theorie der topologischen Ordnung und der Vektorfelder in Banachschen Räumen. Compositio Math. 5 (1937), 177-197.
g) Gradient mappings and extrema in Banach spaces. Duke Math. Journal 15 (1948), 421-431.
h) A note on gradient mappings. Proc. Amer. Math. Soc. 10 (1959), 931-935.

58. Rutitskiĭ, Ia. B.
a) *On a nonlinear operator defined in Orlicz spaces. Dop. Akad. Nauk Ukr. SSR 3 (1952), 161-166.
b) *On a class of normed linear spaces and some of their applications to the study of nonlinear integral equations. Dissertation, Kiev State Univ., 1952.

59. Schauder, J.
a) Der Fixpunktsatz in Funktional Raumen. Stud. Math. 2 (1930), 1-6.
b) Über den Zusammenhang zwischen der Eindeutigkeit und Lösbarkeit partieller Differentialgleichungen zweiter Ordnung von elliptischen.Typus. Math. Ann. 106 (1932), 661-721.

60. Schmidt, E.
Zur Theorie der linearen und nichtlinearen Integralgleichungen, III Theil. Über die Auflösung der nichtlinearen Integralgleichungen und die Verzweigung ihrer Lösungen. Math. Ann. 65 (1908), 370-399.

61. Shmul'ian, V. L.
*On certain geometric properties of the unit sphere in spaces of type (B). Matem, sb. 6 (48) (1940), 77-94.

62. Shnirel'man, L. G.
Über eine neue kombinatorische Invariante Monat. für Math. und Phys. 37 (1930), 131-134.

63. Sobolev, S. L.
a) *General theory of diffracted waves on Riemann surfaces. Trudy Steklov Inst. 9 (1935), 39-106.
b) *On a boundary problem for quasi-harmonic equations. Matem. sb. 2 (44) (1937), 465-498.
c) *Some applications of functional analysis to mathematical physics. Izd. Leningrad State Univ., 1950.

64. Sobolev, V. I.
a) *On proper elements of certain nonlinear operators. Dissertation, Moscow State Univ. (1940), 1-47.
b) *On proper elements of certain nonlinear operators. Dokl. Akad. Nauk USSR 31, No. 8 (1941), 734-736.
c) *On a nonlinear integral equation. Dokl. Akad. Nauk 71, No. 5 (1950), 831-834.

65. Steinhaus, H.
Additive und stetige Funktionaloperationen. Math. Zeitschr. 5 (1919), 186-221.

66. Stone, M. H.
Linear transformations in Hilbert spaces. New York, 1932.

67. Tsitlanadze, É. S.
a) *Certain problems of proper values for nonlinear operators in Hilbert spaces. Dokl. Akad. Nauk USSR 53, No. 4 (1946), 311-314.
b) *Certain problems of conditional extrema and the variational theory of proper values. Dokl. Akad. Nauk USSR 56, No. 1 (1947), 17-20.
c) *On the problem of proper values of completely continuous nonlinear operators in Hilbert spaces. Dokl. Akad. Nauk USSR 57, No. 9 (1947), 879-881.
d) *Proof of the principle of critical points for conditional extrema in spaces of type B . Soobshch. Akad. Nauk Gruz. SSR 8 (1947), 7-10.
e) *On integral equations of Lichtenstein type. Soobshch. Akad. Nauk Gruz. SSR 8 (1947), 359-363.
f) *On the variational theory of a class of nonlinear operators in the spaces L_p $(p > 1)$. Dokl. Akad. Nauk USSR 71, No. 3 (1950), 441-444.
g) *Certain problems of the calculus of variations in functional spaces. Dissertation, Moscow State Univ., 1950.
h) *On the extrema of functionals in linear spaces. Dokl. Akad. Nauk USSR 74, No. 6 (1951), 797-800.
i) *On the differentiation of functionals. Matem. sb. 29 (71) (1951), 3-12.
j) *Theorems on the existence of minimax points in Banach spaces and their applications. Trudy Mosk. Matem. ob.-va. 2 (1953), 235-274.

68. Vaĭnberg, M. M.
a) *On proper values of a class of nonlinear integral equations and branching of their solutions. Dissertation, Moscow State Univ., 1940.
b) *On a theorem of Hammerstein for nonlinear integral equations. Uch. Zap. Moscow State Univ. 1, vyp. 100 (1946), 93-103.
c) *Theorems on the existence of proper values for a class of nonlinear integral equations. Uch. Zap. Moscow Ped. Inst. 15, vyp. 1 (1950), 103-127.
d) *Theorems on the existence of proper values for a class of systems of nonlinear integral equations. Matem. sb. 26 (68) (1950), 365-394.
e) *On the continuity of certain operators of special types. Dokl. Akad. Nauk USSR 73, No. 2 (1950), 253-255.
f) *On proper elements of a class of nonlinear operators. Dokl. Akad. Nauk USSR 75, No. 5 (1950), 609-612.

g) *On weak continuity of functionals and their gradients. Dokl. Akad. Nauk USSR 78, No. 5 (1951), 841-844.

h) *Existence of proper functions for nonlinear integral equations with non-positive kernels. Dokl. Akad. Nauk USSR 78, No. 6 (1951), 1077-1080.

i) *Existence theorems for systems of nonlinear integral equations. Uch. Zap. Moscow Ped. Inst. 18, vyp. 2 (1951), 225-257

j) *On the variational theory of proper values of nonlinear integral equations. Dokl. Akad. Nauk 80, No. 3 (1951), 309-312.

k) *On the question of the variational theory of proper values of nonlinear integral equations. Matem. sb. 30 (72) (1952), 3-10.

l) *On some variational principles in the theory of operator equations. Uspekhi Matem. Nauk 7, vyp. 2(1952), 197-200.

m) *On the differentials and gradients of functionals. Uspekhi Matem. Nauk 7, vyp. 3 (1952), 139-143.

n) *On certain topics in differential calculus in linear spaces. Uspekhi Matem. Nauk 7, vyp. 4 (1952), 55-102.

o) *Potential operators and the variational theory of nonlinear operator equations. Doctoral Dissertation, Moscow State Univ., 1952.

p) *The existence of proper functions of nonlinear integral operators with nonpositive kernels and of the product of self-conjugate and potential operators. Matem. sb. 32 (74) (1953), 665-680.

q) *On the structure of an operator. Dokl. Akad. Nauk USSR 92, No. 2 (1953), 213-216.

r) *On the soluability of certain operator equations. Dokl. Akad. Nauk USSR 92, No. 3 (1953), 457-460.

s) *Variational theory of proper functions of nonlinear integral and other operators. Trudy Mosk. Matem. ob.-va. 3 (1954), 375-406.

t) *The Urysohn integral equation. Uch. Zap. Moscow Ped. Inst. 21 (1954), 49-64.

u) *On a form of the (c)-property of functions. Uch. Zap. Moscow Ped. Inst. 21 (1954), 65-72.

v) *On certain properties of quadratic forms in the spaces L^q $(q < 2)$. Dokl. Akad. Nauk USSR 100, No. 5 (1955), 845-848.

w) *On invariant directions of products of certain operators. Dokl. Akad. Nauk USSR 85, No. 2 (1952), 261-263.

x) *Variational methods for the investigation of nonlinear operators. Gostehkizdat, Moscow, 1956.

69. Vaǐnberg, M. M., and Kachurovskiǐ, R. I.
*On the variational theory of nonlinear operators and equations. Dokl. Akad. Nauk USSR 129, No. 6 (1959), 1199-1202.

70. Voskresenskiǐ, E. P., and Sobolev, V. I.
*On a class of nonlinear integral equations. Dokl. Akad. Nauk USSR 79, No. 5 (1951), 747-748.

71. Wiener, N.
Note on a paper of M. Banach. Fund. Math. 4 (1923), 136-143.

JOHN A. NOHEL

Problems in Qualitative Behavior of Solutions of Nonlinear Volterra Equations

1. Introduction

In this paper we consider some questions regarding global behavior of solutions of nonlinear Volterra equations. Of particular interest are questions of global existence, boundedness, behavior of solutions as the independent variable approaches infinity, existence of periodic solutions. In the absence of general theories (comparable in scope to qualitative theory for ordinary differential equations) some of the problems which we discuss deal with integral equations of rather special form. Therefore, we stress that our survey is by no means exhaustive, and the selection of problems and methods discussed is motivated by the author's interests in this area.

We first discuss in Section 2 a general result which compares solutions of the real system

$$x(t) = h(t) + \int_0^t f(t, \tau, x(\tau))\, d\tau \qquad (t \geq 0), \tag{1.1}$$

where h, f are given vectors with n components, and x is a vector to be determined, with solutions of a related scalar equation obtained by taking norms of (1.1). This comparison enables us to draw a number of consequences of a qualitative nature. Since for a particular solution much information is lost by taking norms of both sides of (1.1), these results need not be readily applicable in many situations. For this reason we present a number of results by several authors for special cases of (1.1) which, at the same time illustrate different techniques.

In many situations Volterra equations occur as integro-differential equations of the form

$$x' = \int_0^t F(t, \tau, x(\tau))\, d\tau + h(t) \qquad (' = d/dt) \tag{1.2}$$

where h, F are given functions (possibly vectors) and x is a function (vector) to be determined. From a particular point of view there is a general stability theory for such equations. Namely, the system (1.2) may be regarded as a special case of a system of Volterra functional differential equations (also known as differential equations with retarded arguments) and there does exist a recently developed stability theory for such systems which parallels theories developed for ordinary differential equations. However, we know of no instance where this theory is applied specifically to nontrivial cases of (1.2); this theory, (some aspects of which have close connections with integral equations) has been developed mainly for the purpose of dealing with differential-difference equations with both bounded and unbounded delays; however, the basic equations considered are, in fact, much more general. Since this theory would require a separate and extensive survey we do not attempt this task here. We do, however, present in the appendix a very brief sketch together with some references to recent literature. In the absence of a readily applicable qualitative theory for (1.2), we discuss in Section 3 below a number of results on the global behavior of solutions of equations which are interesting special cases of (1.2). The methods used in some of these problems may be regarded as an extension of Liapunov's second method employed in part of the general theory referred to above.

As is the case in ordinary differential equations, the equations discussed in this paper are of considerable mathematical interest, yet have their origin in important questions of physics and engineering. We attempt to point out some of these connections throughout.

For the convenience of the reader we list in the bibliography some additional papers dealing with problems of qualitative behavior of solutions of nonlinear integral equations which are not referred to in the manuscript.

2. Nonlinear Volterra Integral Equations

We consider real systems of the form

$$x(t) = h(t) + \int_0^t f(t, \tau, x(\tau))\, d\tau \qquad (t \geq 0), \tag{2.1}$$

where h, f are given vectors with n components. Questions of existence and uniqueness of solutions, by both iterative and fixed point methods, have been discussed in this symposium in papers by Wouk [45] and Thielman [41]. We therefore turn our attention to other problems.

For any vector x let $|x| = \sum_{i=1}^{n} |x_i|$ (any other equivalent norm could be used); for any square matrix A, let $|A| = \sum_{i,j=1}^{n} |a_{ij}|$.

One problem of considerable interest is existence in the large and boundedness of continuous solutions of (2.1). A general result in this direction has recently been obtained by the author [36]. For the sake of simplicity of presentation we assume

$$(2.2) \qquad f(t, \tau, x) = q(t - \tau)\, g(\tau, x)$$

where q is a $n \times n$ matrix and g is a vector. We remark that the assumptions (2.2-2.4) can easily be weakened, especially if the requirement of continuous solutions is dropped. Let the following conditions be satisfied:

(2.3) h, g are continuous in t and (t, x) respectively for $0 \leq t < t_0$ and $0 \leq t < t_0$, $|x| < \infty$, where $t_0 > 0$ is arbitrary and $t_0 = +\infty$ is not excluded,

(2.4) for any c, $0 < c < t_0$, $|q(t)| \in L[0, c]$.

While these hypotheses pertaining to the dependence on (t, τ) are easily relaxed it is, in fact, the case in most problems arising in the applications that g is a function of x alone and that $q(t)$ is continuous for $t > 0$, except for a singularity of the form $t^{-\gamma}$, $0 < \gamma < 1$, at $t = 0$. We remark that under assumptions (2.2, 2.3, 2.4) existence (but not uniqueness) of solutions follows either from Schauder's fixed point theorem or by a modification of the Caratheodory Theorem for ordinary differential equations [10], [36]. By using the latter technique it can be shown, Lemma 1.2 [36], that with assumptions (2.3, 2.4) satisfied, a solution ϕ can be continued to the right for as long as $|\phi|$ is bounded.

To state the general theorem let there exist nonnegative functions H, Q, w such that

$$(2.5) \qquad |h(t)| \leq H(t), \quad |q(t)| \leq Q(t), \quad |g(t, x)| \leq w(t, |x|), \qquad (0 \leq t < t_0, \ |x| < \infty).$$

We compare solutions of the system (2.1) with solutions of the scalar equation

$$(2.6) \qquad r(t) = H(t) + \int_0^t Q(t - \tau)\, w(\tau, r(\tau))\, d\tau \qquad (0 \leq t < t_0).$$

The following result is proved in [36].

Theorem 2.1. Let (2.3, 2.4, 2.5) be satisfied. Let H be continuous for $0 \leq t < t_0$; let $Q \in L$ on every finite subinterval of $[0, t_0)$. Let w be continuous in (t, r) for $0 \leq t < t_0$, $0 \leq r < \infty$, and nondecreasing in r for each fixed t. For some $0 < b \leq t_0$ let r_M be the maximum solution of (2.6) on $0 \leq t < t_0$. Then if ϕ is a solution of (2.1), ϕ can be continued to the right as far as r_M exists and

$$|\phi(t)| \leq r_M(t) \qquad (0 \leq t < b).$$

This theorem is an extension of the comparison technique for ordinary differential equations due to Conti [11] and Wintner [44]. We refer to [36] for the proof of existence of the maximum solution of (2.6) under the stated conditions which, of course, could also be weakened. We refer to Satō [39], also Satō and Iwasaki [40]* for a different approach with some overlap of results.

In the proof of Theorem 2.1 it is first shown that it suffices to establish $|\phi(t)| \leq r(t, \epsilon)$, for $\epsilon > 0$ sufficiently small, where $r(t, \epsilon)$ is any solution of the scalar equation (2.6) having ϵ added to its right-hand side. The conclusion then follows by showing that the assumption of existence of values of t such that $|\phi(t)| > r(t, \epsilon)$ leads to a contradiction. For details see [36].

It follows immediately from Theorem 2.1 that existence and boundedness of $r_M(t)$ on $0 \leq t < \infty$ implies the same conclusion for solutions ϕ of the system. Also if $r_M(t) \to 0$ as $t \to \infty$ so does $|\phi(t)|$. In particular, one may establish the following analogue of the well known result of Poincaré-Liapunov-Perron in ordinary differential equations.

Corollary 2.1. Let there exist constants $\eta, \sigma, \kappa > 0$ such that

$$|h(t)| \leq \eta e^{-\sigma t}, \; |q(t)| \leq \kappa e^{-\sigma t} \qquad (0 \leq t < \infty).$$

Let $g(t,x)$ be continuous in (t,x) for $0 \leq t < \infty$, $|x|$ small and and let $g(t,x) = o(|x|)$ as $|x| \to 0$, uniformly in t, $0 \leq t < \infty$. Then if η is sufficiently small all solutions of (2.1, 2.2) exist on $0 \leq t < \infty$ and approach zero as $t \to \infty$.

---

*The author was unaware of the existence of this paper and is grateful to Drs. Anselone and Wouk for calling it to his attention.

For the proof one merely takes $H(T) = \eta e^{-\sigma t}$, $Q(t) = \kappa e^{-\sigma t}$, $w(t,r) = \frac{\epsilon}{\kappa} r$ in (2.6) is equivalent to a first order differential equation from which the result follows trivially. For other results of this type involving linearization of integral equations see Neĭmark [34].

We refer to [36] for other applications of this theorem and method. In particular the interested reader will find there as special cases analogues for (2.1) of several known theorems in ordinary differential equations pertaining to global existence and boundedness of solutions of (2.1). Also the method of proof of Theorem 2.1 yields a general uniqueness theorem for solutions of (2.1), see also [39], and a general theorem on the convergence of the Picard successive approximations. For other recent results of this type see papers by Dinghas [12] and Reichert [38].

The comparison integral equation (2.6) arises formally by taking norms of both sides of (2.1) and assuming that the equality holds in the resulting equation. Naturally a great deal of information is lost by taking norms. It is therefore not surprising that much deeper results can be obtained in many special cases if this step is not taken. We now illustrate this with a number of such problems which have been studied recently by various methods of interest in themselves.

In studying the transfer of heat between gases and liquids a nonlinear boundary initial value problem for the heat equation, Mann and Wolf [29] are led to the study of the integral equation

$$y(t) = \frac{1}{\sqrt{\pi}} \int_0^t \frac{G(y(\tau))}{(t-\tau)^{1/2}} \, d\tau \qquad (t \geq 0), \tag{2.7}$$

where (i) $G(1) = 0$, (ii) $G(u)$ is continuous for all u, (iii) $G(u)$ is strictly decreasing.* The main problem, as far as (2.7) is concerned in the context of [29], is to prove the following result.

Theorem 2.2. *Let (i), (ii), (iii) be satisfied. Let $T > 0$ be given. Then there exists at least one solution $y(t)$ of (2.7) on $0 \leq t \leq T$ and such that $0 < y(t) \leq 1$.*

The essential part of the proof consists in showing that the mapping $\mathcal{F}$ defined by

$$\mathcal{F}[z](t) = \int_0^t \frac{G^*[z(\tau)]}{\pi^{1/2}(t-\tau)^{1/2}} \, d\tau ,$$

---

*Further remarks regarding equations (2.7), (2.8) from the numerical point of view may be found in B. Noble, "The numerical solution of nonlinear integral equations", these proceedings, pp. 232-41.

where

$$G*[z(t)] = \begin{cases} G(z(t)) & \text{if } z(t) \le 1 \\ 0 & \text{if } z(t) > 1, \end{cases}$$

of the Banach space $C[0, T]$, of functions continuous on $0 \le t \le T$, with the usual topology, satisfies the hypothesis of Schauder's fixed point theorem; namely that $\mathcal{F}$ carries a convex, compact subset H of C continuously into itself. It is then shown that if $y(t)$ is a continuous fixed point of $\mathcal{F}$ for $0 \le t \le T$, then $y(t) \le 1$ for $0 \le t \le T$ which easily leads to the result. Refinements of Theorem 2.2 are given requiring more smoothness of G. For some generalizations we refer to papers by Mann and Roberts [30] and Padmavally [37].

We mention also an application of Tychonov's fixed point Theorem by Beneš [5, 7] to study an integral equation arising in nonlinear servomechanisms. The fixed point theorem is used to obtain ultimately periodic behavior of solutions; see also additional remarks in Section 3.

A more complicated problem than discussed in Theorem 2.2 above arises in the theory of superfluidity developed recently by C. C. Lin. The physical problem is again a boundary initial value problem for the heat equation which, because of a more complicated boundary condition leads to the integral equation

$$(2.8) \qquad y(t) + f(t) = -\frac{1}{\pi^{1/2}} \int_0^t \frac{\Phi(y(\tau))}{(t-\tau)^{1/2}} d\tau \qquad (t \ge 0),$$

where $f(t)$ is a given periodic function. This problem has recently been studied by N. Levinson [28]. He establishes the following results.

<u>Theorem 2.3. Let $f(t)$ be continuous on $0 \le t < \infty$ and satisfy a uniform Hölder condition of exponent $\beta > 0$ on any finite interval. Let $\Phi(y)$ be monotone increasing on $-\infty < y < \infty$, $\Phi(0) = 0$; let Φ satisfy a local Lipschitz condition. Then (2.8) possesses a unique continuous solution $y(t)$ on $(0, \infty)$.</u>

<u>Theorem 2.4. Let the hypothesis of Theorem 2.3 be satisfied and in addition let $f(t)$ have period ω and let $\max |f(t)| = M$. Suppose that there exists a positive monotone increasing function $k(u)$ for $u > 0$ such that</u>

$$\Phi(y_2) - \Phi(y_1) \ge k(y_2 - y_1)$$

for $y_2 - y_1 > 0$ and $|y_1|, |y_2| \leq 2M$. Then there exists a continuous periodic function $\phi(t)$ of period ω such that the solution $y(t)$ of (2.8) satisfies

$$\lim_{t \to \infty} (y(t) + f(t) - \phi(t)) = 0$$

Moreover $|y(t) + f(t)| \leq \max |f(t)|$.

It is also shown that the periodic function $\phi(t)$ is itself the only periodic solution of a certain integral equation, and that the average value of $\Phi(\phi(t) - y(t)) = 0$. The methods used throughout are elementary. The main tool is the following formula. Let p, q be continuous for $0 \leq t < c$ for some $c > 0$ and let

$$q(t) = \int_0^t p(s)(t-s)^{-1/2} ds \qquad (0 \leq t < c).$$

Then with p, q satisfying Hölder conditions with suitable exponents,

$$t^{-1/2} q(t) + \frac{1}{2} \int_0^t (q(t) - q(\sigma))(t-\sigma)^{-3/2} d\sigma = \pi p(t).$$

Such a formula is needed in the analysis as it takes the place of differentiation of $q(t)$ which in general is not permitted. It is easily seen that the change of variable $H(t) = y(t) + f(t)$ transforms (2.8) to

$$H(t) = -\frac{1}{\pi^{1/2}} \int_0^t \frac{\Phi(H(s) - f(s))}{(t-s)^{1/2}} ds,$$

and the applicability of the formula with sufficient smoothness is evident; indeed, it is used e.g. in Theorem 2.3 to deduce continuation of a solution, which exists on some finite interval by classical successive approximations, to the interval $0 \leq t < \infty$. This solution is bounded if $|f(t)|$ is bounded. The proof of Theorem 2.4 is accomplished by showing that for $j \geq i \to \infty$, $\lim [H(t+j\omega) - H(t+i\omega)] = 0$, uniformly with respect to t on $0 \leq t \leq 2\omega$. This requires some extremely delicate estimates and again makes use of the above formula and properties of q. It seems clear (oral discussion with Professor H. E. Conner] that these results can be extended to the case of (2.8) with the kernel $(t - \tau)^{-1/2}$ replaced by $(t - \tau)^{-\gamma}$, $0 < \gamma < 1$. We refer to Hellman [19] for another problem of this type.

3. Asymptotic Behavior of Nonlinear Volterra Integrodifferential Equations

We first consider the real scalar equation

$$(3.1)\qquad x'(t) = -\int_0^t a(t-\tau)g(x(\tau))\,d\tau \qquad (t \geq 0),$$

which is a special case of (1.2). We assume that the kernel $a(t)$ is positive in the sense that

$$(3.2)\qquad a(t) \in C[0,\infty),\quad (-1)^k a^{(k)}(t) \geq 0 \qquad (0 < t < \infty;\ k = 0, 1, 2, 3),$$

and that $g(x)$ is a "nonlinear spring":

$$(3.3)\qquad g(x) \in C(-\infty,\infty),\quad xg(x) > 0\ (x \neq 0),\quad G(x) = \int_0^x g(\xi)\,d\xi \to \infty,\quad (|x| \to \infty).$$

The following result was established by J. J. Levin [24].

Theorem 3.1. Let (3.2, 3.3) be satisfied. Then given any x_0 there exists a solution $x = u(t)$, $u(0) = x_0$, on $0 \leq t < \infty$. Moreover, there exists a constant $K = K(x_0)$, such that

$$(3.4)\qquad |u^{(j)}(t)| \leq K \qquad (j = 0, 1, 2;\ 0 \leq t < \infty).$$

If also $a(t) \not\equiv a(0)$, then

$$(3.5)\qquad \lim_{t\to\infty} u^{(j)}(t) = 0 \qquad (j = 0, 1, 2).$$

Equation (3.1) arises in connection with a problem in nuclear reactor dynamics. There $g(x) = e^x - 1$ is a physically important nonlinearity which satisfies (3.3) and $a(t)$ occurs as a Laplace transform which not only satisfies (3.2) but also

$$(3.6)\qquad (-1)^k a^{(k)}(t) \geq 0 \qquad (0 < t < \infty,\ k = 0, 1, \ldots);$$

i.e. $a(t)$ is completely monotonic on $[0,\infty)$. We shall return to (3.6) presently.

In previous work Levin and Nohel [25] studied the asymptotic behavior of solutions of (3.1) in the linear case $g(x) \equiv x$ by using a Tauberian theorem for Laplace transforms; such methods do not lend themselves to the nonlinear problem. We note that if $g(x)$ fails to satisfy the condition $G(x) \to \infty$ as $|x| \to \infty$ in (3.3), the conclusion of the theorem still holds for all solutions $u(t)$ with $|u(0)| = |x_0|$ sufficiently small. Since $g(0) = 0$, $u(t) \equiv 0$ is a solution of (3.1) and the conclusion (3.5, $j = 0$) states that the identically zero solution is asymptotically stable in the large. However, the method used to prove this statement establishes also (3.5, $j = 1, 2$) and the conclusion for $j = 1, 2$ is also of some physical significance. As the method of proof makes use of a Liapunov functional referred to in the appendix, a brief sketch and additional remarks will now be given.

Sketch of proof of Theorem 3.1: Hypothesis (3.2) implies the following properties of $a(t)$ which are needed to justify various formal calculations in the sketch below:

$$(3.7) \quad \begin{cases} t\,a'(t),\ t^2 a''(t) \to 0 & (t \to 0^+) \\ a'(t),\ ta''(t),\ t^2 a'''(t) \in L_1(0,\infty) & \\ \text{Either } -a'(t),\ a''(t) > 0 \quad (0 < t < \infty), \text{ or there exists} & \\ \text{a } t_0 > 0 \text{ such that } -a'(t),\ a''(t) > 0 \quad (0 < t < t_0) \text{ and} & \\ a(t) \equiv a(t_0) \quad (t_0 < t < \infty). & \end{cases}$$

We remark that if $g(x)$ also satisfies a Lipschitz condition on every interval $|x| \leq X < \infty$, the existence (and uniqueness) of a local solution $u(t)$, $u(0) = x_0$, follows from the usual method of successive approximations. This fact together with the apriori bounds (3.4) imply that every such solution can be continued (uniquely) to the right to the entire interval $0 \leq t < \infty$. Under the present hypothesis (3.3) existence on $0 \leq t < \infty$ (but not necessarily uniqueness) follows also from these bounds and results of the author [36] mentioned in section 2.

Let $u(t)$ be a solution of (3.1), $u(0) = x_0$, and define the (Liapunov) functional

$$(3.8) \quad E(t,u) = G(u(t)) + \frac{1}{2}a(t)\Big[\int_0^t g(u(\tau))\,d\tau\Big]^2 - \frac{1}{2}\int_0^t a'(t-\tau)\Big[\int_\tau^t g(u(s))\,ds\Big]^2 d\tau .$$

Clearly the function $E(t) = E(t, u(t)) \geq 0$ for as long as $u(t)$ exists. Differentiating (3.8) and using (3.1) gives

$$(3.9) \quad E'(t) = \frac{1}{2}a'(t)\Big[\int_0^t g(u(\tau))\,d\tau\Big]^2 - \frac{1}{2}\int_0^t a''(t-\tau)\Big[\int_\tau^t g(u(s))\,ds\Big]^2 d\tau \leq 0,$$

for as long as $u(t)$ exists. With reference to the general theory of the appendix note that (3.9) is not negative definite, and therefore no conclusion regarding asymptotic stability of the zero solution can be drawn from the general theory. From (3.8, 3.9) it follows that $G(u(t)) \leq E(t) \leq E(0) = G(x_0) < \infty$ for as long as $u(t)$ exists. This together with (3.3) and the remark regarding continuation proves (3.4, j = 0). Differentiating (3.1) gives

$$(3.10)\quad u''(t) + a(0)g(u(t)) = -\int_0^t a'(t-\tau)g(u(\tau))\,d\tau \qquad (0 \leq t < \infty),$$

which together with (3.3), (3.4, j = 0), (3.7) gives (3.4, j = 2), where K is increased if necessary. Then (3.4, j = 0, 2) and the mean value theorem give (3.4, j = 1).

We remark that (3.10) can be interpreted as a nonlinear oscillator with a hereditary term — see also Theorem 3, 3 and 3.4 below. It is clear from (3.3) and (3.10) that if $a(t) \equiv a(0) \neq 0$ all solutions of the resulting equation (and in particular of (3.1)) are periodic. Thus the assumption $a(t) \not\equiv a(0)$ is essential for what follows.

A calculation using (3.4, 3.7, 3.9) shows that $E''(t)$ is bounded on $0 \leq t < \infty$. This together with $E(t) \geq 0$, $E'(t) \leq 0$ and the mean value theorem implies $\lim_{t\to\infty} E'(t) = 0$. Thus, in particular from (3.9)

$$\lim_{t\to\infty} \int_0^t a''(t-\tau)\Big[\int_\tau^t g(u(s))\,ds\Big]^2 d\tau = 0$$

From this it is not difficult to establish (3.5, j = 0) by using $a''(t) \geq 0$ and a contradiction argument. But then (3.4, 3.10) readily yield (3.5, j = 1, 2) as well. This completes a sketch of the proof.

Returning to (3.6) we note that by using the Liapunov functional

$$(3.11)\quad V(t,u) = G(u(t)) + \frac{1}{2}\int_0^t\int_0^t a(\tau+s)g(u(t-\tau))g(u(t-s))\,d\tau\,ds,$$

Levin and the author [26] have established the following weaker version of Theorem 3.1.

<u>Theorem 3.2.</u> <u>Let</u> (3.3, 3.6) <u>be satisfied.</u> <u>Then the conclusions of Theorem</u> 3.1 <u>hold.</u>

This result is of some interest, as the functional (3.11) and the proof of Theorem 3.2 draw together such different notions of positivity as Liapunov functionals, complete monotonicity and kernels of positive type (see second term in (3.11)). It is obvious that if

$a(t) \equiv a(0)$ then the functionals (3.8) and (3.11) are the same. It can also be shown that if $u(0) \neq 0$ and if $E(t) \equiv V(t) = V(t, u(t))$, $0 \leq t \leq t_0 < \infty$, where $u(t)$ is a solution of (3.1) existing on $0 \leq t \leq t_0$, then $a(t) \equiv a(0)$, $0 \leq t < \infty$. Thus (3.11) provides another Liapunov functional for (3.1). Since (3.3, 3.6) are satisfied in the reactor problem [25] referred to above, it is of interest to note that the first term in (3.11) may be interpreted as a potential energy and the second as a kinetic energy. The proof of Theorem 3.2 differs from that of Theorem 3.1 essentially in technical details.

By modifying the Liapunov functionals we have recently obtained analogous results for the case of (3.1) with an integrable forcing term added on the right-hand side (unpublished). This requires further restriction of the function g.

We next turn to the nonlinear delay equation

$$x'(t) = -\int_{t-L}^{t} a(t-\tau)\, g(x(\tau))\, d\tau \qquad (0 \leq t < \infty), \tag{3.12}$$

where $L > 0$ is a constant. By using the functional

$$\widetilde{E}(t, u) = G(u(t)) - \frac{1}{2} \int_{t-L}^{t} a'(t-\tau)\Big[\int_{\tau}^{t} g(u(s))\, ds\Big]^2 d\tau \geq 0, \tag{3.13}$$

Levin and Nohel [27] have established the following result, completely analogous (both in statement and proof) to Theorem 3.1.

<u>Theorem 3.3.</u> <u>Let</u> $g(x)$ <u>be continuous and satisfy</u> (3.3). <u>Let</u> $a(t)$ <u>satisfy</u>

$$a(t) \in C[0, L], \quad a(L) = 0, \quad (-1)^k a^{(k)}(t) \geq 0 \qquad (0 < t \leq L,\ k = 1, 2, 3). \tag{3.14}$$

<u>Let</u> $\Psi(t) \in C[-L, 0]$ <u>be given.</u> <u>If</u> $a''(t) \not\equiv 0$, <u>then there exists a function</u> $x = u(t)$ <u>which coincides with</u> $\psi(t)$ <u>on</u> $-L \leq t < 0$, <u>satisfies</u> (3.12) <u>on</u> $0 \leq t < \infty$, <u>and is continuous at</u> $t = 0$. <u>Moreover</u>

$$\lim_{t \to \infty} u^{(j)}(t) = 0 \qquad (j = 0, 1, 2).$$

The same remarks with reference to the possibility of applying the general Liapunov theory mentioned in the proof of Theorem 3.1 are relevant here; this in spite of the fact that (3.12) has a bounded delay. Note that assumptions (3.14) are completely analogous to (3.2), but now on $[0, L]$. Note also that for existence one now specifies an initial function rather than an initial point. In case g

also satisfies a Lipschitz condition standard successive approximations yield both existence and uniqueness. If g is merely continuous the results of the author [36] are applicable.

Differentiating (3.12) one obtains

$$x''(t) + a(0)g(x(t)) = -\int_{t-L}^{t} a'(t-\tau)g(x(\tau))\,d\tau,$$

which may be compared with the linear delay equation

$$x''(t) + cx(t) = \int_{t-L}^{t} F(t-\tau)x(\tau)\,d\tau,$$

where c and L are given positive constants, studied by Volterra [42] in his formulation of the theory of heredity. It is by way of highly modified versions of the quadratic functionals employed by Volterra that [42] influences the results discussed here and in Theorem 3.1.

Of considerably more interest than Theorem 3.3 is the case of equation (3.12) with $a''(t) \equiv 0$. We therefore consider the delay equation

$$(3.15) \qquad x'(t) = -\frac{1}{L}\int_{t-L}^{t} (L-(t-\tau))g(x(\tau))\,d\tau \qquad (0 \le t < \infty),$$

whose kernel $a(t) = \frac{1}{L}(L-t)$ has $a''(t) \equiv 0$. This case, excluded from Theorem 3.3, permits phenomena which cannot occur in the seemingly more general situation. Differentiating (3.15) yields

$$(3.16) \qquad x''(t) + g(x(t)) = \frac{1}{L}\int_{t-L}^{t} g(x(\tau))\,d\tau \qquad (0 \le t < \infty),$$

from which it is, perhaps, not surprising that the behavior of solutions of (3.15) for large t is intimately related to those of the equation

$$(3.17) \qquad x'' + g(x) = 0,$$

together with its equivalent system

$$(3.18) \qquad x' = y, \quad y' = -g(x).$$

If $g(x)$ satisfies (3.3) and is locally Lipschitzian, let $x = \varphi(t) = \varphi(t, t_0, \alpha, \beta)$ be the solution of (3.17) such that $\varphi(t_0, t_0, \alpha, \beta) = \alpha$, $\varphi'(t_0, t_0, \alpha, \beta) = \beta$. Then $x = \varphi(t)$, $y = \varphi'(t)$ is the solution of (3.18) passing through the point (α, β) in the phase plane at $t = t_0$. Recalling that all solutions of (3.17) are periodic, let ($\rho = \rho(\alpha,\beta) > 0$ denote the common least period of all solutions of (3.18) passing through $(\alpha,\beta) \neq (0,0)$. Let $\Gamma = \Gamma(\alpha,\beta)$ be the orbit of (3.18) through (α,β); in particular, $\Gamma(0,0) = (0,0)$. Levin and the author [27] have established the following result.

Theorem 3.4. Let $g(x)$ be locally Lipschitzian and satisfy (3.3). Let $\psi(t) \in C[-L, 0]$ be given.

(i) Then there exists a unique function $x = u(t)$ which coincides with $\psi(t)$ on $-L \leq t \leq 0$, satisfies (3.15) on $0 \leq t < \infty$, and is continuous at $t = 0$. Moreover,

$$(3.19) \qquad |u^{(j)}(t)| \leq K_1 < \infty \qquad (0 \leq t < \infty;\ j = 0,1,2)$$

for some constant K_1.

(ii) Let $\Omega = \Omega(\psi)$ be the limit set as $t \to \infty$ of the curve $x = u(t)$, $y = u'(t)$ in the phase plane. (Ω is nonempty by (3.19).) Then there exists an orbit $\Gamma = \Gamma(\psi)$ of (3.18) such that

$$(3.20) \qquad \Omega = \Gamma.$$

If $\Omega = \Gamma \neq (0,0)$, then there exists an integer $m \geq 1$ such that

$$(3.21) \qquad L = m\rho(\alpha,\beta) \qquad ((\alpha,\beta) \in \Gamma).$$

Further, if $(\alpha,\beta) \in \Gamma$ and if $0 < K_2 < \infty$ is a constant, then

$$(3.22) \quad \lim_{n\to\infty} \left[\max_{0\leq t\leq K_2} \left| u^{(j)}_{(t+nL)} - \varphi^{(j)}_{(t,t_n,\alpha,\beta)} \right| \right] = 0 \qquad (j=0,1,2),$$

for some sequence $\{t_n\}$, where $0 \leq t_n \leq \rho(\alpha,\beta)$ if $\Gamma \neq (0,0)$ and t_n is arbitrary if $\Gamma = (0,0)$.

Although (3.22) includes (3.20), the proof of (3.21, 3.22) is a by-product of the proof of (3.20); the latter seems to show more clearly the geometric simplicity of the result and is reminiscent of familar results in autonomous systems of ordinary differential equations. The proof itself combines the use of these methods with the use of the functional (3.12), where $a(t) = 1/L(L-t)$. See additional remarks below.

It follows from Theorem 3.4 that if $u(t)$ is a periodic solution of (3.15) then there exist t_0, α,β such that $u(t) = \varphi(t,t_0,\alpha,\beta)$. Moreover, if $(\alpha,\beta) \neq (0,0)$, there exists an integer $m \geq 1$ such that $L = m\rho(\alpha,\beta)$. The converse of this statement is also true but requires a separate proof. Therefore it is clear that a limit set of solutions of (3.15) consists of a one parameter family of periodic solutions of (3.15) which differ by translation.

It is possible that given $g(x)$ and L there does not exist a triple α, β, m with $(\alpha, \beta) \neq (0,0)$ and $m \geq 1$ an integer, such that $L = m\rho(\alpha, \beta)$ (e.g. $g(x) = 2x$, $L = 2\pi$). Theorem 3.4 then asserts that for any initial function $\psi(t)$, $\Omega = (0,0)$. The author, [35], examined (3.15) in the close to linear case

$$g(x) = kx + o(x) \qquad (x \to 0),$$

where $k > 0$ and where $\max_{-L \leq t \leq 0} |\psi(t)|$ is small, by using an entirely different method which converts (3.15) to a nonlinear integral equation (see also discussion at the beginning of the appendix). It is shown in [35], see also Bellman and Cooke [3], that if $k \neq n^2 (\frac{2\pi}{L})^2$ $(n = 1, 2, \ldots)$ and if $g(x)$ is almost linear, all solutions u of (3.15) with $\max_{-L \leq t \leq 0} |\psi(t)|$ sufficiently small approach zero as $t \to \infty$. This, of course, precludes the existence of any triple α, β, m with $(\alpha, \beta) \neq (0,0)$ and $m \geq 1$ an integer, satisfying $L = m\rho(\alpha, \beta)$. Thus Theorem 3.4 includes the earlier result as a very special case.

Brownell and Ergen [8] have also considered (3.15) by still different methods than those of [35] and [27]. They require that

$$g(x) \in C', \quad g'(x) > 0, \quad g(0) = 0, \quad g(x) > -K > -\infty \qquad (-\infty < x < \infty),$$

for some constant K, and that

$$\{\alpha \mid \rho(\alpha, 0) = \frac{L}{m}\} \qquad \text{is a finite set for } m = 1, 2, \ldots .$$

Clearly these conditions are much more severe than the hypotheses of Theorem 3.4. Under the first of these assumptions, which excludes the linear case $g(x) = kx$, $k > 0$, a very weak form of Theorem 3.4 is obtained in [8]. To obtain (3.22) (or even (3.20)) both of the above hypotheses are invoked in [8]. Their analysis is based on a theorem on rearrangements due to Hardy, Littlewood, Polya.

We remark that if $g(x) = kx$, $k > 0$, equation (3.16) is of the form considered by Volterra and referred to above with $c = k$ and $F(t) = \frac{k}{L}$. Hence neither of Volterra's critical assumptions

$$\text{(i)} \quad F(t) > 0, \quad F'(t) < 0, \quad \text{(ii)} \quad m = c - \int_0^L F(\tau)\, d\tau > 0$$

are satisfied in the present analysis. Indeed, Volterra shows that under his assumptions the (linear) problem has no periodic solutions.

Equation (3.15) with $g(x) = c(e^x - 1)$, c a constant, describes the dynamic behavior of a circulating fuel nuclear reactor; references may be found in [8] and [35]. It is of considerable importance physically to know the behavior of both $u(t)$ and $u'(t)$.

A detailed proof of Theorem 3.4 is given in [27]. Here we remark about the salient points. The functional (3.12) with $a(t) = \frac{1}{L}(L-t)$ for which

$$\widetilde{E}'(t) = \widetilde{E}'(t, u(t)) = -\frac{1}{2L}\left[\int_{t-L}^{t} g(u(\tau))\, d\tau\right]^2 \leq 0,$$

yields (3.19) and the proof of (i), much as (3.4) is obtained in the first part of the proof of Theorem 3.1. From $\widetilde{E}(t) \geq 0$, $\widetilde{E}'(t) \leq 0$, $0 \leq t < \infty$ one has $\lim_{t\to\infty} \widetilde{E}(t) = \nu \geq 0$ for some constant $\nu < \infty$. If $\nu = 0$ all the remaining assertions of Theorem 3.4 follow readily with $\Omega = (0,0) = \Gamma(0,0)$. It also follows that $\nu > 0$ if and only if $\Omega \neq (0,0)$. It is next shown, using $|E''(t)| \leq K < \infty$, $0 \leq t < \infty$, that

$$f(t) = \frac{1}{L}\int_{t-L}^{t} g(u(\tau))\, d\tau \to 0 \qquad (t \to \infty).$$

Then it is seen from (3.16) that, at least intuitively, a solution $u(t)$ of (3.15) stays arbitrarily close to solutions of (3.17) for longer and longer intervals of time as $t \to \infty$. This key fact is made precise and used repeatedly in the remainder of the proof. In particular, one obtains: if $(\alpha, \beta) \in \Omega$, then $\Gamma(\alpha, \beta) \subset \Omega$. Further, for any two points (α_1, β_1), (α_2, β_2), define the annular type region $D(\alpha_1, \beta_1; \alpha_2, \beta_2)$ in the phase plane as the closed connected set whose boundary consists of the two curves $\Gamma(\alpha_1, \beta_1)$ and $\Gamma(\alpha_2, \beta_2)$. One then proves that $\Omega = D(\alpha_1, \beta_1; \alpha_2, \beta_2)$ for some (α_1, β_1), (α_2, β_2). To establish the conclusion (3.20), it must be shown that this annulus is always degenerate. This requires a detailed study of the limiting form of the functional $\widetilde{E}(t, u)$. Conclusions (3.21) and (3.22) follow easily from the proof of (3.20).

We now remark briefly about a different problem for a Volterra equation similar to (3.1). V. E. Beneš [4] considers the real equation

$$(3.23) \qquad x'(t) = \omega - \int_0^t k(t-s) F(x(s))\, ds \qquad (t \geq 0,\ \omega \text{ a constant}),$$

which arises in the study of nonlinear control mechanisms such as synchronous motors or phase controlled oscillators. It is assumed that

(a) $k(t)$ is bounded on $0 \leq t < \infty$ and $k(t) \in L_1[0, \infty)$,

(b) $F(x)$ is bounded and satisfies a uniform Lipschitz condition on $(-\infty, \infty)$.

The problem is to determine choices of ω, k, F for which a solution $x(t)$ of (3.23) satisfies $\lim_{t\to\infty} x(t) = 0$. In [4] the fixed point theorem of Tychonov is used to study properties of solutions of (3.23) by showing that a fixed point of an appropriate transformation lies in a specific set of a function space (this requires restrictions in addition to (a), (b) above.). In [6] Beneš considers by similar methods the question of existence of ultimately periodic solutions of (3.23), where it is now assumed that F is periodic.

Many other problems lead to integrodifferential equations, e.g., the free-boundary problem studied by I. Kolodner [20]. We also mention an entirely different problem. In [31] Z. A. Melzak considers the scalar transport equation

$$(3.24) \quad \frac{\partial f}{\partial t}(x,t) = \frac{1}{2}\int_0^x f(y,t)f(x-y,t)\,\phi(y,x-y)\,dy - f(x,t)\int_0^\infty f(y,t)\,\phi(x,y)\,dy - \frac{f(x,t)}{x}\int_0^x y\psi(x,y)\,dy + \int_x^\infty f(y,t)\,\psi(y,x)\,dy.$$

The variables x, y, t are nonnegative and the functions $f(x, 0)$, $\phi(x, y)$, $\psi(x, y)$ are given and satisfy suitable conditions too lengthy to be given here. It is shown that there exists a continuous solution $f(x, t)$ of (3.24) existing for $x, t \geq 0$. This solution is nonnegative, analytic in t for each x, integrable in x for each t; moreover, this solution satisfies the condition

$$\int_0^\infty |f(x,t)|\,dx \leq K < \infty \qquad (0 \leq t \leq T < \infty)$$

which is enough to insure uniqueness of the initial value problem associated with (3.24). In [32] these results are extended to the more general case of (3.24) with $\phi(x, y)$, $\psi(x, y)$ replaced by $\phi(x, y, t)$, $\psi(x, y, t)$. A further generalization to operator equations of the form

$$\frac{\partial f}{\partial t} = K[f(x,t)] \qquad (0 \leq x, t < \infty),$$

where $K(f) = \sum_1^\infty K_n(f)$, is considered in [33], with each $K_n(f)$ being derived from an n-linear operator by equating the argument functions. It would seem of considerable interest to consider questions of asymptotic behavior as $t \to \infty$. For a connection between transport theory, invariant imbedding and two point boundary value problems we refer to a recent paper of G. M. Wing [43] where an extensive bibliography is given.

APPENDIX

Remarks On Volterra Functional Differential Equations

As pointed out in the Introduction and Section 3, systems such as (1.2), (3.1), (3.12) are a special case of the real system

$$y' = \mathcal{F}(t, y(\cdot)) \qquad (t > t_0) \tag{A. 1}$$

where $\mathcal{F} = (\mathcal{F}_1, \ldots, \mathcal{F}_n)$ and each $\mathcal{F}_i$ is a given functional whose value is determined by t and values of the vector $y(s)$ on some interval $\alpha \leq s \leq t$, $t > t_0$, $\alpha = -\infty$ not excluded (if $\alpha = -\infty$, $[\alpha, t] = (-\infty, t]$.) Thus both bounded and unbounded "delays" are admitted. Clearly (A. 1) includes not only the systems mentioned above, but also systems of ordinary differential equations ($\alpha = t$), differential-difference equations ($\alpha < t$) with both bounded and unbounded delays and more general functional equations.

A great deal is known about stability and asymptotic behavior of solutions of differential equations (see e.g. books by Coddington and Levinson [10], Cesari [9], Bellman [2], Lefschetz [23], LaSalle and Lefschetz [22], and others). Much of the analysis is concerned with systems of the form

$$x' = A(t)x + F(t, x), \tag{A. 2}$$

where F is sufficiently smooth and small in norm in some sense when $|x|$ is small, and where the unperturbed system is linear (in many instances with constant or periodic coefficients). A central problem is given the behavior of solutions of the unperturbed system, what perturbations are admissible in order that solutions of the perturbed system exhibit a similar qualitative behavior. Analogous problems have been discussed for differential-difference equations and certain other delay equations with bounded delays (see Bellman and Cooke [3] for an up to date account and references). The usual approach to these questions is to employ the variations of constants formula in the case of (A. 2), and an analogous integral representation using Laplace transforms in the case of difference-differential equations with bounded delays to convert the problem to a nonlinear Volterra integral equation (most often of convolution type) with a very well behaved kernel (e.g. exponential decay). Such methods will ordinarily not be successful if the unperturbed system has variable coefficients since a useful representation for solutions is lacking, and they certainly cannot be used if the unperturbed system is nonlinear. Even more to the point, consider the linear analogue of equation (3.1)

$$x' = -\int_0^t a(t-\tau)x(\tau)\,d\tau \qquad t \geq 0.$$

It is shown in [25], referred to in Section 3, that under certain conditions which include $a(t) = \int_0^\infty \exp(-s^2 t)h(s)ds$, $h \in L_1[0,\infty)$, $h(s) \geq 0$ with inequality holding on a set of positive measure, all solutions $x(t)$ approach zero, but $x(t) = O(\frac{1}{t^{3/2}})$ as $t \to \infty$. Because of this order condition if in (3.1) $g(x) = x + o(|x|)$ as $x \to 0$, it is unlikely that a perturbation technique for this problem will be successful.

Another basic technique for studying asymptotic behavior of solutions of differential equations is based on ideas of the Second Method of Liapunov (see e.g. LaSalle and Lefschetz [22]). By using the notion of a Liapunov functional a number of authors have recently extended these ideas to various equations of the form (A.1). We refer to N. N. Krassovskiĭ [21] for such results pertaining to delay equations with bounded delays; the reader will find there an extensive bibliography also for such results for differential equations. Equation (A.1) with possibly unbounded delays has been studied by R. Driver [13] who extended many of the earlier results of [21] and simplified a number of the proofs. For recent research on systems of neutral type we refer to Driver [14], [15]; see especially Theorems 4 and 5 of [14] for results on asymptotic behavior.

The main advantages in using Liapunov functionals for studying asymptotic behavior and stability are as follows: (i) The system in question need not be almost linear; (ii) in cases of perturbation systems the unperturbed system can be either linear or nonlinear and one does not require an integral representation for solutions.

As in ordinary differential equations the stability of any solution of (A.1) can be reduced to the study of the trivial solution. Roughly speaking, the basic idea of Liapunov's Second Method for ordinary differential equations is to select (this may be the whole difficulty) a nonnegative function $V(t,y)$ which gives some estimate of the norm of y. Then if for a solution $\phi = \phi(t, t_0)$(where $\phi(t_0, t_0) = y_0$

is a given vector, $|y_0|$ small), $V(t, \phi(t, t_0))$ is small whenever $|\phi(t, t_0)|$ is small, then the zero solution of the system in question is stable. If in addition $V(t, \phi(t, t_0)) \to 0$ as $t \to \infty$, the zero solution is asymptotically stable. Liapunov's theorems merely give sufficient conditions under which such a function V exhibits this behavior. For (A. 1) these underlying ideas still hold, but one must in general use a functional $V(t, y(\cdot))$ since the right-hand side of (A. 1) depends as a rule on values of the solution at times previous to t.

The chief difficulty in applying these methods to many problems is that little is known about systematic constructions of suitable Liapunov functionals. In this connection we point out, however, that interesting new results (even for ordinary differential equations) have recently been obtained by J. K. Hale [16], [17], [18] for systems of functional differential equations with bounded delays by employing "converse theorems" (see e.g. H. A. Antosiewicz [1] for differential equations and N. N. Krassovskiĭ [21] for equations of the form (A. 1) and with bounded delays. As implied by Driver [13] such results could also be obtained in the case of (A. 1) with unbounded delays.

While the general Liapunov theory of [21] and [13] applies in principle to integrodifferential equations such as (1. 2) or (3. 1), it is, in fact, the case that essentially [21] and [13] have given only examples dealing with difference-differential equations. As can be seen in Section 3, this theory can at best be applied to deduce stability of the zero solution, but not asymptotic stability, by using the various Liapunov functionals defined there. The reason for this is essentially that these functionals do not have a negative definite derivative. Furthermore, we are also interested in global asymptotic behavior which these authors do not consider. In this connection it seems clear that such results, e.g. Massera's theorem [1], for ordinary differential equations will hold in this more general setting. Another point to bear in mind from Section 3, Theorems 3. 1, 3. 2, 3. 3, 3. 4, is that much more than $\lim_{t\to\infty} u(t) = 0$ is actually established, and this is of considerable practical interest. Thus these theorems may be regarded as a further extension of Liapunov's method.

BIBLIOGRAPHY

1. Antosiewicz, H. A., A survey of Liapunov's second method, Annals of Math. Studies, #41, Princeton, 1958.

2. Bellman, R., Stability Theory for Ordinary Differential Equations, McGraw-Hill, New York, 1953.

3. Bellman, R. , and Cooke, K. L. , Differential-Difference Equations, Academic Press, New York, 1963.

4. Beneš, V., A fixed point method for studying the stability of a class of integrodifferential equations, J. Math. and Phys., 40 (1961), 55-67.

5. Beneš, V., A nonlinear integral equation from the theory of servo-mechanisms, Bell Syst. Tech. J., 40(1961), 1309-1321.

6. Beneš, V., Ultimately periodic solution to a nonlinear integrodifferential equation, Bell Syst. Tech. J., 41 (1962), 257-268.

7. Beneš, V., Ultimately periodic behaviour in a class of nonlinear servomechanisms, Nonlinear differential equations and nonlinear mechanics, New York, Academic Press, 1963, pp. 384-392.

8. Brownell, F. H., and Ergen, W. K., A theorem on rearrangements and its application to certain delay differential equations, J. Rational Mech. and Anal. 3(1954), 565-579.

9. Cesari, L., Asymptotic Behaviour and Stability Problems for Ordinary Differential Equations, Berlin, Springer, 1959.

10. Coddington, E. A. and Levinson, N., Theory of Ordinary Differential Equations, New York, McGraw-Hill, 1955.

11. Conti, R., Sulla prolungabilita delle soluzioni di nu siptema di equazioni differenziali ordinarie, Bull. Un. Mat. Ital. 11 (1956), 510-514.

12. Dinghas, A. , Zur Existenz von Fixpunkten bei Abbildungen vom Abel-Liouvilleschen Typus, Math. Z. 70(1958), 174-189.

13. Driver, R. D., Existence and stability of solutions of a delay-differential system, MRC Tech. Summ. Rep. #300, Univ. of Wis. (1962).

14. Driver, R. D., A two-body problem of classical electrodynamics: The one dimensional case, Ann. Phys., 21 (1963), 122-141.

15. Driver, R. D., A functional-differential system of neutral type arising in a two-body problem of classical electrodynamics, Nonlinear Differential Equations and Nonlinear Mechanics, New York, Academic Press, 1963, pp. 474-483.

16. Hale, J. K., Asymptotic behaviour of the solutions of differential-difference equations, Rias Tech. Rep. 61-10, to appear Proc. Symp. Nonlinear Oscillations, IUTAM, Kiev, USSR, Sept. 1961.

17. Hale, J. K., A class of functional-differential equations, to appear.

18. Hale, J. K., Functional-differential equations with parameters, to appear.

19. Hellman, O., On the periodicity of the solution of a certain nonlinear integral equations, Pac. J. Math. 8 (1958), 219-226.

20. Kolodner, I. I., Free boundary problem for the heat equation with applications to problems of change of phase, I. Comm. Pure Appl. Math. 9 (1956), 1-31.

21. Krasovskiĭ, N., Stability of Motion (translated by J. L. Brenner), Stanford, 1963.

22. LaSalle, J. P., and Lefschetz, S., Stability of Liapunov's Direct Method with Applications, New York, Academic Press, 1961.

23. Lefschetz, S., Differential Equations: Geometric Theory, New York, Interscience, 1957.

24. Levin, J. J., The asymptotic behaviour of the solution of a Volterra equation, to appear, Proc. Amer. Math. Soc.

25. Levin, J. J., and Nohel, J. A., On a system of integrodifferential equations occurring in reactor dynamics, J. Math. Mech. 9, 347-368 (1960).

26. Levin, J. J., and Nohel, J. A., Note on a nonlinear Volterra equation, to appear Proc. of the Amer. Math. Soc.

27. Levin, J. J., and Nohel, J. A., On a nonlinear delay equation, to appear J. Math. Anal. and Appl.

28. Levinson, N. , A nonlinear Volterra equation arising in the theory of superfluidity, J. Math. Anal. and Appl. 1 (1961), 1-11.

29. Mann, W. R., and Wolf, F., Heat transfer between solids and gasses under nonlinear boundary conditions, Quart. Appl. Math., 9 (1951), 163-184.

30. Mann, W. R., and Roberts, J. H., On a certain nonlinear integral equation of Volterra type, Pacific J. Math., 1 (1951), 431-435.

31. Melzak, Z. A., A scalar transport equation, Trans. of the Amer. Math. Soc., 85 (1957), 547-560.

32. Melzak, Z. A., A scalar transport equation, II, Mich. Math. J., 4 (1957), 193-206.

33. Melzak, Z. A., Entire operators and functional equations, Proc. of the Amer. Math. Soc. 10 (1959), 438-447.

34. Neǐmark, Yu. I., On the permissibility of linearization in studying stability, Dokl. Akad. Nauk SSSR, 127 (1959), 961-964. (Russian).

35. Nohel, J. A., A class of nonlinear delay equations, J. Math. Phys., 38 (1960), 295-311.

36. Nohel, J. A., Some problems in nonlinear Volterra equations, Bull. of the Amer. Math. Soc. 68 (1962), 323-329.

37. Padmavally, K., On a nonlinear integral equation, J. Math. Mech. 7 (1958), 533-555.

38. Reichert, M., Uber die Fixpunkte einer Klasse Singulären Volterrascher Abbidungen (Thesis), Math. Inst. der Freien Universität Berlin, July 1962.

39. Satō, T., Sur l'équation intégrale nonlinéaire de Volterra, Compositio Math. 11 (1953), 271-290.

40. Satō, T., and Iwasaki, A., Sur l'équation intégrale de Volterra, Proc. Japan Acad. 31 (1955), 395-398.

41. Thielman, H. P., Applications of fixed point theorems by Russian mathematicians, these proceedings, pp. 35-48.

42. Volterra, V., Sur la theorie mathematique des phenomenes hereditaires, J. de Math. Pures et Appliquees, 7 (1928), 249-298.

43. Wing, G. M., Transport theory, invariant imbedding, and two point boundary value problems. Nonlinear Differential Equations and Nonlinear Mechanics, New York, Academic Press, 1963, pp. 172-183.

44. Wintner, A., Ordinary differential equations and Laplace transforms (appendix), Amer. J. Math. 79 (1957), 265-294.

45. Wouk, A., Integral and differential equations — direct iteration, these proceedings, pp. 3-33.

Some Additional References On Nonlinear Volterra Equations Not Discussed In The Text

46. Baumann, V., Eine nichlineare Integrodifferentialgleichung der Warmeñbertragung bei Warmeleitung und Strahlung, Math. Z., 64 (1956), 353-384.

47. Cameron, R. H., Lingren, B. W. and Martin, W. T., Linearization of certain nonlinear functional equations, Proc. of the Amer. Math. Soc. 3 (1952), 138-143.

48. Cameron, R. H. , and Shapiro, J. M., Nonlinear integral equations, Ann. of Math. 62 (1955), 472-497.

49. Cameron, R. H., Nonlinear Volterra functional equations and non linear parabolic differential systems, J. Analyse Math. (1956/57), 136-182.

50. Picone, M., Nuove determinazioni concernenti l'equazione integrale nonlineare di Volterra, Ann. Mat. Pura Appl. 50 (1960), 97-113 (English Summary).

51. Picone, M. Sull'equazione integrale nonlineare di Volterra, Ann. Mat. Pura Appl. 49 (1960), 1-10 (English Summary).

52. Satō, T., The fixed point theorem in functional a spaces, Mem. Fac. Sci. Krusyu Univ. A. 5 (1950), 65-67.

53. Satō, T., Sur la limitation des solutions d'une systѐme d'équations integrales de Volterra, Tôhoku Mat. J. 2 (1952), 272-274.

54. Satō, T., Determination unique de solution de l'equation integrale de Volterra, Proc. Japan Acad. 27 (1951), 276-278.

55. Satō, T. Sur l'equation intégrale $xu(x) = f(x) + \int_0^x k(x,t,u(t))\,dt$, J. Math. Soc. Japan 5(1953), 145-153.

56. Zitarosa, A., Sulle equazioni funzionali di Volterra-Tonelli, Ricerch Mat. 3 (1954), 108-126.

Preparation of this paper was partly supported by the National Science Foundation (G-24335).

B. NOBLE

The Numerical Solution of Nonlinear Integral Equations and Related Topics

Contents

1. Introduction

Since explicit solutions of nonlinear integral equations can be obtained only in isolated instances, one might expect that a voluminous literature would exist on their numerical solution. This is not altogether true. In comparison with the enormous number of papers on the numerical solution of differential equations, there are comparatively few systematic investigations of methods for the numerical solution of nonlinear integral equations. Even for existing methods, much work remains to be done in connection with the experimental verification that the methods are numerically effective, and in connection with theoretical error analysis. At this stage in the development of the subject, no account of the numerical solution of nonlinear integral equations can hope to be definitive.

The bibliography given at the end of this paper indicates that there are a number of papers which solve nonlinear equations numerically in order to provide answers to problems of physical interest, but for the most part the methods used are elementary standard techniques borrowed from other fields of numerical analysis. Applications tend to fall into certain well-defined areas in which nonlinear integral equations are especially appropriate, as illustrated by some of the headings in the bibliography. Perhaps this is to be expected since it is usually easier and more straightforward to deal with differential equations rather than integral equations when describing physical phenomena (though this may be partly due to familiarity and training). As a rough generalization, it would seem that, as physical problems become more complicated, integral equations become more useful.

In view of these remarks (remembering the intention of this advanced seminar), the present paper is devoted to the following limited objectives:

(i) To summarize the numerical methods commonly used for solving nonlinear integral equations, together with a survey of the literature.

(ii) To indicate some of the applications of nonlinear integral equations where numerical solutions have been found useful.

(iii) To indicate areas in which further work might be carried out, in connection with both numerical methods and applications.

The problems considered in this paper are distinguished by two features. In the first place, the interest of these problems is primarily physical, in the sense that the nonlinear integral equations describe and are motivated by physical phenomena. In the second place, the object of the analysis is ultimately to represent the solution of the integral equation in terms of an approximate formula or a table of numbers.

It is of course of great interest if a numerical procedure can be justified rigorously, but reliable numerical results can be obtained even if the theoretical justification is not as satisfactory as might be desired. It may be necessary to adopt the point of view that when solving integral equations numerically, the calculations should be arranged so as to provide a posteriori justification. We can repeat calculations with different step-lengths, when using finite-difference methods. We can also verify directly that the integral equation is satisfied approximately by the numerical solution. In this connection it is important to possess information concerning the uniqueness of the solution; existence and convergence theorems are not so important. If a solution does not exist, no solution will be produced by a properly devised numerical procedure. From a numerical point of view, once certain basic principles are established, it is often cheaper and simpler to see whether an iterative procedure converges, or a step-by-step method is unstable, by merely testing the method in practice, incorporating suitable internal checks in the numerical work. An illustration of these remarks is given in §4 below.

We adopt the usual distinction between Volterra and Fredholm integral equations. When the equation is of Volterra type, one of the limits of integration is variable. An example is:

$$f(x) + \int_0^x k(x,t; f(t))\, dt = g(x), \qquad (x \geq 0) \quad . \tag{1}$$

When both limits are fixed, the equation is of Fredholm type, for example

$$f(x) + \int_0^1 k(x,t; f(t)\, dt = g(x), \qquad (0 \leq x \leq 1) \quad . \tag{2}$$

From a numerical point of view, the distinction between Volterra and Fredholm equations corresponds to a distinction between initial-value and boundary-value problems. Equations of Volterra type are generally solved by a step-by-step procedure in which approximate values of the unknown function $f(x)$ are computed for $x = x_r = rh$, with $r = 1, 2, 3, \ldots$ in succession, where h is a suitable step-length. On the other hand, equations of Fredholm type can be reduced to a set of simultaneous algebraic equations for the unknown quantities $f_r = f(x_r)$, $r = 0, 1, \ldots n$, where the x_r are $n + 1$ points in the range $0 \leq x \leq 1$. Precisely the same distinction between initial-value and boundary-value problems occurs when solving differential equations numerically.

Because of this distinction, the remainder of this paper falls naturally into two parts. After §2, in which some of the connections between differential and integral equations are elaborated, §§3-8 deal with Volterra equations, §§9-15 deal with Fredholm equations.

2. Connections and analogies between differential and integral equations.

We start by reminding the reader of a well-worn example. Suppose that we wish to solve the differential equation

$$(3) \qquad d^2y/dx^2 = f(x,y), \qquad (x \geq 0) \;,$$

with

$$y(0) = a, \quad y'(0) = b \;.$$

An integration with respect to x gives

$$dy/dx = \int_0^x f(t, y(t))\, dt + b \;.$$

A further integration, with subsequent change of the order of integration, gives

$$(4) \qquad y(x) = \int_0^x (x-t)\, f(t, y(t))\, dt + bx + a \;.$$

This is a Volterra integral equation, and in fact it is a special case of (1). If, on the other hand, we wish to solve the boundary-value problem represented by solving (3) in $0 \leq x \leq 1$ with

$$y(0) = y(1) = 0 \;,$$

then (4) is still true, with $a = 0$. The constant b is determined by applying the boundary condition at $x = 1$:

$$0 = \int_0^1 (1-t)\, f(t, y(t))\, dt + b \;.$$

If this value of b is inserted in (4) with $a = 0$ we obtain the Fredholm equation (compare (2)):

$$(5) \qquad y(x) = \int_0^1 K(x,t)\, f(t, y(t))\, dt \;,$$

where

$$K(x,t) = \begin{cases} -t(1-x)\;, & 0 \leq t \leq x \leq 1\;, \\ -x(1-t)\;, & 0 \leq x \leq t \leq 1\;. \end{cases}$$

The function K(x,t) is of course the Green's function of the differential operator d^2/dx^2 for boundary conditions $y(0) = y(1) = 0$:

$$\frac{d^2K(x,t)}{dx^2} = \delta(x-t) , \tag{6}$$

where δ is the Diric delta-function. The Green's function often has physical significance. Thus in considering the static deflection of a string, K(x,t) is the deflection at the position t due to a point force at the position x. The above example illustrates the remark made in the introduction, that Volterra equations correspond to initial-value problems, and Fredholm equations correspond to boundary-value problems.

The equation (4) is not the only integral equation that can be derived for y, when considering the initial-value problem stated in connection with (3). If equation (3) is written in the form

$$d^2y/dx^2 + k^2y = \{f(x,y) + k^2\} ,$$

the solution of this equation such that $y(0) = a$, $y'(0) = b$, regarding the right-hand side as known, is

$$y = \frac{1}{k}\int_0^x \sin k(x-t) \ \{f(t,y(t)) + k^2\}\,dt + a\cos kx + \frac{b}{k}\sin kx . \tag{7}$$

The parameter k, which is at our disposal, can be chosen so that the term involving y under the integral sign is as small as possible. Thus if $a = b = 0$ and

$$f(t,y) = -y - \epsilon y^3 + \cos wt ,$$

where ϵ is small, then, on choosing $k = 1$, equation (7) gives the following iterative procedure which is convenient if it is desired to carry out the iteration analytically:

$$y_{n+1} = -\epsilon\int_0^x \sin(x-t)\, y_n^3(t)\,dt + \int_0^x \sin(x-t)\cos wt\,dt .$$

It should be noted that this equation is entirely equivalent to the procedure

$$\frac{d^2y_{n+1}}{dx^2} + y_{n+1} = -\epsilon y_n^3 + \cos wt . \tag{8}$$

If we wish to solve the problem numerically it may be more convenient to deal with finite difference forms of the differential equation (8), rather than the integral equation.

We next consider an example which occurs in connection with the nonlinear axially symmetrical bending of a circular plate. The differential equations for the problem can be reduced to the form ([52], p. 274):

$$(9a) \qquad L\,\alpha(x) = x\frac{d}{dx}\frac{1}{x}\frac{d}{dx}\{x\,\alpha(x)\} = -\alpha(x)\,\gamma(x) - Px^2, \qquad (0 \le x \le 1),$$

$$(9b) \qquad L\,\gamma(x) = x\frac{d}{dx}\frac{1}{x}\frac{d}{dx}\{x\,\gamma(x)\} = \frac{1}{2}\,\alpha^2(x), \qquad (0 \le x \le 1),$$

where α, γ are the unknown functions, x is the radial coordinate, and P is a given constant. The boundary conditions are that α, γ are finite at the center of the plate, $x = 0$, and, on the circumference, for a clamped plate with zero radial displacement,

$$\alpha = 0, \quad d\gamma/dx = \nu\gamma, \qquad x = 1,$$

where ν is Poisson's ratio, a known constant. The method used above to derive (5) readily generalises, and the integral equations corresponding to (9) are:

$$(10a) \qquad \alpha(x) = \int_0^1 g_1(x,t)\,\alpha(t)\,\gamma(t)\,dt + \frac{1}{8}Px(1-x^2),$$

$$(10b) \qquad \gamma(x) = -\int_0^1 g_2(x,t)\,\alpha^2(t)\,dt,$$

where, for $i = 1, 2$,

$$g_i(x,t) = \begin{cases} -\frac{1}{2}t\left(\frac{1}{x} + \frac{x}{m_i}\right), & (x > t), \\ -\frac{1}{2}x\left(\frac{1}{t} + \frac{t}{m_i}\right), & (x < t), \end{cases}$$

and

$$m_1 = -1, \qquad m_2 = (1-\nu)/(1+\nu).$$

This problem was solved by iterative procedures in [52]. The following comments can be made

(i) In [52], the theoretical analysis of the convergence of the iterative procedures is based on the integral equation formulation (10).

(ii) In [52], the actual numerical work is performed using a finite difference form of the differential equations (9). Direct numerical solution of the integral equation would seem to be quite practicable, though care might have to be taken since the kernels have discontinuous derivatives at $x = t$.

(iii) In [53], a different method is proposed for direct solution of integral equations related to (10), by means of a series expansion.

The general situation in connection with the conversion of a differential equation, say $My = g$, into an integral equation is the following. The operator M, which is not necessarily linear, is split into two parts, $M = L + N$, in such a way that

(i) The equation $Ly = h$ can be solved explicitly to give $y = L^{-1}h$ for arbitrary h. This usually means that L is a linear operator, and the kernel of the resulting integral equation will involve the Green's function defined by $LG(x,t) = \delta(x-t)$. (Compare (6)).

(ii) If we write $My = g$ as $Ly = -Ny + g$ and apply L^{-1} to obtain

$$y = -L^{-1} Ny + L^{-1}g ,$$

then the part of the first term on the right of this equation which depends on y is as small as possible.

In applications, a simple way of splitting the operator is often suggested by the physical system. Thus in elasticity with a nonlinear stress-strain law, it is often possible to take a linear law as a first approximation. Suppose that the relation between the stress σ and the strain ϵ is given by the solid curve in Figure 1. The total strain ϵ is written in the form

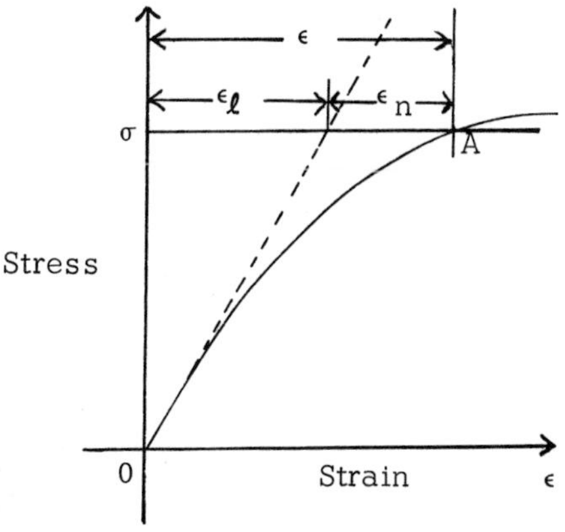

Figure 1

$$\epsilon = \epsilon_\ell + \epsilon_n$$

where we assume

$$\epsilon_\ell = k\sigma ,$$

k being a suitable constant. It is often convenient (as well as natural) to take k to be the constant corresponding to small strains, i.e. corresponding to the dotted line in Figure 1, which is the tangent to the stress-strain curve at the origin. However there is no necessity to do this, and k could be chosen so as to minimize the integral part of the final integral equation. For instance it might correspond to the straight line joining 0A in Figure 1. As a simple example, given in [57], consider a flat plate of thickness $2c$, with coordinates x, y in the plane of the plate, and z perpendicular to the plate. Suppose that there is a given temperature distribution $T(z)$ across the plate, independent of x and y, and suppose that this causes the plate to bend into a circular shape in the x-z plane. It is assumed that the plate is constrained in such a way that lines which were parallel to the y-axis before bending are still parallel to the y-axis after the temperature distribution is applied. If the plate lies initially in, say, $-a \leq x \leq a$, where $a \gg c$, we ignore end effects near $x = \pm a$. Assuming that sections which are originally plane in the y - z plane remain plane after bending, the geometry of the situation shows that

$$\epsilon_t(z) = a + bz \tag{11a}$$

where ϵ_t denotes the total strain, and a, b are constants which have to be determined. The stress-strain law states that

$$\epsilon_t(z) = \epsilon(z) + \alpha T(z) = k\sigma(z) + \epsilon_n(z) + \alpha T(z) \ , \tag{11b}$$

where k is a suitable constant, as discussed above, and $\alpha T(z)$ is the contribution to the strain from the expansion due to temperature. The conditions of equilibrium are that there is no resulting force or moment over the whole cross-section, i. e.

$$\int_{-c}^{c} \sigma(z)\,dz = 0, \quad \int_{-c}^{c} z\sigma(z)\,dz = 0 \ . \tag{12}$$

If we eliminate ϵ_t from (11a, b) and substitute the resulting expression for σ in (12) we obtain two equations from which a, b can be determined in terms of $\epsilon_n(z)$. If these are substituted in (11a) we obtain the following nonlinear integral equation:

$$\epsilon(z) = -\alpha T(z) + \frac{\alpha}{2c}\int_{-c}^{c}\left(1 + \frac{3zu}{c^2}\right) T(u)\,du$$

$$+ \frac{1}{2c}\int_{-c}^{c}\left(1 + \frac{3zu}{c^2}\right)\epsilon_n(u)\,du \ .$$

The nonlinear part of the strain ϵ_n is a known function of ϵ (see Figure 1) so that this is a nonlinear integral equation. It is solved by assuming first of all that $\epsilon_n = 0$. This gives a first approximation for $\epsilon(z)$, and from the stress-strain curve (Figure 1) we can make a first estimate of ϵ_n which leads, from the integral equation, to a second estimate of $\epsilon(z)$, and so on. This is an example of the simplest type of iterative procedure for solving nonlinear integral equations (see §§10, 11). It turns out that the nonlinear strains are usually close to the first linear estimates of the strains, although the final stresses can be quite different from the stresses estimated on a linear basis. This indicates that the above integral equation in terms of strains is more satisfactory than integral equations involving unknown stresses. Although we have discussed only a very simple example, the same general principles can be applied to much more complicated problems. The reader is referred to references [54]-[60].

Another way of converting differential into integral equations is the following. Consider the initial-value problem defined in connection with (3) at the beginning of this section. If we set

$$z = d^2y/dx^2 , \tag{13}$$

then

$$\frac{dy}{dx} = b + \int_0^x z(t)\,dt ,$$

$$y = a + bx + \int_0^x (x-t)\,z(t)\,dt .$$

Hence (3) becomes

$$z(x) = f\left(x,\ a + bx + \int_0^x (x-t)\,z(t)\,dt\right) .$$

This is a Volterra integral equation for $z(x)$ which may be more convenient than (4) for numerical work.

An application of this method occurs in connection with boundary-layer flow (see [27]-[30]). Consider, for instance, the problem of solving

$$y'''(x) + y''(x)\,y(x) = 0 , \tag{14a}$$

with

$$y(0) = 0,\quad y'(0) = \alpha,\quad y''(0) = 1 , \tag{14b}$$

where α is a known constant. We introduct the function $z(x) = y''(x)$ defined as in (11). From (14a)

$$(z'/z) + y = 0 ,$$

and integration gives

$$\log z(x) + \int_0^x y(u)\,du = 0 . \tag{15}$$

On integrating (13) three times, using (14b), we obtain the result

$$\int_0^x y(u)\,du = \frac{1}{2}\int_0^x (x-t)^2 z(t)\,dt + \frac{1}{2}\alpha x^2 .$$

On combining this equation with (15), we obtain the following integral equation for $z(x)$:

$$\log z(x) = -\frac{1}{2}\int_0^x (x-t)^2 z(t)\,dt - \frac{1}{2}\alpha x^2 . \tag{16}$$

Since $z(x)$ tends to zero rapidly as x tends to infinity, this can be solved efficiently by an iterative procedure:

$$\log z_{n+1}(x) = -\frac{1}{2}\int_0^x (x-t)^2 z_n(t)\,dt - \frac{1}{2}\alpha x^2$$

where $z_n(x)$ is the nth approximation to $z(x)$. The numerical procedure involves nothing more than the repeated calculation of an indefinite integral. The integral equation (16) is also useful for obtaining approximate analytical solutions (see, for instance, [27]). Similar conversions of a differential to an integral equation are convenient in certain nonlinear problems in heat conduction (and diffusion) when the heat conductivity (or diffusivity) depend on the temperature (concentration). Examples can be found in [40], Chapter 9.

Some illustrations are given in [23] of the determination of appromate analytical solutions to problems of engineering interest, by converting differential into integral equations. For instance, the dynamic braking of a synchronous motor is considered in [23], p. 299. The system is governed by a pair of complicated nonlinear differential equations. By converting these into Volterra integral equations, a comparatively simple expression is obtained for the number of rotations before the rotor comes to rest.

When considering ordinary differential equations (i.e. when only one independent variable is involved) there is usually little advantage in solving numerically an equivalent integral equation rather than the original differential equation. (See, for example, the remark following equation (8) above). However when several independent variables are involved, it is often preferable to deal with the integral equation, since in many cases a problem involving a partial differential equation in two (three) independent variables can be converted into an integral equation in one (two) variables. Examples will be given later in connection with heat-conduction (§§4, 5) and conformal mapping (§13). Here we consider a simple dynamical problem, namely the impact of a sphere on an elastic beam.

The deflection $\phi(x,t)$ of an elastic beam is governed by the equation

$$c^2 \partial^4 \phi / \partial x^4 = \partial^2 \phi / \partial t^2 \tag{17}$$

where c is a known constant. Suppose that the beam extends from $x = 0$ to $x = 1$, and that suitable boundary conditions are prescribed at the ends. Without going into detail, the motion of the beam, starting from rest, under a point force of magnitude $p(t)$ applied at a point, say $x = a$, is given by a formula of the form

$$\phi(a,t) = \int_0^t K(t-\tau)\, p(t)\, d\tau \ , \tag{18}$$

where K has the form

$$K(u) = \sum_{n=1}^{\infty} a_n \sin \lambda_n u \ ,$$

for suitable constants a_n, λ_n which need not be specified here. (The explicit form of K can be obtained by solving (17) by the Laplace transform, or by separation of variables.) Suppose that the pressure $p(t)$ is produced by a sphere hitting the beam normally at the point $x = a$, and suppose that the position of the sphere at any instant is denoted by y where y is a distance normal to the beam. Assume that at $t = 0$ the sphere just starts to touch the beam with velocity V normal to the beam, and that $y = \phi(a, 0) = 0$ at $t = 0$. The sphere and the beam exert equal and opposite reactions on each other, so that the equation of motion of the sphere is

$$m\, d^2 y / dt^2 = -\, p(t) \ ,$$

where m is the mass of the sphere, and $p(t)$ is the pressure defined previously. On integrating twice,

$$y(t) = Vt - \frac{1}{m} \int_0^t (t-\tau)\, p(\tau)\, d\tau \, . \tag{19}$$

The quantity $y - \phi$ represents the depth of indentation of the beam by the sphere at time t. From Hertz's law of contact, the relationship between the depth of indentation and the pressure is

$$y(t) - \phi(\lambda, t) = k p^{2/3}(t) \, , \tag{20}$$

where k is a known constant depending on the materials of the beam and sphere and the radius of the sphere. It is of course this equation that introduces nonlinearity into the problem. On combining (18), (19), (20) we obtain the following nonlinear Volterra integral equation for $p(t)$:

$$kp^{2/3}(t) = Vt - \int_0^t \left\{\frac{t-\tau}{m} + K(t-\tau)\right\} p(\tau)\, d\tau \, . \tag{21}$$

This equation can be solved easily by numerical methods, for example by the finite difference methods discussed in the next section. Note that although the motion of the beam is governed by a partial differential equation, the final integral equation involves only one independent variable, namely the time. Equation (21) holds only when the sphere and the beam are in contact. A discussion of this problem is given in [24].

An example of an integro-differential equation is given by the classical Volterra theory of the growth of a population consisting of a single species when a hereditary effect is present (see [22], [25]). If the growth is unchecked, we assume that the population increases exponentially. If the number of individuals in the population is measured by a continuous variable x, then an exponential growth means that

$$dx/dt = ax, \quad (a > 0) \, . \tag{22}$$

However in practice there is only a limited amount of food available and, when the population starts to grow, individuals compete. Volterra assumed that (22) is replaced by

$$\frac{dx(t)}{dt} = ax - bx^2 - cx \int_{-\infty}^t k(t-\tau)\, x(\tau)\, d\tau \, .$$

The term bx^2 comes from the instantaneous inhibiting effect of individuals competing with each other for the available food. The number of encounters of individuals is assumed to be proportional to x^2. The integral term represents a hereditary effect. Individuals do not reach maturity instantaneously, and the amount of food available at any given time may depend on the amount consumed by the population at previous times. The presence of the hereditary term has a marked effect on the behavior of the solution of the equation. A discussion of the case where $k(t-\tau)$ is simply a constant, and a simplified discussion of the case where there are two competing populations can be found in [22], Chapter 13. No extensive discussion of the numerical solution of equations of this type has been located.

3. The solution of nonlinear Volterra integral equations by finite differences

There are close connections and analogies between methods for the numerical solution of differential and integral equations. Corresponding to many methods for the step-by-step solution of differential equations we can invent similar methods for the solution of Volterra integral equations. This provides the motivation for the treatment which follows.

Suppose that we wish to solve the differential equation

$$y' = f(x, y), \quad x \geq 0, \tag{23}$$

with

$$y(0) = y_0,$$

by finding, in succession,

$$y_r = y(x_r), \quad x_r = rh, \quad r = 1, 2, \ldots .$$

Equation (23) can be integrated from x_r to x_{r+1} to give, exactly,

$$y_{r+1} = y_r + \int_{x_r}^{x_{r+1}} f(u, y(u))\, du . \tag{24}$$

In Euler's method it is assumed that the value of $f(u, y(u))$ in the interval $x_r \leq u \leq x_{r+1}$ is given, approximately, by its value at the beginning of the interval. We denote the approximate value of y_r found at any stage of the calculation by Y_r. The formula for the determination of Y_{r+1} from Y_r is then

(25) $$Y_{r+1} = Y_r + h\, f(x_r, Y_r) \ .$$

The initial value $Y_0 = y_0$ is known, so that $Y_1, Y_2, \ldots$ can be computed in succession. The error per step, ϵ_{r+1}, is defined as the error in Y_{r+1}, assuming that Y_r is exactly correct, i.e. $Y_r = y_r$. By subtracting (2.5) from (2.4) we see that, in this case,

$$\epsilon_{r+1} = y_{r+1} - Y_{r+1} = \int_{x_r}^{x_{r+1}} f(u, y(u))\, du - h\, f(x_r, y_r)$$

(26) $$= \frac{1}{2} h^2 f'(x_r, y_r) + O(h^3)$$

where $f'(x,y) = f_x + f_y y'$. The cumulative error e_{r+1} is defined as the difference between y_{r+1} and Y_{r+1}, and it can be found in the following way. From (24), (25),

$$e_{r+1} = e_r + \int_{x_r}^{x_{r+1}} f(u, y(u))\, du - h\, f(x_r, Y_r)$$

(27) $$= e_r + h\,\{f(x_r, y_r) - f(x_r, Y_r)\} + \frac{1}{2} h^2 f'(x_r, y_r) + O(h^3)$$

$$= e_r + h\left(\frac{\partial f}{\partial y}\right)_r e_r + \frac{1}{2} h^2 f'(x_r, y_r) + O(h^3) \ .$$

Since $Y_0 = y_0$ we have $e_0 = 0$ and $e_1, e_2, \ldots$ can be estimated, in succession, by (27). If we define $E(x)$ to be a solution of the differential equation

(28) $$dE/dx = g(x)\, E + \psi(x), \quad E(0) = 0 \ ,$$

where

$$g(x) = \partial f(x,y)/\partial y, \quad \psi(x) = \frac{1}{2} f'(x,y) \ ,$$

then on applying Euler's method (i.e. a finite difference formula of the type (25)) to the equation (28) and comparing the result with (27) we see that

$$e_r = h\, E(x_r) + O(h^2) \ .$$

Since $E(x)$ is of order unity, this result shows that the cumulative error is of order h. From (26), the error per step is of order h^2.

The reason for discussing these differential equation results in such detail is that we wish to develop similar procedures for the non-linear Volterra integral equation

$$y(x) = g(x) + \int_0^x k(x,t;\, y(t))\,dt \quad . \tag{29}$$

On setting $x = 0, h, 2h, \ldots$ in succession in this equation, and using the same approximation as that used to derive (25), we obtain

$$y_0 = Y_0 = g_0 \;,$$

$$Y_1 = g_1 + h\,k(x_1, x_0;\, Y_0) \;,$$

$$Y_2 = g_2 + h\,\{k(x_2, x_0;\, Y_0) + k(x_2, x_1;\, Y_1)\} \;,$$

and, in general,

$$Y_{r+1} = g_{r+1} + h\sum_{s=0}^{r} k(x_{r+1}, x_s;\, Y_s) \;, \tag{30}$$

where Y_r is the approximation to $y(x_r)$, and $g_r = g(x_r)$. The values of $Y_1, Y_2, Y_3, \ldots$ can be computed in succession from these equations.

The cumulative error $e_{r+1} = y_{r+1} - Y_{r+1}$ can be discussed by a method similar to that used above for the differential equation. We require the result:

$$\int_0^{x_{r+1}} f(t)\,dt = h\sum_{s=0}^{r} f_s + \tfrac{1}{2}h(f_{r+1} - f_0) + O(h^2) \quad .$$

Then

$$e_{r+1} = y_{r+1} - Y_{r+1} = \int_0^{x_{r+1}} k(x_{r+1}, t;\, y(t))\,dt - h\sum_{s=0}^{r} k(x_{r+1}, x_s;\, Y_s)$$

$$= h\sum_{s=0}^{r} \{k(x_{r+1}, x_s;\, y_s) - k(x_{r+1}, x_s;\, Y_s)\} + h\psi_{r+1} + O(h^2) \tag{31}$$

$$= h\sum_{s=0}^{r} \left(\frac{\partial k}{\partial y}\right)_s e_s + h\,\psi_{r+1} + O(h^2) \tag{32}$$

where

$$(\partial k/\partial y)_s = \{\partial k(x_{r+1}, x_s; y)/\partial y\}_{y=y_s} , \tag{33}$$

$$\psi_{r+1} = \frac{1}{2}\{k(x_{r+1}, x_{r+1}; y_{r+1}) - k(x_{r+1}, x_0; y_0)\} .$$

We define $E_1(x)$ to be the solution of the linear integral equation

$$E_1(x) = \int_0^x \frac{\partial k(x, t; y(t))}{\partial y} E_1(t)\, dt + \psi_1(x) \tag{34}$$

where

$$\psi_1(x) = \frac{1}{2}\{k(x, x; y(x)) - k(x, x_0; y_0)\} . \tag{35}$$

If (34) is solved by the finite-difference procedure (30), and the resulting equations are compared with (32), we see that

$$e_r = h\, E_1(x_r) + O(h^2) . \tag{36}$$

Since $E_1(x)$ is of order unity this means that the cumulative error involved in solving a nonlinear Volterra integral equation by Euler's method is of order h.

The above method has been introduced as the natural analogue of Euler's method for differential equations, but it is unnecessarily crude, and with practically no additional complication we can improve the accuracy by a factor of h. Consider the following modification. We write

$$\begin{aligned} y_{r+1} &= g_{r+1} + v_{r+1} + \int_{x_r}^{x_{r+1}} k(x_{r+1}, x; y(x))\, dx , \\ Y_{r+1} &= g_{r+1} + V_{r+1} + h\, k(x_{r+1}, x_r; Y_r) , \end{aligned} \tag{37}$$

where

$$\begin{aligned} v_{r+1} &= \int_0^{x_r} k(x_{r+1}, x; y(x))\, dx , \\ V_{r+1} &= h\{\tfrac{1}{2}k(x_{r+1}, x_0; Y_0) + \sum_{s=0}^{r-1} k(x_{r+1}, x_s; Y_s) + \tfrac{1}{2}k(x_{r+1}, x_r; Y_r)\} . \end{aligned} \tag{38}$$

Note that the quantity V_{r+1} is formed by the trapezoidal rule which is more accurate than the crude integration rule used to approximate the integral from x_r to x_{r+1}. We have $Y_0 = y_0 = g_0$, and it is still possible to compute $Y_1, Y_2, Y_3, \ldots$ in succession from (37), in a straightforward way.

The cumulative error analysis proceeds as follows: We have

$$\int_0^{x_r} f(x)\,dx = h\{f_0 + \sum_{s=1}^{r-1} f_s + \frac{1}{2} f_r\} - \frac{1}{12} h^2 (f_r' - f_0') + O(h^3) .$$

Hence

$$e_{r+1} = y_{r+1} - Y_{r+1}$$

$$= (v_{r+1} - V_{r+1}) + \int_{x_r}^{x_{r+1}} k(x_{r+1}, x; y(x))\,dx - h\,k(x_{r+1}, x_r; Y_r)$$

$$= h\{\frac{1}{2}\left(\frac{\partial k}{\partial y}\right)_0 e_0 + \sum_{s=0}^{r-1}\left(\frac{\partial k}{\partial y}\right)_s e_s + \frac{1}{2}\left(\frac{\partial k}{\partial y}\right)_r e_r\}$$

$$-\frac{1}{12} h^2 \{k'(x_{r+1}, x_r; y_r) - k'(x_{r+1}, x_0; y_0)\} + \frac{1}{2} h^2 k'(x_{r+1}, x_r; y_r) + O(h^3) ,$$

where $(\partial k/\partial y)_s$ has been defined in (33), and

$$k'(x_{r+1}, x; y(x)) = dk/dx = k_x + k_y y', \quad y' = dy/dx .$$

On remembering that $k'(x_{r+1}, x_r; y_r)$ and $k'(x_{r+1}, x_{r+1}; y_{r+1})$ differ by terms of order h, we see that if $E_2(x)$ is defined as the solution of

(39) $$E_2(x) = \int_0^x \frac{\partial k(x,t;y(t))}{\partial y} E_2(t)\,dt + \psi_2(x) ,$$

where

(40) $$\psi_2(x) = \frac{1}{12}\{5k'(x, x; y(x)) + k'(x, x_0; y_0)\}$$

then

$$e_r = h^2 E_2(x_r) + O(h^3) .$$

The cumulative error is now of order h^2, and this has been achieved with little increase in complication of the calculation.

Of course, if the integral equation is linear, the procedure can be simplified. If

$$y(x) = g(x) + \int_0^x K(x,t)\, y(t)\, dt \ ,$$

we write

$$(41)\quad Y_{r+1} = g_{r+1} + h\{\tfrac{1}{2} K_{r+1,0} Y_0 + \sum_{s=1}^{r} K_{r+1,s} Y_s + \tfrac{1}{2} K_{r+1,r+1} Y_{r+1}\} \ ,$$

where

$$K_{rs} = K(x_r, x_s) \ .$$

On rearranging,

$$(42)\quad Y_{r+1}(1 - \tfrac{1}{2} h K_{r+1,r+1}) = g_{r+1} + h\{\tfrac{1}{2} K_{r+1,0} Y_0 + \sum_{s=1}^{r} K_{r+1,s} Y_s\} \ ,$$

so that Y_{r+1} can be found directly.

If we attempt to apply the same method to the nonlinear equation (29), the equation analogous to (41) is

$$(43)\qquad Y_{r+1} = g_{r+1} + U_{r+1} + \tfrac{1}{2} h\, k(x_{r+1}, x_{r+1}; Y_{r+1}) \ ,$$

where

$$(44)\qquad U_{r+1} = h\{\tfrac{1}{2} k(x_{r+1}, x_0; Y_0) + \sum_{s=1}^{r} k(x_{r+1}, x_s; Y_s)\} \ .$$

Equation (43) is a nonlinear algebraic equation for Y_{r+1}. This is the point of using the Euler approximation for the part of the integral from x_r to x_{r+1} in (37), to give an equation which yields Y_{r+1} explicitly. Suppose first of all that (43) is solved iteratively by means of the procedure

$$(45)\qquad Y_{r+1}^{(p+1)} = g_{r+1} + U_{r+1} + \tfrac{1}{2} h\, k(x_{r+1}, x_{r+1}, Y_{r+1}^{(p)}), \quad p = 0, 1, \ldots \ ,$$

where $Y_{r+1}^{(p)}$ is the pth approximation to Y_{r+1}, and the process is started by choosing any convenient estimate for $Y_{r+1}^{(0)}$ (for instance

(49) below). No convergence difficulties are to be expected, in general, since the term on the right containing Y_{r+1} is multiplied by h . Then

$$e_{r+1} = y_{r+1} - Y_{r+1}$$

$$= h\{\frac{1}{2}(\frac{\partial k}{\partial y})_0 e_0 + \sum_{s=1}^{r} (\frac{\partial k}{\partial y})_s e_s + \frac{1}{2}(\frac{\partial k}{\partial y})_{r+1} e_{r+1}\}$$

$$- \frac{1}{12} h^2 \{k'(x_{r+1}, x_{r+1}; y_{r+1}) - k'(x_{r+1}, x_0; y_0)\} + O(h^3) .$$

If $E_3(x)$ is the solution of

(46) $$E_3(x) = \int_0^x \frac{\partial k(x, t; y(t))}{\partial t} E_3(t)\, dt + \psi_3(x) ,$$

where

(47) $$\psi_3(x) = -\frac{1}{12} \{k'(x, x; y(x)) - k'(x, x_0; y_0)\} ,$$

then

(48) $$e_r = h^2 E_3(x_r) + O(h^3) .$$

The error is again of order h^2, but on comparing (47) with (40) we see that the error is likely to be smaller for the method (43) than for (37), as we should expect. However the orders of the two procedures are the same.

We next show that the improvement in accuracy obtained by carrying out the iteration in (45) until successive iterates agree to a high degree of accuracy is marginal compared with the gain obtained by iterating only once. (However if it is easy to iterate one would usually in practice iterate until convergence is achieved, unless a predictor-corrector method with error estimation is used, as explained in §5 below). Consider the following one-step iteration. Define

(49) $$Y_{r+1}^{(0)} = g_{r+1} + U_{r+1} + \frac{1}{2} h\, k(x_{r+1}, x_r; Y_r) ,$$

(50) $$Y_{r+1} = g_{r+1} + U_{r+1} + \frac{1}{2} h\, k(x_{r+1}, x_{r+1}; Y_{r+1}^{(0)}) ,$$

where U_{r+1} has been defined in (44) . To perform an error analysis of this procedure we first of all subtract the second equation from the first:

$$Y^{(0)}_{r+1} - Y_{r+1} = \frac{1}{2}h\,\{k(x_{r+1}, x_{r+1}; Y^{(0)}_{r+1}) - k(x_{r+1}, x_{r+1}; Y_{r+1})\}$$

$$+ \frac{1}{2}h\,\{k(x_{r+1}, x_{r+1}; Y_{r+1}) - k(x_{r+1}, x_r; Y_r)\}$$

$$= \frac{1}{2}h\left(\frac{\partial k}{\partial y}\right)_{r+1}(Y^{(0)}_{r+1}\ 0\ Y_{r+1}) + \frac{1}{2}h^2 k'(x_{r+1}, x_{r+1}, Y_{r+1}) + O(h^3) .$$

Hence

$$(51) \qquad Y^{(0)}_{r+1} = Y_{r+1} + O(h^2) .$$

On substituting this result in (50),

$$(52) \qquad Y_{r+1} = g_{r+1} + U_{r+1} + \frac{1}{2}h\,k(x_{r+1}, x_{r+1}; Y_{r+1}) + O(h^3) .$$

If an error analysis is carried out on this equation similar to that following (43) it appears that the $O(h^3)$ term does not affect the dominant part of the error which is still given by (48). This confirms the earlier statement that the accuracy of the one-step iterative procedure (49), (50) is comparable with the accuracy of the complete iteration (45), in the sense that the orders of the errors are the same.

Summing up this section, we have considered four elementary methods for the numerical solution of the nonlinear Volterra integral equation (29) by step-by-step procedures:

(i) The crude Euler method (30).

(ii) The method (37) in which the main integration is performed by the trapezoidal rule, and the last step by the Euler approximation.

(iii) The iterative method (45) in which the integration is carried out by the trapezoidal rule.

(iv) The one-step iteration method (49), (50) for which the basic formula is the same as in (iii), but only the first step of the iteration is performed.

The cumulative error is of order h in method (i) and of order h^2 in methods (ii)-(iv). Generalizations which give higher-order accuracy will be considered in §5. In §4 we consider a numerical example involving a singular kernel. A method will be illustrated for obtaining some idea of the accuracy of the calculations, when performing the numerical work.

4. A numerical example: heat conduction with a nonlinear boundary condition.

In the theory of heat transfer, the Stefan-Boltzmann boundary condition for loss of heat by radiation from a solid body states that the rate of loss of heat between the surface of the solid body and an external medium is given by a fourth-power law:

$$K\ \partial T/\partial x = -\sigma\ E(T_0^4 - T^4) \tag{53}$$

where T is the temperature of the surface of the body measured from absolute zero, T_0 is the temperature of the surrounding medium, K is the thermal conductivity of the solid, $\partial T/\partial x$ is the thermal gradient at the surface, evaluated in the direction of the interior normal of the solid, σ is the Stefan-Boltzmann constant, and E is the emissivity of the surface. When T and T_0 are close together, we can set $T = T_0 + v$, where v is small compared with T_0. The neglecting higher-order terms, (53) gives

$$K\ \partial v/\partial x = 4\sigma E T_0^3\ v\ .$$

It is a linear law of this type that is usually assumed in the theory of heat loss by radiation, since boundary-value problems involving the heat-conduction equation can be solved easily only when the boundary conditions are linear. However problems involving the nonlinear law (53) can be reduced to nonlinear integral equations, and we consider a simple problem to illustrate the method.

Consider one-dimensional heat-conduction in a semi-infinite medium governed by the equations:

$$K\ \partial^2 u/\partial x^2 = \partial u/\partial t, \qquad 0 \le x < \infty,\ t \ge 0\ , \tag{54}$$

$$u(x, 0) = 0, \qquad 0 \le x < \infty\ , \tag{55}$$

$$\partial u/\partial x = -\ G(u, t)\ , \qquad x = 0,\ t > 0\ . \tag{56}$$

It is a standard result that the solution of (54) satisfying the initial condition (55), with boundary condition

$$\partial u/\partial x = -\ g(t)\ , \qquad x = 0,\ t > 0\ ,$$

is given by

$$u(x, t) = \frac{1}{(\pi K)^{1/2}} \int_0^t \frac{g(\tau)}{(t-\tau)^{1/2}} \exp\left\{-\frac{x^2}{4K(t-\tau)}\right\} d\tau\ .$$

From (56), on replacing $g(\tau)$ by $G(u, \tau)$,

$$u(x, t) = \frac{1}{(\pi K)^{1/2}} \int_0^t \frac{G(u(0, \tau), \tau)}{(t-\tau)^{1/2}} \exp\left\{-\frac{x^2}{4K(t-\tau)}\right\} d\tau\ . \tag{57}$$

Hence $u(x,t)$ is known for all values of x and t if $u(0,t)$ is known. A nonlinear integral equation for $u(0,t)$ is obtained by setting $x = 0$ in (57):

$$(58) \qquad u(0,t) = \frac{1}{(\pi K)^{1/2}} \int_0^t \frac{G(u(0,\tau),\tau)}{(t-\tau)^{1/2}} d\tau .$$

The existence and uniqueness of solutions of this equation have been examined in [33]under the following physically reasonable assumptions:

(i) $G(u,t)$ is a continuous function of u.

(ii) $G(T_0,t) = 0$, where T_0 is the temperature of the surrounding medium (compare (53)).

(iii) If $u_1 > u_2$, then $G(u_1,t) < G(u_2,t)$.

References [32], [34], [35] deal with existence and uniqueness for related equations. (See also the paper by Dr. J. Nohel in this volume.)

For our numerical study, we consider the special form

$$G(u,t) = p(T_0^k - u^k)$$

where p, k, T_0 are given constants. Since $u(0,0) = 0$, we have, for small t,

$$(59) \qquad u(0,t) \approx \frac{pT_0^k}{(\pi K)^{1/2}} \int_0^t \frac{dt}{(t-\tau)^{1/2}} = \frac{pT_0^k}{2(\pi K)^{1/2}} t^{1/2} .$$

Hence $u(0,t)$ behaves like $t^{1/2}$ for small t. Since the derivative of $t^{1/2}$ tends to infinity as t tends to zero, it is advisable for numerical work to make a change of variable to eliminate this singularity. We also include constants in the change of variable to simplify the form of the equations. Let

$$t = \beta^2 x^2, \qquad \tau = \beta^2 y^2 ,$$

where

$$\beta = K^{1/2} T_0^{1-k}/p ,$$

and introduce $f(x) = u(0,t)/T_0$ as the unknown function. Then (58) becomes

$$(60) \qquad f(x) = \frac{2}{\pi^{1/2}} \{x - \int_0^x \frac{f^k(y)}{(x^2-y^2)^{1/2}} y\,dy\} .$$

Because of the singularity in the kernel when x is nearly equal to y, the formulae given in the last section do not apply directly. We can, however, obtain analogous procedures by developing generalized integration formulae.

The analogue of the crude Euler formula (30) is obtained by dividing the range of y into steps of equal length h, and assuming that in the step x_s to x_{s+1}, $f(y)$ has the constant value f_s. Then

$$\int_0^{x_{r+1}} \frac{f^k(y)}{(x^2-y^2)^{1/2}}\, y\,dy = \sum_{s=0}^{r} f_s^k \int_{x_s}^{x_{s+1}} \frac{y\,dy}{(x_{r+1}^2-y^2)^{1/2}} + R$$

$$(61) \qquad = h \sum_{s=0}^{r} K_{r+1,\, s+\frac{1}{2}}\, f_s^k + R\ ,$$

where R is a remainder term, and

$$K_{r+1,\, s+\frac{1}{2}} = \left\{ (x_{r+1}^2 - x_s^2)^{1/2} - (x_{r+1}^2 - x_{s+1}^2)^{1/2} \right\} \Big/ h$$

$$(62) \qquad = \frac{(2s+1)}{((r+1)^2-s^2)^{1/2} + ((r+1)^2-(s+1)^2)^{1/2}}\ ,$$

where this last expression is convenient for numerical work. The original integral equation (60) is replaced by:

$$(63) \qquad f_{r+1} = \frac{2h}{\pi^{1/2}} \left\{ r+1 - \sum_{s=0}^{r} K_{r+1,\, s+\frac{1}{2}}\, f_s^k \right\} .$$

The analogue of the trapezoidal rule is obtained by assuming that

$$f^k(y) = \left\{ (x_{s+1}-y)\, f_s^k - (y-x_s)\, f_{s+1}^k \right\} \Big/ h, \qquad x_s \le y \le x_{s+1} .$$

Then

$$\int_{x_s}^{x_{s+1}} \frac{f^k(y)}{(x_{r+1}^2-y^2)^{1/2}}\, y\,dy \approx \frac{1}{2} h \left\{ (K_{r+1,\, s+\frac{1}{2}} + L_{r+1,\, s+\frac{1}{2}})\, f_s^k + \right.$$

$$\left. (K_{r+1,\, s+\frac{1}{2}} - L_{r+1,\, s+\frac{1}{2}})\, f_{s+1}^k \right\} ,$$

where $K_{r+1,\, s+\frac{1}{2}}$ has been defined in (61), (62) above, and

$$L_{r+1,\,s+\frac{1}{2}} = 2\int_{x_s}^{x_{s+1}} \frac{(x_{s+\frac{1}{2}} - y)}{(x_{r+1}^2 - y^2)^{1/2}}\, y\, dy$$

$$= (r+1)^2 \left\{ A_{r+1,\,s+\frac{1}{2}} - \sin^{-1} A_{r+1,\,s+\frac{1}{2}} \right\},$$

$$A_{r+1,\,s+\frac{1}{2}} = \frac{2s+1}{(s+1)[(r+1)^2 - s^2]^{1/2} + s[(r+1)^2 - (s+1)^2]^{1/2}} .$$

We can now write down the analogues of the procedures (43), (45), and (49)-(50) developed in the last section. We define:

$$W_{r+1} = \frac{1}{2}\left\{ (K_{r+1,\frac{1}{2}} + L_{r+1,\frac{1}{2}})\, f_0^k + \sum_{s=1}^{r} (K_{r+1,\,s-\frac{1}{2}} - L_{r+1,\,s-\frac{1}{2}} + K_{r+1,\,s+\frac{1}{2}} + L_{r+1,\,s+\frac{1}{2}})\, f_s^k \right\}.$$

Then the analogue of (43) is:

$$f_{r+1} = \frac{2h}{\pi^{1/2}}\left\{ r+1 - W_{r+1} - \frac{1}{2}(K_{r+1,r+\frac{1}{2}} - L_{r+1,r+\frac{1}{2}})\, f_r^k \right\}. \tag{64}$$

The analogue of (49)-(50) is given by

$$f_{r+1}^{(0)} = \frac{2h}{\pi^{1/2}}\left\{ r+1 - W_{r+1} - \frac{1}{2}(K_{r+1,r+\frac{1}{2}} - L_{r+1,r+\frac{1}{2}})\, f_r^k \right\} \tag{65a}$$

$$f_{r+1} = \frac{2h}{\pi^{1/2}}\left\{ r+1 - W_{r+1} - \frac{1}{2}(K_{r+1,r+\frac{1}{2}} - L_{r+1,r+\frac{1}{2}})\, (f_{r+1}^{(0)})^k \right\}. \tag{65b}$$

The analogue of (45) is given by

$$f_{r+1}^{(p+1)} = \frac{2h}{\pi^{1/2}}\left\{ r+1 - W_{r+1} - \frac{1}{2}(K_{r+1,r+\frac{1}{2}} - L_{r+1,r+\frac{1}{2}})\, (f_{r+1}^{(p)})^k \right\}, \tag{66}$$

where $f_{r+1}^{(0)}$ can be taken to be the value in (65a), and the iteration is repeated until the procedure has converged to the required degree of accuracy.

An error analysis of the type given in §3 could be carried out, but instead we shall obtain an empirical check on the error in the following way. Suppose that the cumulative error is proportional to Ch^q where C and q are unknown constants, independent of h. We denote the estimates of $f(x)$, for a given value of x, obtained by using step-lengths h, $2h$, $4h$, by F_1, F_2, F_4 respectively. Then our assumption is that

$$f(x) - F_1 = Ch^q ,$$

$$f(x) - F_2 = C(2h)^q ,$$

$$f(x) - F_4 = C(4h)^q .$$

Hence

$$\frac{f(x) - F_1}{f(x) - F_2} = \frac{f(x) - F_2}{f(x) - F_4} = \frac{1}{2^q} .$$

On solving for $f(x)$ we obtain the Aitken extrapolation formula:

(67) $$f(x) = F_1 - \frac{(F_1 - F_2)^2}{F_1 - 2F_2 + F_4} .$$

It is sometimes convenient to introduce the parameter

(68) $$t = \frac{F_4 - F_2}{F_2 - F_1}$$

where the theoretical value of t is 2^q. Then (67) can be written:

(69) $$f(x) = F_1 + \frac{1}{t-1}(F_1 - F_2) .$$

We now examine some numerical results. It is convenient to illustrate the basic principles by considering the simple Euler procedure (63). Computer runs were made, using this formula, with $h = 0.4$, 0.2, 0.1, 0.05 and 0.025 up to $t = 2.0$, with $k = 1$ and 4. It is found that instability is present, and this can be pronounced for large h. The degree of instability can be readily established by forming difference tables. As an example, consider the results in Table 1, for $h = 0.4$ and 0.2, with $k = 1$. By altering the function values f_r so as to smooth the higher-order differences we see that the instability is of the order of several digits in the second decimal place for $h = 0.4$, and several digits in the fourth decimal place when $h = 0.2$. A similar examination of the results for $h = 0.1$ shows that then the effect of instability is less than the inherent inaccuracy of the results due to truncation error, as established below. These results hold for $k = 1$. The effect of instability is more marked for $k = 4$. The reason for this is not yet clear. As an example, the values of f_r for $h = 0.4$, $k = 4$, are given by 0.000, 0.451, 0.870, 0.764, 1.179, -0.669, which should be compared with those for $k = 1$ in Table 1.

Table 1 Results for $k = 1$, using the Euler procedure.

$h = 0.4$

x_r	f_r	Δ
0.0	0.000	
		451
0.4	451	
		99
0.8	550	
		128
1.2	678	
		31
1.6	709	
		73
2.0	0.782	

$h = 0.2$

x_r	f_r	Δ	Δ^2	Δ^3	Δ^4
0.0	0.0000				
		2257			
0.2	2257		-883		
		1374		514	
0.4	3631		-369		-406
		1005		108	
0.6	4636		-261		- 14
		744		94	
0.8	5380		-167		- 49
		577		45	
1.0	5957		-122		- 9
		455		36	
1.2	6412		- 86		- 15
		369		21	
1.4	6781		- 65		- 6
		304		15	
1.6	7085		- 50		- 4
		254		11	
1.8	7339		- 39		
		215			
2.0	0.7554				

The results in Table 1 indicate that in practice it will be desirable to take h to be small for small values of t, and increase h as t increases. This will not be done here since we are interested in checking experimentally our theoretical predictions of the way in which the error depends on h.

We next consider the application of the Aitken extrapolation formula (67). The theoretical value of t for the Euler method is 2. Some typical numerical results are presented in Table 2. The empirical value of t is given by the ratio of successive numbers in the difference column (see (68) above). Estimates of t obtained in this way agree, as closely as would be expected, with the theoretical value of 2. If we apply Aitken's formula to the set of numbers for $x_r = 0.4$, $h = 0.1$, 0.05 and 0.025 we obtain the extrapolated value

$$0.3323 - (0.0036)^2 / 0.0080 \approx 0.3294 .$$

The figures indicate that this should be accurate to within a few digits in the fourth decimal place. For $k = 4$, the results for $h = 0.2$

Table 2 Results for various h, using the Euler procedure.

k = 1	$x_r = 0.4$		$x_r = 1.0$		$x_r = 2.0$	
h	f_r	Diffce.	f_r	Diffce.	f_r	Diffce.
0.2	0.3631		0.5957		0.7554	
		192		123		55
0.1	3439		5834		7499	
		80		54		27
0.05	3359		5777		7472	
		36		24		13
0.025	3323		5750		7459	
Extrap. value:	0.3294		0.5726		0.7447	
Accurate value:	0.329,213		0.572,417		0.744,605	

k = 2	$x_r = 0.4$		$x_r = 1.0$		$x_r = 2.0$	
h	f_r	Diffce.	f_r	Diffce.	f_r	Diffce.
0.1	0.4472		0.8183		0.9215	
		25		68		14
0.05	4447		8115		9201	
		14		33		7
0.025	4433		8082		9194	
Extrap. value:	0.4419		0.8049		0.9187	
Accurate value:	0.44198_5		0.80514		0.91878	

are too unstable to be useful, and the accuracy of the values for $h = 0.1$ are in doubt, so that the theoretical value of $t = 2$ has been used in conjunction with (69) for extrapolation, in this case, rather than (67).

Finally consider three procedures which are more accurate than the Euler method:

A. Procedure (64)

B. Procedure (65), i.e. one step of the iteration (66).

C. Two steps of the iteration (66).

(In practice we should probably iterate until successive iterates differ by less than a specified amount, but from the point of view of error analysis it is instructive to consider the results obtained by using precisely one or two steps of the iterative procedure.) For all three procedures the error is of order h^2, i.e. $q = 2$, and the theoretical value of t is 4 . However we should expect that procedure B will be more accurate A, and C will be somewhat more accurate than B . Some numerical results are given in Table 3. The empirical

Table 3 Results for procedures A, B, C .

$k = 1, x = 2.0$

	A		B		C	
h	f	Diffce.	f	Diffce.	f	Diffce.
0.2	0.747018		0.736165		0.747124	
		-1562		6318		2024
0.1	745456		743483		745100	
		- 561		1021		404
0.05	744895		744404		744696	
		- 190		159		74
0.025	744705		744563		744622	
		- 65		33		14
0.0125	744640		744596		744608	
Extrap. value:	0.744606		0.744605		0.744605	

$k = 4, x = 1.0$

h	f	Diffce.	f	Diffce.	f	Diffce.
0.1	0.810492		0.786988		0.810131	
		3436		15489		4038
0.05	804056		802477		806093	
		1239		2185		782
0.025	805817		804662		805311	
		436		394		137
0.0125	805381		805056		805174	
Extrap. value:	0.80514		0.80514		0.80514	

$k = 4, x = 2.0$

h	f	Diffce.	f	Diffce.	f	Diffce.
0.05	0.918836		unstable		0.919009	
		36				164
0.025	918800		0.918433		0.918845	
		12		313		50
0.0125	918788		918746		0.918795	
Extrap. value:	0.91878		0.91882		0.91878	

value of t is about 3 for procedure A, and 5 for procedures B and C . The results are of course much more accurate than those for the simple Euler procedure. Extrapolation gives remarkably constant results for $k = 1$, and this holds for all values of x up to 2.0, which was as far as the runs were taken. However in the case $k = 4$ the extrapolation is consistent to only five decimals for $x = 1.0$, and instability is starting to affect the fifth decimal place when 2.0 is reached.

5. Further comments on error analysis and error control

We first consider briefly the question of the statistical analysis of round-off error. Suppose that we are solving the integral equation

$$y(x) = g(x) + \int_0^x k(x, t; y(t))\,dt \quad . \tag{70}$$

Assume that, if round-off errors are negligible, the estimates Y_r of $y(x_r)$ are given by

$$Y_r = g_r + h \sum_{s=0}^{r} w_{r,s}\, k(x_r, x_s; Y_s) \quad , \tag{71}$$

where the $w_{r,s}$ are suitable weights in an integration formula such that

$$h \sum_{s=0}^{r} w_{r,s} f_s \approx \int_0^{x_r} f(t)\,dt \quad . \tag{72}$$

Some possible values for $w_{r,s}$ were discussed in §§3, 4, and further possibilities will be discussed in §6 below, but the exact values for the $w_{r,s}$ are not important here. If a round-off error ϵ_r is introduced at the rth step, we denote the resulting estimates of $y(x_r)$ by Y_r^*, so that

$$Y_r^* = g_r + h \sum_{s=0}^{r}{}' \, w_{r,s}\, k(x_r, x_s; Y_s^*) + \epsilon_r \quad . \tag{73}$$

On subtracting (73) from (71) we see that

$$Y_r^* - Y_r = h \sum_{s=0}^{r} w_{r,s} \left(\frac{\partial k}{\partial y}\right)_{r,s} (Y_s^* - Y_s) + \epsilon_r \tag{74}$$

where we assume that the quantities

$$(\partial k/\partial y)_{r,s} = [\partial k(x,t;y(t))/\partial y]_{x=x_r,\ t=x_s}$$

exist, and that terms in $(y-Y_s)^2$ and $(y-Y_s^*)^2$ can be neglected. Since (74) is linear, its solution can be written in the form

$$Y_r^* - Y_r = \sum_{j=0}^{r} d_{rj}\,\epsilon_j\ , \tag{75}$$

where the d_{rj} are suitable coefficients which satisfy equations which can be determined by substituting (75) in (74). These equations turn out to be

$$d_{rj} = h\sum_{s=j}^{r} w_{r,s}\left(\frac{\partial k}{\partial y}\right)_{r,s} d_{sj} + \delta_{rj} \tag{76}$$

where δ_{rj} is the Kronecker delta, $\delta_{rj} = 0\ (r \neq j)$, $1(r = j)$.

The statistical properties of $Y_r^* - Y_r$ can be derived from (75), assuming that the round-off errors ϵ_j are independent of each other. Suppose that the mean and standard deviation of ϵ_j are given by $\mu p(x_j)$ and $\sigma q(x_j)$, where μ, σ are constants, and $p(x)$, $q(x)$ are assumed to be continuous functions of the variable x. These functions depend on the way in which the calculation is performed, for instance whether fixed or floating point working is used. Denote the mean and variance of $Y_r^* - Y_r$ by m_r, v_r, respectively. From (75), since the mean and the variance of the sum of independent random variables is the sum of the means and variances of the individual variables, we see that

$$m_r = \mu\sum_{j=0}^{r} d_{rj}\, p(x_j) \tag{77a}$$

$$v_r = \sigma^2\sum_{j=0}^{r} d_{rj}^2\, q^2(x_j) \tag{77b}$$

An integral equation can be established from which m_r can be deduced. Consider

$$h \sum_{s=0}^{r} w_{r,s} \left(\frac{\partial k}{\partial y}\right)_{r,s} m_s = \mu h \sum_{s=0}^{r} w_{r,s} \left(\frac{\partial k}{\partial y}\right)_{r,s} \sum_{j=0}^{r} d_{rj} \, p(x_j)$$

$$= \mu h \sum_{j=0}^{r} p(x_j) \sum_{s=j}^{r} w_{r,s} \left(\frac{\partial k}{\partial y}\right)_{r,s} d_{sj}$$

$$= \mu \sum_{j=0}^{r} p(x_j) \{ d_{rj} - \delta_{rj} \}$$

$$= m_r - \mu p(x_r) ,$$

where we have used (76), (77a). From this result, and (72), if we let $m(x)$ be the solution of the linear integral equation

(78) $$m(x) = \int_0^x \frac{\partial k(x, t; y(t))}{\partial y} m(t) \, dt + p(x) ,$$

then m_r is given, approximately, by $\mu m(x_r)$. The kernel of the integral equation is precisely the kernel which appeared in the error analyses in §3, for example (46), but of course the nonhomogeneous term in (46) depended on the finite difference formula used to solve the integral equation, whereas the nonhomogeneous term in (78) depends only on the statistical behavior of the round-off error.

An approximate expression for the variance can be obtained in the following way. We introduce the notation

$$\frac{\partial k(x, t; y(t))}{\partial y} = K(x, t) , \quad K_{rs} = K(x_r, x_s) .$$

Then, from (76),

$$d_{rr}(1 - h w_{rr} K_{rr}) = 1 ,$$

$$d_{rj} = h w_{rj} K_{rj} d_{jj} + h \sum_{s=j+1}^{r} w_{rs} K_{rs} d_{sj}, \quad (j < r) .$$

The quantity d_{jj} is unity to within terms of order h. Also, although the coefficients w_{rs} refer to integration from $x = 0$ to $x = x_r$, it will introduce only first-order errors to replace the sum in this equation by an integral. This gives the following result. If $D(x, u)$ is a function which satisfies the equation

$$D(x, u) = K(x, u) + \int_u^x K(x, t) \, D(t, u) \, dt ,$$

then

$$d_{rj} \approx h\, w_{rj}\, D(x_r, x_j), \quad (j < r) \;.$$

The quantity $D(x,u)$ is of course the resolvent of the integral equation

$$y(x) = \int_0^x K(x,t)\, y(t)\, dt + f(x) \quad ,$$

and, in fact,

$$y(x) = f(x) + \int_0^x D(x,u)\, f(u)\, du \;.$$

If we apply these results to (77) we see that

$$m_r = \mu \{d_{rr}\, p(x_r) + h \sum_{j=0}^{r-1} w_{rj}\, D(x_r, x_j)\, p(x_j)\}$$

so that if

$$m(x) = p(x) + \int_0^x D(x,u)\, p(u)\, du \quad ,$$

then $m_r \approx \mu\, m(x_r)$, which is precisely the form obtained from (78) by finding the solution of this equation by means of the resolvent kernel.

We can now deal with the variance. From (77b),

$$v_r = \sigma^2 \{d_{rr}^2\, q^2(x_r) + h^2 \sum_{j=0}^{r-1} w_{rj}^2\, D^2(x_r, x_j)\, q^2(x_j)\} \;.$$

The sum is of the order of h times an integral, so that it can be neglected compared with the first term if h is small. We then have the simple formula:

(79) $$v_r \approx \sigma^2 q^2(x_r) \;.$$

By means of these results we can examine the way in which round-off error depends on the step-length h. The quantity h does not appear explicitly in the expressions we have derived for the mean and the variance. Hence the h-dependence of the error is given by the way in which the error ϵ_r in (73) varies with h. Suppose that the second term on the right of (73) is found by first evaluating the sum and then multiplying by h. Suppose also that the error involved in evaluating $k(x_r, x_s; Y_s^*)$ is independent of h. Then if the step-length is halved, the number of terms in the series is doubled, but the factor h multiplying the series is halved, so that the mean and variance of the statistical error is unchanged. In this case, the mean and variances of the random error will not depend on the step-length. The ϵ_r can of course be determined empirically from (73), so that the h-dependence of the mean and variance of the ϵ_r can be determined experimentally.

The above analysis makes essential use of the fact that there is a term in $y(x)$ outside the integral sign, so that the analysis must be modified when dealing with integral equations of the first kind (§7 below). It is to be expected that the effect of round-off errors will increase as h decreases when solving equations of the first kind, unless special precautions are taken.

At this point it is appropriate to mention the question of ill-conditioning. The equation (70) is said to be ill-conditioned if small changes in the non-homogeneous term $g(x)$ produce large changes in the solution. Suppose that if $g(x)$ is changed to $g(x) + \delta(x)$, the solution changes to $y(x) + \epsilon(x)$. Then

$$y(x) + \epsilon(x) = g(x) + \delta(x) + \int_0^x k(x,t;y(t)+\epsilon(t))\,dt \ .$$

In subtracting (70) we have, approximately,

$$\epsilon(x) = \int_0^x \frac{\partial k(x,t;y(t))}{\partial y}\,\epsilon(t)\,dt + \delta(x) \ . \tag{80}$$

Hence the original equation (70) will be ill-conditioned if the solution of this equation (80) increases much more rapidly with x than the solution of (70). As one would expect, the kernel of (80) is the same as the kernel which appeared in connection with the analysis of truncation error in §3 (for instance in (46)), and in connection with round-off error in (78) above.

We next make a comment on error control. Formulae (49), (50) are reminiscent of predictor-corrector methods for ordinary differential equations. Formula (49) corresponds to the 'predictor' and (50) to the 'corrector'. When dealing with differential equations, predictor-corrector formulae are chosen so that they give a current check on the accuracy of the calculation. This is achieved by arranging that the dominant part of the error per step of the 'predictor' formula is a constant multiple of that for the 'corrector'. Formulae of this type can be obtained for solving nonlinear integral equations by taking advantage of the fact that 'open' and 'closed' integration formulae can be found which have the same form of the error term. Thus consider

(81) $$\int_0^m f(x)\,dx = h\{\tfrac{1}{2}f_0 + \sum_{s=0}^{m-1} f_s + \tfrac{1}{2}f_m\} - \tfrac{1}{12}h^2(f'_m - f'_0) + O(h^3) ,$$

(82) $$\int_0^{2n} f(x)\,dx = 2h\sum_{t=1}^{n} f_{2t-1} + \tfrac{1}{6}h^2(f'_{2n} - f'_0) + O(h^3) ,$$

$$\int_0^{2n+1} f(x)\,dx = h\{\tfrac{1}{4}f_0 + f_1 + \tfrac{7}{4}f_2 + 2\sum_{t=2}^{n} f_{2t}\} + \tfrac{1}{6}h^2(f'_{2n+1} - f'_0) + O(h^3) .$$

Slightly different formulae are required for even and odd r. The coefficients of f_0, f_1, f_2 in the last formula have been chosen so that the form of the error term agrees with that in (82). In order to solve the integral equation (70) we set:

$$Y^{(0)}_{2n} = g_{2n} + 2h\sum_{t=1}^{n} k(x_{2n}, x_{2t-1}; Y_{2t-1}) ,$$

(83) $$Y^{(0)}_{2n+1} = g_{2n+1} + h\{\tfrac{1}{4}k(x_{2n+1}, x_0; Y_0) + k(x_{2n+1}, x_1; Y_1) + \tfrac{7}{4}k(x_{2n+1}, x_2; Y_2) + 2\sum_{t=2}^{n} k(x_{2n+1}, x_{2t}; Y_{2t})\} ,$$

$$Y_{r+1} = g_{r+1} + h\{\tfrac{1}{2}k(x_{r+1}, x_0; Y_0) + \sum_{s=1}^{r} k(x_{r+1}, x_s; Y_s) + \tfrac{1}{2}k(x_{r+1}, x_{r+1}; Y_{r+1})\} .$$

From (70), (81), the exact value of $y(x_{r+1}) = y_{r+1}$ satisfies the equation

$$y_{r+1} = g_{r+1} + h\{\tfrac{1}{2}k(x_{r+1}, x_0; y_0) + \sum_{s=1}^{r} k(x_{r+1}, x_s; y_s) + \tfrac{1}{2}k(x_{r+1}, x_{r+1}; y_{r+1})\} - \tfrac{1}{12}h^2(k'_{r+1} - k'_0) + O(h^3) ,$$

where

$$k' = dk(x, t; y(t))/dt .$$

In subtracting (83) from this expression, and introducing a function $e(t)$ such that $e(x_r) = y_r - Y_r$, it can be shown that

$$(84)\quad y_{r+1} - Y_{r+1} = \int_0^{x_{r+1}} \frac{\partial k(x_{r+1}, t; y(t))}{\partial y} e(t)\,dt - \frac{1}{12} h^2 (k'_{r+1} - k'_0) + O(h^3) \, .$$

In a similar way we can show that, whether r is odd or even

$$y_{r+1} - Y^{(0)}_{r+1} = \int_0^{x_{r+1}} \frac{\partial k(x_{r+1}, t; y(t))}{\partial y} e(t)\,dt + \frac{1}{6} h^2 (k'_{r+1} - k'_0) + O(h^3) \, .$$

Subtraction of these equations gives

$$Y_{r+1} - Y^{(0)}_{r+1} = \frac{1}{4} h^2 (k'_{r+1} - k'_0) + O(h^3) \, .$$

On comparing (84) with (46)-(48), we see that the end-result of the analysis is that the non-homogeneous term in the error integral equation (46), namely (47), can be estimated empirically in the course of the calculation by means of the relation

$$h^2 \psi_3(x_r) \approx -\frac{1}{3}(Y_r - Y^{(0)}_r) \, .$$

Although this formula gives an estimate of the current error, and not the cumulative error, it can be used to control the step length during the course of a calculation, in exactly the same way as error-per-step estimates are used in predictor-corrector formulae for ordinary differential equations.

Of course the above procedure is not the only method that can be invented to give predictor-corrector formulae. If the final accuracy is to be of order h^q, we might prefer to use a formula of accuracy h^{q+2} in the range x_0 to x_{r-p} for some suitable p, so as to eliminate the contribution to the dominant error term from the start of the range of integration, i.e. the term involving k'_0 in the above formulae. Two suitable integration formulae can then be chosen in the range x_{r-p} to x_{r+1}, to give the predictor and corrector formulae.

6. Higher-order procedures

Before considering details, we first of all make the general remark that much insight into methods for the solution of nonlinear equations can be obtained by studying the literature on numerical methods for linear integral equations. This is the reason for including references [4]-[8]. Reference [6] is an excellent elementary introduction.

When discussing the numerical solution of ordinary differential equations, it is not customary to discuss the linear and nonlinear cases separately, since the nonlinear case is not much more difficult than the linear one. It is easy to first develop general methods, and then specialize to the linear case by simply stating that formulae can then be rearranged to avoid iteration, or to make the method more efficient. This point of view does not seem to be adopted in the literature on Volterra integral equations, although many of the methods proposed for linear equations can be generalized, with little trouble, to apply to equations of the form

$$y(x) = F(x, y(x), \int_0^t k(x,t; y(x), y(t))\, dt) .$$

These remarks are not intended to minimize the difficulties which may arise in connection with the existence and uniqueness of the solution of a nonlinear integral equation. In this respect nonlinear equations can be completely different from linear equations. In applications, even if the physical system is determinate, if the mathematical formulation leads to a nonlinear integral equation, this may not possess a unique solution. An interesting example of the non-uniqueness of the solution of a Fredholm integral equation occurs in connection with problems in radiative transfer (see §11 below). On the other hand, if a numerical method can be devised which gives a unique solution for an integral equation, it may be possible to convert this constructive method into an existence and uniqueness proof.

We now consider some possible methods for obtaining solutions of higher-order accuracy for Volterra equations. The most accurate formula developed in §3 used the trapezoidal rule. To obtain increased accuracy we must use a more accurate integration formula. One possibility is the Gregory formula:

$$(85) \qquad \int_0^{x_m} f(x)\, dx = h\{\tfrac{1}{2} f_0 + \sum_{s=1}^{m-1} f_r + \tfrac{1}{2} f_m + \Delta\}$$

where the correction term Δ is given, in terms of forward and backward differences, by

$$\Delta = -(\tfrac{1}{12}\nabla + \tfrac{1}{24}\nabla^2 + \tfrac{19}{720}\nabla^3 + \dots) f_m + (\tfrac{1}{12}\Delta - \tfrac{1}{24}\Delta^2 + \tfrac{19}{720}\Delta^3 - \dots) f_0 .$$

When computing by hand, it may be convenient to use this formula as it stands, including as many differences as are necessary to give the required accuracy. However we shall examine only one method, in which the order of differences is fixed in advance.

If we wish to solve

$$(86)\qquad y(x) = g(x) + \int_0^x k(x,t;g(t))\,dt \ ,$$

using an integration formula of order h^4, we neglect the effect of third and higher-order differences in (85), to obtain

$$(87)\qquad Y_{r+1} = g_{r+1} + W_{r+1} + \frac{3}{8}h\,k(x_{r+1}, x_{r+1};\, Y_{r+1}) \ ,$$

where

$$W_{r+1} = h\sum_{s=0}^{r} a_s\,k(x_{r+1},\, x_s;\, Y_s) \ ,$$

with

$$a_1 = \frac{3}{8},\quad a_2 = a_r = \frac{7}{6},\quad a_3 = a_{r-1} = \frac{23}{24} \ ,$$

$$a_s = 1, \qquad s = 3,\, 4,\, \dots\, r-2 \ .$$

Equation (87) can be solved iteratively for Y_{r+1} . If $Y_{r+1}^{(p)}$ is the pth estimate of Y_{r+1}, then

$$Y_{r+1} - Y_{r+1}^{(p+1)} = h\left(\frac{\partial k}{\partial y}\right)_{r+1}(Y_{r+1} - Y_{r+1}^{(p)}) + O(h^2) \ .$$

If we choose $Y_{r+1}^{(0)} = Y_r$, then, since Y_r and Y_{r+1} differ by order h, Y_{r+1} and $Y_{r+1}^{(p)}$ will differ by h^{p+1} . There would therefore seem to be little point in performing more than three iterations, since the overall procedure is of accuracy h^4 .

A new complication which arises is that in order to secure an h^4 accuracy in Y_1, Y_2, Y_3 it is necessary to devise a special starting procedure. One possibility is the following sequence, which should be self-explanatory:

$$Y_1^{(0)} = g_1 + h\,k(x_1,\, x_0;\, Y_0), \qquad y_1 - Y_1^{(0)} = O(h^2) \ .$$

$$Y_1^{(1)} = g_1 + \frac{1}{2}h\{k(x_1,\, x_0;\, Y_0) + k(x_1,\, x_1;\, Y_1^{(0)})\} \ ,$$

$$y_1 - Y_1^{(1)} = O(h^3) \ .$$

$$Y_2^{(0)} = g_2 + 2h\,k(x_2,\, x_1;\, Y_1^{(1)}), \qquad y_2 - Y_2^{(0)} = O(h^3) \ .$$

$$Y_3^{(0)} = g_3 + \frac{3}{2} h \{k(x_3, x_1; Y_1^{(1)}\} + k(x_3, x_2; Y_2^{(0)})\} ,$$

$$y_3 - Y_3^{(0)} = O(h^3) .$$

$$Y_1 = g_1 + \frac{1}{24} h \{9k(x_1, x_0; Y_0) + 19k(x_1, x_1; Y_1^{(1)})$$

$$-5k(x_1, x_2; Y_2^{(0)}) + k(x_1, x_3; Y_3^{(0)})\} ,$$

$$Y_2 = g_2 + \frac{1}{3} h \{k(x_2, x_0; Y_0) + 4k(x_2, x_1; Y_1) + k(x_2, x_2; Y_2^{(0)})\} ,$$

$$Y_3 = g_3 + \frac{3}{8} h \{k(x_3, x_0; Y_0) + 3k(x_3, x_1; Y_1)$$

$$+ 3k(x_3, x_2; Y_2) + k(x_3, x_3; Y_3^{(0)})\} .$$

The last three formulae give results of accuracy h^4.

Another way in which (85) can be used is to employ the method of deferred correction in which relatively crude estimates of Y_s ($s = 1, 2, \ldots n$) are obtained by neglecting Δ in (85), i.e. by using the methods of §3. The difference correction Δ is computed for $s = 1, 2, \ldots n$ from the crude estimates of Y_s, and the solution is then repeated using the difference corrections. In the general case this would involve the recomputation of the quantities $k(x_r, x_s; Y_s)$ which is a disadvantage of the method, which is not however present if the kernel is of the form $K(x, t)\ F(y(t))$.

Instead of (85), it is possible to use other integration formulae, for instance Simpson's rule. This will not be examined in detail. A special starting procedure will again be necessary. The calculation of Y_r for even and odd values of r will involve slightly different formulae. This usually introduces the minor, though sometimes annoying, difficulty that if we try to pass a smooth curve through the points (x_r, Y_r), the resulting curve will exhibit a small oscillation or ripple due to systematic differences in the values for even and odd ordinates. It is more satisfactory to consider the sets Y_{2s} and Y_{2s-1} ($s = 1, 2, 3, \ldots$) separately. Alternatively, it is possible to alter the sets Y_{2s} and Y_{2s-1} systematically, for instance by examining a difference table of the Y_r, so that the higher-order differences of the modified function are smooth.

A number of papers exist which propose various higher-order difference formulae for solving nonlinear Volterra integral equations, for example [17], [18], the papers in [3] referred to under the heading V in the bibliography, and references given in all these papers.

There are a very large number of possibilities, and a definitive comparative study of the various methods has still to be undertaken.

We have already considered one special starting procedure for producing accurate values of Y_r for small r. If $y(x)$ can be expanded in a Taylor series about the origin, another possibility is to find the coefficients of the Taylor series by repeated differentiation of the integral equation:

$$y^{(n)}(x) = g^{(n)}(x) + \sum_{s=0}^{n-1} \frac{d^{n-1-s}k^{(s)}(x, x; y(x))}{dx^{n-1-s}} + \int_0^x k^{(s)}(x, t; y(t))dt,$$

where

$$k^{(s)}(x, t; y(t)) = \partial^s k(x, t; y(t))/\partial x^s .$$

The coefficients in the Taylor series can be obtained by setting $x = 0$ in these formulae, in which case the integral terms vanish, and $y^{(n)}(0)$ can be found for $n = 0, 1, 2, \ldots$ in succession. Whether this method is practicable will depend on the form of the kernel k. Even if $y(x)$ cannot be expanded as a Taylor series, it may be possible to obtain sufficiently accurate analytical formulae for small x by some approximate procedure. An example is given in §7 below.

If the unknown function $y(x)$ also occurs under the integral sign, for example

$$y(x) = g(x) + \int_0^x k(x, t; y(x), y(t))\, dt ,$$

the finite-difference formulae become

$$Y_{r+1} = g_{r+1} + h \sum_{s=0}^{r+1} w_{r,s}\, k(x_r, x_s; Y_{r+1}, Y_s) , \tag{88}$$

where the $w_{r,s}$ are suitable weight constants. The unknown Y_{r+1} now enters into every single term on the right-hand side. Since each term on the right is multiplied by h, there will in general be no fundamental difficulty in solving this nonlinear equation iteratively for Y_{r+1}, although the iteration procedure may involve an annoying amount of recomputation of the k-functions, unless k has a particularly simple form. Another possibility is to compute the right-hand side for various values of Y_{r+1}, and then use inverse interpolation to find precisely the number which, when substituted in the formula on the right of (88), gives precisely itself as the end-result of the calculation. A method of this type is mentioned at the end of §7 below, in connection with a specific example.

7. Volterra equations of the first kind

An integral equation of the form (86) which has a term $y(x)$ outside the integral sign, is called a Volterra integral equation of the second kind, in contrast to the following equation, which has no term in $y(x)$ outside the integral sign, and is called an equation of the first kind:

$$(89) \qquad \int_0^x k(x,t;\ y(t))\,dt = g(x), \qquad (x \geq 0) .$$

Equations of the second kind are usually easier to solve numerically than equations of the first kind. Consider for example the finite difference replacement (87) for (86). A first approximation can be obtained immediately for Y_{r+1} by simply replacing Y_{r+1} by Y_r in the term containing Y_{r+1} on the right. This approximation can then be improved by iteration. The formula corresponding to (84) for (89) is

$$W_{r+1} + \frac{3}{8} h\, k(x_{r+1}, x_{r+1}; Y_{r+1}) = g_{r+1} .$$

This is not necessarily a well-conditioned equation for Y_{r+1}.

It is instructive to consider the linear case. If the kernel of (86) is of the form

$$(90) \qquad k(x, t;\ y(t)) = K(x,t)\, y(t) ,$$

then, as in (42), the integral equation is replaced by a set of simultaneous linear algebraic equations for which the matrix of coefficients is triangular, with dominant diagonal terms. The set of equations for (89), with kernel of form (90), is

$$\frac{1}{2} K_{r+1,r+1} Y_{r+1} = g_{r+1}/h - \frac{1}{2} K_{r+1,0} Y_0 - \sum_{s=0}^{r} K_{r+1,s} Y_s .$$

This does not necessarily have diagonal dominance. In a sense, the Volterra equation of the second kind is a limiting case of a Volterra equation of the first kind in which the kernel has a delta-function singularity at $x = t$. This argument also leads us to expect that Volterra equations of the first kind in which the kernel is large when $x \approx t$, for example Abel-type equations where the kernel behaves like $(x-t)^{-1/2}$ for t near x, will be amenable to numerical solution. A simple example for which trouble occurs is

$$(91) \qquad \int_0^x (x-t)^{r-1} y(t)\,dt = g(x) , \qquad r = 1, 2, \ldots .$$

The solution of this equation is $y(x) = g^{(r)}(x)/r!$. The kernel is zero when $x = t$. In any event, numerical differentiation tends to be an inaccurate procedure, and this is an indirect indication that numerical difficulties will arise in connection with using (91) to deduce $y(t)$ from a numerical table of $g(x)$. It is instructive to consider the trivial case $r = 1$ of (91) in a little more detail, i.e.

$$\int_0^x y(t)\,dt = g(x) \quad . \tag{92}$$

Using the trapezoidal rule, as in §3, we obtain

$$\frac{1}{2}(Y_0 + Y_1) = g_1 \, ,$$

$$\frac{1}{2}(Y_0 + 2Y_1 + Y_2) = g_2 \, , \quad \text{etc.} \quad .$$

In the first place, this set of equations is not determinate. Suppose that we know that $y_0 = g'(0)$, obtained by taking the derivative of (92), and then setting $x = 0$. In solving the resulting set of difference equations, we find that

$$Y_r = \{2g_r + 4\sum_{s=1}^{r-1} (-1)^s g_{r-s}\}/h + (-1)^r g'(0) \quad . \tag{93}$$

This would not seem to be a very suitable approximation for the exact solution $y(x) = g'(x)$, and in fact formulae based on the trapezoidal rule, as in the above example, do not give satisfactory results for the numerical solution of Volterra equations of the first kind. A much better procedure is to introduce approximate values $Y_{r+1/2}$ for the function-values at half-way points, and write

$$hY_{1/2} = g_1 \, ,$$

$$h(Y_{1/2} + Y_{3/2}) = g_2, \quad \text{etc.} \quad .$$

It is readily seen that then

$$Y_{r+1/2} = (g_{r+1} - g_r)/h \, , \tag{94}$$

which is a reasonable approximation to the exact value $g'(x_{r+1/2})$. In the general case of (89) we should have

$$h\,k(h, \tfrac{1}{2}; Y_{1/2}) = g_1 ,$$

$$h\,\{k(2h, \tfrac{1}{2}h; Y_{1/2}) + k(2h, \tfrac{3}{2}h; Y_{3/2})\} = g_2, \quad \text{etc.} \; .$$

The difference between (93) and (94) is reminiscent of the phenomenon of instability which is well-known in connection with difference methods for solving differential equations. It is found that certain finite difference schemes give results which oscillate wildly, and bear little relation to the desired solution of the equation. Sometimes unstable results are obtained merely because the step-length h is too large, and the instability can be removed merely by reducing h. An example of this type occurred in §4. However the trouble can be more fundamental. (The phenomenon of instability should be distinguished from that of ill-conditioning, mentioned earlier. Ill-conditioning is an inherent property of the original equation. Instability is an undesirable property of the finite-difference scheme.) In the case of differential equations, instability can result if the order of the finite-difference equations is greater than the order of the differential equation, and the extra solutions of the difference equations have undesirable properties. It seems to be difficult to devise a corresponding general theory for integral equations. It would seem that instability troubles will be more serious for Volterra integral equations of the first kind, than for equations of the second kind. The term in $y(x)$ outside the integral sign is a stabilizing factor.

An equation of the first kind can sometimes be reduced to an equation of the second kind by differentiation, and this is in general desirable, when possible. Thus differentiation of (89) gives

$$k(x, x; y(x)) + \int_0^x \frac{\partial k(x,t;y(t))}{\partial x}\, dt = g'(x) \; ,$$

provided that $k(x,x;y(x))$ is not infinite. This is an integral equation of the second kind if $k(x,x;y(x))$ is not zero. It will usually be preferable to solve this equation numerically, rather than (89). If $g(x)$ is given numerically, then the accuracy with which $g'(x)$ can be determined will place an inherent limit on the accuracy of the solution.

An interesting example has been considered by G. F. Miller [16], namely

$$(95) \qquad \int_0^x \frac{y(t)}{\{1+y(x)-y(t)\}^{1/2}}\, dt = x^2, \qquad (x \geq 0) \; .$$

Differentiation gives

$$(96) \qquad y(x) - \tfrac{1}{2}y'(x)\int_0^x \frac{y(t)}{\{1+y(x)-y(t)\}^{3/2}}\,dt = 2x, \qquad (x \geq 0) .$$

It is required to find a real solution of (95), so that the quantity under the square root must be positive, and this implies that

$$(97) \qquad y(x) \geq y(t) - 1, \qquad x \geq t .$$

Hence $y(0)$ cannot be infinite. From (96), $y'(x)$ exists. For small x and t, $y(x) - y(t)$ will be small, so that the integral equation (95) is then, approximately,

$$\int_0^x y(t)\,dt = x^2 ,$$

and $y(x)$ is approximately equal to $2x$ when x is small. This means that the integral in (96) is approximately x^2 when x is small, and we write (96) in the form

$$(98) \qquad \{x^2 - S(x)\}\,y'(x) - 2y(x) = -4x, \qquad x \geq 0 ,$$

where, on using (95), (96),

$$(99) \qquad S(x) = \int_0^x \frac{y(t)\{y(x)-y(t)\}}{\{1+y(x)-y(t)\}^{3/2}} .$$

As a first approximation, (98) gives, on neglecting $S(x)$ and solving the resulting ordinary differential equation,

$$y(x) = 4e^{-2/x}\left\{\int_0^1 \frac{1}{u}\,e^{2/u} + C\right\} ,$$

where C is an arbitrary constant. One interesting feature of this solution is that it tends asymptotically to $2x$ as x tends to zero, whatever the value of the constant C. The solution has an essential singularity at $x = 0$, and in order to fix the solution uniquely some extra condition must be known. This is provided by the physical problem which requires that $y(x)$ must tend to zero as x tends to infinity. Miller has shown that this condition can be applied in an unusual way. From (96) we see that when $y'(x) = 0$ we have $y(x) = 2x$. By differentiating (96) and examining $y''(x)$ we can show that a point where $y'(x) = 0$ is never a point of inflection. Hence, since $y(x)$ is approximately $2x$ when x is small, and tends to zero as x tends to infinity, $y(x)$ has precisely one maximum, and $y(x)$ is never negative. Denote the maximum value of $y(x)$ by m. On considering (97) for large x we see that $m \le 1$. But if $m < 1$

$$x^2 = \int_0^x \frac{y(t)}{\{1+y(x)-y(t)\}^{1/2}}\,dt \le \frac{m}{(1-m)^{1/2}} \int_0^x dt = \frac{mx}{(1-m^2)^{1/2}} .$$

Since this inequality is not true if x is greater than $m/(1-m^2)^{1/2}$, m must be precisely unity. Since $y(x) = 2x$ at the maximum, we see that $y(x) = 1$ at $x = \frac{1}{2}$. Miller now obtains the solution of the integral equation by writing (98) in the form

$$\{x^2 - S_{(r)}(x)\}(y_{(r+1)})' - 2y_{(r+1)} = -4x , \tag{100}$$

where $y_{(r+1)}$ denotes the $(r+1)$th approximation to $y(x)$. $S_{(0)}(x)$ is taken to be the approximation to $S(x)$ obtained by substituting $y(x) = 2x$ in (99). The ordinary differential equation (98) is then solved numerically from $x = \frac{1}{2}$ to $x = 0$, using the initial condition $y(\frac{1}{2}) = 1$. A second approximation $S_{(1)}(x)$ to $S(x)$ is obtained by inserting $y_{(1)}(x)$ in (99), performing the integration numerically, and so on. It is found that this iterative procedure converges quickly, and $y_{(3)}(x)$ is accurate to four decimals.

The solution for $x > \frac{1}{2}$ can be obtained by the method of inverse interpolation mentioned in connection with equations of the second kind at the end of §6. Knowing $y(x_s)$ for $x_s = sh$, $s = 1, 2, \ldots r+1$, $x_r > \frac{1}{2}$, we tabulate numerically the quantity

$$I(\alpha_n) = \int_0^{x_r} \frac{y(t)}{\{1+\alpha_n - y(t)\}^{1/2}}\,dt ,$$

for various guessed values $\alpha_1, \alpha_2, \ldots$ of $y(x_r)$. By inverse interpolation, we then find the value of α_n such that $I(\alpha_n)$ is precisely x_r^2. Details of one method for doing this can be found in [16].

8. Moving boundary problems involving the heat-conduction equation

In physical problems involving a change of phase, for example melting or evaporation, the location of the boundary between the two phases is often unknown. The mathematical solution of such problems requires the determination of the position of a moving boundary or interface. It is possible to obtain a formulation in terms of nonlinear Volterra integral equations. There does not seem to be any fundamental difficulty in solving these integral equations numerically, though little work has been done in this connection. Since moving boundary problems of this type are of current interest, and the integral equation approach seems to be promising, we give a brief discussion of the formulation of the appropriate integral equations for some simple situations.

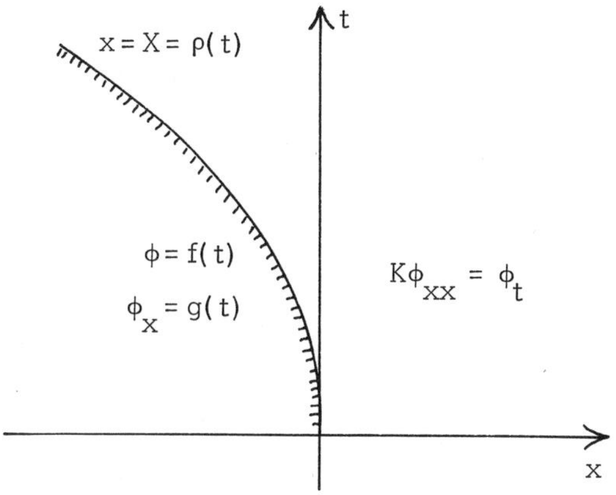

Figure 2

Consider the behavior of a physical quantity ϕ, such as the temperature or the vapor density, in a region $X \leq x < \infty$ where the boundary $x = X$ is a function of time which at present we assume to be known, $X = \rho(t)$.

For simplicity we assume that $\rho(0) = 0$ (see Figure 2). The quantity ϕ satisfies the heat-conduction equation

(101) $$K\phi_{xx} = \phi_t, \qquad t \geq 0, \quad X \leq x < \infty ,$$

with

(102) $$\phi(x, 0) = 0, \qquad 0 \leq x < \infty ,$$

(103) $$\phi = f(t), \quad \phi_x = g(t), \quad \text{on } x = X, \quad t \geq 0 .$$

We use the method of Fourier transforms. Define

$$\Phi(\alpha) = \int_{\rho(t)}^{\infty} \phi e^{i\alpha x} dx .$$

Then

$$\frac{d\Phi}{dt} = -\frac{d\rho}{dt} f(t)\, e^{i\alpha\rho(t)} + \int_{\rho(t)}^{\infty} \frac{\partial\phi}{\partial t} e^{i\alpha x} dx ,$$

$$\int_{\rho(t)}^{\infty} \frac{\partial^2\phi}{\partial x^2} e^{i\alpha x} dx = \{-g(t) + i\alpha f(t)\} e^{i\alpha\rho(t)} - \alpha^2 \Phi .$$

On multiplying the heat-conduction equation (101) by $\exp(i\alpha x)$ and integrating with respect to x from $\rho(t)$ to infinity, we therefore obtain

$$\frac{d\Phi}{dt} + K\alpha^2 \Phi = \{-Kg(t) - \frac{d\rho(t)}{dt} + i\alpha K f(t)\} e^{i\alpha\rho(t)} .$$

The solution of this equation, remembering that $\Phi = 0$ when $t = 0$, is

$$\Phi = e^{-K\alpha^2 t} \int_0^t \{-Kg(\tau) - \frac{d\rho(\tau)}{d\tau} + i\alpha K f(\tau)\} e^{i\alpha\rho(\tau) + K\alpha^2\tau} d\tau .$$

On inverting and interchanging orders of integration, we find that the resulting inner integrals can be evaluated by means of the formula:

$$\int_{-\infty}^{\infty} e^{i\alpha z - \alpha^2 u} d\alpha = \pi^{1/2} u^{-1/2} \exp(-\tfrac{1}{4} z^2/u) ,$$

and the derivative of this formula with respect to z. The final result can be written in the form

$$(104) \quad \phi = \frac{K^{1/2}}{2\pi^{1/2}} \int_0^t \left\{ -\frac{g(\tau)}{(t-\tau)^{1/2}} + f(\tau) \frac{d}{d\tau}\left(\frac{x-\rho(\tau)}{K(t-\tau)^{1/2}} \right) \right\} \exp\left\{ -\frac{(x-\rho(\tau))^2}{4K(t-\tau)} \right\} d\tau .$$

From this result we can deduce that

$$\frac{\partial\phi}{\partial x} = \frac{1}{2\pi^{1/2}} \int_0^t \frac{g(\tau)}{t-\tau} z(x,\tau)\, e^{-z^2(x,\tau)}\, d\tau$$

(105)
$$+ \frac{1}{2(\pi K)^{1/2}} \int_0^t f(\tau) \frac{d}{d\tau}\left\{\frac{1}{(t-\tau)^{1/2}} e^{-z^2(x,\tau)}\right\} d\tau \ .$$

where we have introduced the notation

$$z(x,\tau) = \frac{x-\rho(\tau)}{2K^{1/2}(t-\tau)^{1/2}} \ .$$

These results can be applied directly to the problem of the evaporation of a vapor from a liquid. The vapor lies in $x > X$, and the liquid in $x < X$. The quantity ϕ is the vapor density, and the problem can be formulated in the following way (see [38], p. 16): ϕ satisfies (101),(102) and, instead of (103),

(106)
$$\phi(=f(t)) = 1, \quad \alpha\phi_x(=\alpha g(t)) = d\rho/dt \ ,$$

on $x = X = \rho(t)$, for $t \geq 0$.

By using (106) in conjunction with (104), (105), we can establish two different integral equations for the unknown function $\rho(t)$:

(i) We can let x tend to $\rho(t)+0$ in (104), and set

$$\phi(\rho(t),t) = f(t) = 1, \qquad (t \geq 0) \ .$$

(ii) We can let x tend to $\rho(t)+0$ in (105), and set

(107)
$$(\partial\phi/\partial x)_{x=\rho(t)} = g(t) = \alpha^{-1}\, d\rho/dt, \qquad (t \geq 0) \ .$$

Method (i) leads to a Volterra integral equation of the first kind, and method (ii) gives an equation of the second kind. We establish the integral equation given by method (ii), since integral equations of the second kind are usually more convenient for numerical work. In the usual way, care has to be exercised when taking limits. We have deliberately said that x tends to $\rho(t)+0$, since if we merely set $x = \rho(t)$, or if we take the limit as x tends to $\rho(t)-0$, we obtain different results. This is very clear from the point of view adopted in [38], where the integral equations are established by introducing the heat-potentials of single and double layers. From the present point of view, we establish the limits from first principles.

The first integral on the right of (105) can be written as follows:

$$I = \frac{1}{2\pi^{1/2}} \int_0^t \frac{g(\tau)}{t-\tau}\, z(\rho(t), \tau)\, e^{-z^2(x,\tau)}\, d\tau + \psi(x,t) \tag{108}$$

where

$$\psi(x,t) = \frac{x-\rho(t)}{4(\pi K)^{1/2}} \int_0^t \frac{g(\tau)}{(t-\tau)^{3/2}}\, e^{-z^2(x,\tau)}\, d\tau = \psi_1 + \psi_2 \,, \tag{109}$$

where we split the range of integration into two parts, ψ_1 being the part from $\tau = 0$ to $t-\delta$, and ψ_2 is the part from $\tau = t-\delta$ to t, where δ is a suitable small constant which will be chosen later. On setting $g(\tau) = g(t) + (t-\tau)\, g'(\theta)$, where $\tau < \theta < t$, in the integral ψ_2, we see that

$$\psi_2(x,t) = \frac{\{x-\rho(t)\}}{4(\pi K)^{1/2}} \left\{ g(t) \int_{t-\delta}^{t} \frac{1}{(t-\tau)^{3/2}}\, e^{-z^2(x,\tau)}\, d\tau + O(\delta) \right\} . \tag{110}$$

We now set

$$x = \epsilon + \rho(t)$$

where ϵ is a small constant. Then

$$\{x-\rho(t)\} \int_{t-\delta}^{t} \frac{1}{(t-\tau)^{3/2}}\, e^{-z^2(x,\tau)}\, d\tau$$

$$= \epsilon \int_{t-\delta}^{t} \frac{1}{(t-\tau)^{3/2}} \exp\left\{ -\frac{\epsilon^2}{4K(t-\tau)} \right\} d\tau + O(\epsilon) + O(\delta)$$

$$= 4K^{1/2} \frac{\epsilon}{|\epsilon|} \int_{\frac{|\epsilon|}{2(K\delta)^{1/2}}}^{\infty} e^{-u^2}\, du + O(\epsilon) + O(\delta) \quad . \tag{111}$$

The procedure is now as follows: We choose δ so as to make the terms of order δ in (110), (111) as small as desired. Having fixed δ, we let x tend to $\rho(t) \pm 0$ in (108), i.e. we let $\epsilon \to \pm 0$ in (111). Equations (109)-(111) give

$$\lim_{\epsilon \to \pm 0} \psi(x,t) = \lim_{\epsilon \to \pm 0} \psi_2(x,t) = \left(\lim_{\epsilon \to 0} \frac{\epsilon}{|\epsilon|} \right. \frac{g(t)}{\pi^{1/2}} \int_0^{\infty} e^{-u^2}\, du$$

$$= \pm \frac{1}{2}\, g(t) \quad .$$

We now return to the formulation of the integral equation by method (ii), from (105) and (106). The second integral in (105) can be integrated explicitly since $f(\tau) = 1$. If we then let x tend to $\rho(t) + 0$, we obtain the following integral equation for $\rho(t)$:

$$\frac{d\rho(t)}{dt} = \frac{1}{2(\pi K)^{1/2}} \int_0^t \frac{d\rho(\tau)/d\tau}{(t-\tau)^{3/2}} \left\{\rho(t) - \rho(\tau)\right\} \exp\left\{-\frac{(\rho(t)-\rho(\tau))^2}{4K(t-\tau)}\right\} d\tau$$

(112)

$$- \frac{\alpha}{(\pi K t)^{1/2}} \exp\left\{-\frac{\rho^2(t)}{4Kt}\right\} .$$

This is precisely the integral equation obtained in [38], p. 18, equation (b), by a different method. The equation has in fact an exact solution $\rho = -Ct^{1/2}$, where C is a constant which can be determined by substituting in the integral equation.

Some comments should be made on the above integral equation formulation

(i) In melting and solidification problems there are two media, one in $-\infty < x < \rho(t)$, the other in $\rho(t) < x < \infty$, with

$$\phi = f(t) = 1 \text{ on the interface } x = \rho(t) .$$

The remaining condition across the interface is

(113) $$a_1 g_1(t) - a_2 g_2(t) = d\rho(t)/dt ,$$

where a_1, a_2 are suitable constants, and

$$g_1(t) = (\phi_x)_{x=\rho(t)-0}, \quad g_2(t) = (\phi_x)_{x=\rho(t)+0} .$$

The above method can still be applied. We shall have one integral equation from (105) involving $g_2(t)$ and $\rho(t)$, a second integral equation from the expression analogous to (105) in $-\infty < x < \rho(t)$ involving $g_1(t)$ and $\rho(t)$, and the joining expression (92). However it will not in general be possible to eliminate g_1 and g_2 to obtain a single integral equation for $\rho(t)$. (See [38] §7).

(ii) There is no reason why the transforms should be limited to the Fourier transform in the range $(-\infty, \infty)$. In the problem treated in detail above we could have used a Fourier since a cosine transform in (x_0, ∞) where x_0 is any value of x such that $x_0 < \rho(t)$ in the range of t considered. Similarly, if there had been a solid boundary at $x = d$ on which $\phi_x = 0$, we should have used a Fourier cosine transform in $(-\infty, d)$, or a finite transform in (x_0, d), where x_0 has just been defined.

The integral equations for various other problems are formulated in [38]. The method used in [38], and the above transform method are of course equivalent.

One difficulty appears when we try to solve (112) numerically. In the examples in previous sections, when considering the first step $t = 0$ to h, the contribution from the integral term in the integral equation is small, but this is not true in the present case. This can be seen as follows. The exact solution is of the form $\rho = -Ct^{1/2}$ so that, ignoring a constant multiplying term, the integral gives a contribution

$$\int_0^t \frac{(\sqrt{t}-\sqrt{\tau})}{\tau^{1/2}(t-\tau)^{3/2}} \exp\left\{-\frac{C^2}{4K}\left(\frac{\sqrt{t}-\sqrt{\tau}}{\sqrt{t}+\sqrt{\tau}}\right)\right\} d\tau$$

$$(114) \qquad = \frac{1}{\sqrt{t}} \int_0^{\frac{1}{2}\pi} \sec^2 \tfrac{1}{2}\theta \exp\left\{-\frac{C^2}{4K} \tan^2 \tfrac{1}{2}\theta\right\} d\theta ,$$

where we have used the substitution $\tau = t\cos^2\theta$. This result confirms that the exact solution is of the form $\rho = -Ct^{1/2}$. The integral (114) can be expressed in terms of the error function by means of an obvious substitution and a transcendental equation for the constant C is obtained on substituting the result in (112).

The same starting difficulty for a numerical solution, namely that the integral term is not negligible for small t, will occur in all problems of this type. Fortunately, in more complicated cases, it usually happens that the solution for small t can be approximated analytically. For example, in the above case, if there is a fixed boundary at $x = d$, it is clear physically that for small t the solution will behave like the known exact solution for the case where the medium extends to infinity. If necessary this first approximation for small t can be improved analytically, by iteration or by substituting a series for f in terms of powers of $t^{1/2}$ in the integral equation. When an approximation is known for small t, there is little difficulty in extending the solution to larger values of t by straightforward numerical methods.

A different kind of integral equation formulation for problems involving moving boundaries has been proposed by Boley [36]. In the problem considered at the beginning of this section, Boley would assume that the vapor filled the region $x_0 < x < \infty$, where x_0 is some constant such that $x_0 < \rho(t)$ for the range of t considered. (x_0 may be minus infinity). A fictitious (unknown) vapor density, $\phi = F(t)$, is maintained on the new fixed boundary $x = x_0$. The conditions (106) are then imposed on $x = \rho(t)$, to give two integral equations for $F(t)$ and $\rho(t)$. It is not completely clear how one would justify the existence of a function $F(t)$ which will give the required values of ϕ and ϕ_x on the moving boundary, although the method works, and $F(t)$ can be constructed explicitly, in simple cases which have an analytical solution. Many of the remarks made by Boley concerning the numerical solution of his integral equations are relevant to the numerical solution of the more usual type of equation considered earlier in this section.

Instead of using a transform in the space variable to establish the integral equation, as we did at the beginning of this section, it is possible to use a Laplace transform in the time, as in [37]. The reference [39] has been included mainly for historical reasons.

9. The numerical solution of Fredholm equations by finite differences

Consider the Fredholm equation

$$y(x) + \int_0^a k(x,t;y(t))\,dt = g(x), \quad 0 \le x \le a. \tag{115}$$

If the kernel k is such that the integral can be evaluated efficiently by Simpson's rule, we can replace (115) approximately by

$$Y_r + h\sum_{s=0}^{2n} w_s\, k(x_r, x_s; Y_s) = g_r, \quad r = 0, 1, \ldots 2n, \tag{116}$$

where $x_r = rh$, $h = a/2n$, Y_r is an approximation to $y(x_r)$, $w_0 = w_{2n} = \frac{1}{3}$, and

$$w_{2m} = \tfrac{2}{3}, \quad m = 1, 2, \ldots, n-1, \qquad w_{2m-1} = \tfrac{4}{3}, \quad m = 1, 2, \ldots, n.$$

Equations (116) are a system of $2n+1$ nonlinear simultaneous algebraic equations in $2n+1$ unknowns Y_r. Methods for the solution of systems of this type by iteration are examined in §10 below.

Of course any suitable integration formula will give rise to a similar set of nonlinear equations. If we use the Gregory formula (85), this gives

$$Y_r + h\sum_{s=0}^{N} v_s\, k(x_r, x_s; Y_s) + \Delta_r = g_r, \quad r = 0, 1, \ldots N, \tag{117}$$

where $v_0 = v_N = \frac{1}{2}$, $v_s = 1$ $(s = 1, 2, \ldots N-1)$. The quantity Δ is the difference correction given by the equation following (85). The difference correction can be used in one of two ways:

(i) Differences above a certain order can be neglected. The differences which are retained are expressed in terms of function values. Thus if we keep differences of order three, the error in the integration formula is of order h^4, and we obtain a set of algebraic equations of type (117) in which Δ_r does not appear, but now (compare (79)):

$$v_0 = v_N = \tfrac{3}{8}, \quad v_1 = v_{N-1} = \tfrac{7}{6}, \quad v_2 = v_{N-2} = \tfrac{23}{24},$$

$$v_s = 1, \quad s = 3, 4, \ldots N-3 .$$

(ii) We can use the method of deferred corrections, in which the equations (117) are first solved neglecting Δ_r altogether, to give say $Y_r^{(1)}$. Then the Δ_r are estimated, using the expression for Δ following (85), and the $Y_r^{(1)}$ just found. Second estimates $Y_r^{(2)}$ are then derived, using (117) and the Δ_r which have just been found, and so on. This procedure can be rapidly convergent and efficient in certain cases. A clear exposition for the case of linear equations is given in [6].

Still another possibility is to use Gaussian integration formulae. (See for example [49], and other references to Nystrom's papers given in [49].) This can give accurate results with a small amount of computation, but it is usually difficult to check the accuracy of the results.

If the solution or one of its derivatives has a known type of singularity, which may well happen at the end-points of the range of integration, it is sometimes desirable to use special integration formulae to take care of this. An example occurs in §10.

Equation (115) is a Fredholm equation of the second kind. If no term in $y(x)$ occurs outside the integral sign, the equation is said to be of the first kind, for example

$$\int_0^a k(x,t;y(t))\,dt = g(x), \quad (0 \le x \le a) .$$

Fredholm equations of the first kind which possess solutions invariably have a singular kernel, i.e. the range of integration is infinite, or the kernel is infinite when $x = t$. In either case it is necessary to use special integration formulae to deal with the singular nature of the kernel. An example of special integration formulae in connection with a Fredholm equation of the second kind with singular kernel will be considered in §14.

We next consider error analysis for the above type of method. Suppose that an integration formula is used with error of order h^2, so that

$$\int_0^a f(x)\,dx = h \sum_{s=0}^{N} u_s f_s + Ch^q + O(h^{q+1}) \quad .$$

The integral equation (115) is replaced by

(118) $$Y_r + h \sum_{s=0}^{N} u_s k(x_r, x_s; Y_s) = g_r, \qquad v = 0, 1, \ldots N \; .$$

From (115) we have also, to order h^q,

$$y_r + h \sum_{s=0}^{N} u_s k(x_r, x_s; y_s) + C_r h^q = g_r, \qquad r = 0, 1, \ldots N \; .$$

Subtraction of these equations gives, to order h^q,

$$y_r - Y_r + h \sum_{s=0}^{N} u_s \left(\frac{\partial k}{\partial y} \right)_{r,s} (y_r - Y_r) = - C_r h^q \; ,$$

where

$$(\partial k / \partial y)_{r,s} = [\, \partial k(x, t; y(t)) / \partial y]_{x=x_r, t=x_s} \; .$$

Hence if $e(x)$ is the solution of the linear integral equation

(119) $$e(x) + \int_0^a \frac{\partial k(x, t; y(t))}{\partial y} e(t)\, dt = -C(x) \; ,$$

where $C(x)$ is a function such that $C(x_r) = C_r$, then

(120) $$y_r - Y_r \approx h^q e(x_r) \quad .$$

Since $e(x)$ is of order unity, this means that the truncation error is of order h^q, i.e. it is of the same order as the error in the integration formula.

In numerical work, if we choose a given h and perform calculations for intervals of h, $2h$, $4h$, then an error law like (120) leads to Aitken's extrapolation formula (67). It is also possible to check whether the expirical value of the quantity t defined in (68) agrees with the theoretical value. If the empirical value is much less than the theoretical, this means that the assumptions underlying the theoretical treatment are not valid, and usually it is desirable to modify the method of calculation. An illustration is given in §11.

In practice the quantities Y_r satisfying (118) cannot be calculated exactly. Suppose that the quantities that are in fact calculated are denoted by Y_r^*, and that, exactly,

$$Y_r^* + h \sum_{s=0}^{N} u_s \, k(x_r, x_s; Y_s^*) = g_r + \epsilon_r, \quad r = 0, 1, \ldots N,$$

where the ϵ_r occur because of round-off, or simply because the equations (118) have not been solved exactly. Then

$$(121) \quad Y_r - Y_r^* + h \sum_{s=0}^{N} u_s \left(\frac{\partial k}{\partial y} \right)_{r,s} (Y_s - Y_s^*) = -\epsilon_r, \quad r = 0, 1, \ldots N.$$

Suppose that the mean values of the ϵ_r are given by μp_r. Denote the mean value of $Y_r - Y_r^*$ by m_r. Suppose that $m(x)$ is a solution of the linear integral equation

$$(122) \qquad m(x) + \int_0^a \frac{\partial k(x,t; y(t))}{\partial y} m(t)\, dt = -p(x),$$

where $p(x)$ is a function such that $p(x_r) = p_r$. Then an estimate of m_r is given by

$$m_r \approx \mu m(x_r).$$

The kernels of the integral equations (119) and (122) are the same.

The variance can be examined by a method analogous to that used to obtain the result (79) for the Volterra equation of the second kind in §5. We invert the equations (121) to obtain, say,

$$Y_r - Y_r^* = -\sum_{s=0}^{N} A_{rs} \epsilon_s .$$

The constants A_{rs} can be expressed in terms of the resolvent kernel of a linear Fredholm integral equation of the second kind with the same kernel as (122). There are now two difficulties which did not appear in the Volterra case. These are due to the fact that the Y_r^* are obtained by solving a set of $N+1$ simultaneous integral equations in $N+1$ unknowns.

(i) It is not necessarily true that the ϵ_s are random and independent.

(ii) The way in which the statistical properties of the ϵ_s depend on N (and therefore h) is not clear.

Of course the properties of the ϵ_s can be investigated experimentally. The subject requires further work.

10. Iterative methods for Fredholm equations

We can distinguish between two methods of approach to the study of iterative methods for the solution of nonlinear integral equations. Iterative procedures can be examined for general nonlinear operators, and then nonlinear integral operators can be considered as a special case. This mathematically attractive point of view is adopted in most of the papers in this symposium. An alternative approach is to examine the methods which are available for the solution of algebraic and transcendental equations of the form $f(y) = 0$, where y is an ordinary real or complex variable, and then consider whether these special methods can be generalized to provide practical procedures for solving nonlinear integral equations. This simple-minded approach is the one adopted here.

There are two iterative methods which are commonly used to solve algebraic and transcendental equations of the form $f(y) = 0$:

(i) Suppose that the equation can be written in the form:

$$y = F(y) \quad . \tag{123}$$

An iterative procedure is obtained by writing

$$y_{r+1} = F(y_r) \quad , \tag{124}$$

where the iteration is started by guessing a first approximation to y_0 which is as close as possible to the required root.

(ii) The Newton-Raphson method: If Y is an approximate root, we suppose that the exact root is given by $y = Y + h$, where h is small. Then

$$f(Y+h) = 0 = f(Y) + h\, f'(Y) + O(h^2) \quad ,$$

and, approximately,

$$h \approx -f(Y)/f'(Y) \quad .$$

This leads to the iterative procedure

$$y_{r+1} = y_r - \frac{f(y_r)}{f'(y_r)} \quad . \tag{125}$$

The method is essentially linearization in h, neglecting terms of order h^2 .

If the exact answer to a problem is given by, say, y, and an iterative procedure yields a sequence $y_1, y_2, \ldots$, and if

$$y - y_r \approx a_k(y - y_{r-1})^k, \quad a_k \neq 0 \quad , \tag{126}$$

where k is a constant independent of r, then k is called the order of the iterative procedure. By subtracting (124) from (123) we see that

(127) $$y - y_{r+1} \approx F'(y)\ (y - y_r) \ ,$$

so that method (i) is first-order. From (125),

$$y - y_{r+1} \approx \tfrac{1}{2}(y - y_r)^2\ f''(y)/f'(y) \ ,$$

so that the Newton-Raphson procedure is second-order.

The nature of the convergence of first- and second-order procedures is completely different. For a first-order procedure, repeated application of (126) gives

$$y - y_r \approx a_1^r(y - y_0) \ .$$

Hence the procedure is:

(128) convergent if $a_1 < 1$, divergent if $a_1 > 1$.

On the other hand, for a second-order procedure ($a_2 \neq 0$):

$$y - y_1 \approx a_2(y - y_0)^2, \quad y - y_2 \approx a_2^3\ (y - y_0)^4 \ ,$$

$$y - y_r \approx \{a_2(y - y_0)\}^{2^r}/a_2 \ ,$$

and the procedure is always convergent, whatever the value of a_2, provided that the initial guess y_0 is chosen sufficiently near to the exact result y, so that $a_2(y-y_0)$ is less than unity.

The higher the order of an iterative procedure, the more rapid the convergence. A second-order procedure eventually converges extremely rapidly, for sufficiently large r. The main difficulty in this connection is to choose y_0 sufficiently near to y, to start with. A first-order procedure, on the other hand, may converge too slowly for practical purposes, or it may diverge for any initial estimate y_0. In the case of the simple iterative method (i) above there are several remedies that can be tried:

(a) An elementary point is that often there are many ways of arranging the equation $f(y) = 0$ in the form $y = F(y)$. Thus if we wish to solve the quadratic equation $y^2 + ay + b = 0$, we can rearrange this as

(129a) $$y = (-ay - b)^{1/2} \ ,$$

(129b) $$y = -(y^2 + b)/a \ ,$$

(129c) $$y = -b/(y + a) \ .$$

Each of these gives rise to an iterative procedure. One tries to select the rearrangement of the original equation which gives most rapid convergence to the required root.

(b) If the equation $f(y) = 0$ can be written in the form $y = F(y)$ then we can also write

$$y = (1-c)\,y + c\,F(y) \tag{130}$$

where c is an arbitrary constant which is at our disposal. This gives the iterative procedure

$$y_{r+1} = (1-c)\,y_r + c\,F(y_r) \quad . \tag{131}$$

If we write $y^*_{r+1} = F(y_r)$, then this equation is

$$y_{r+1} = (1-c)\,y_r + c\,y^*_{r+1}$$

which explains the name 'interpolated iteration' which is sometimes used to describe this procedure. The rate of convergence is governed by the size of the derivative of the right-hand side of (130), namely

$$(1-c) + c\,F'(y)$$

which should be as small as possible. In fact the ideal value of this quantity is zero, which gives

$$c = 1/(1-F'(y)) \quad .$$

Substitution in (131) gives

$$y_{r+1} = y_r - \frac{y_r - F(y_r)}{1-F'(y)} \quad .$$

In practice, the best estimate of $F'(y)$ at any stage is given by $F'(y_r)$, and we see that we have been led back to the Newton-Raphson method applied to the equation $y - F(y) = 0$. The point is essentially that in some types of calculation it may be inconvenient to calculate derivatives so as to use the Newton-Raphson method proper, but it may be possible to estimate the optimum value of the constant c in (131). The resulting iterative procedure will still, in general, be first-order, but the convergence may be much faster than in the original method, where $c = 1$. Also the modified method may converge even if the original method diverges.

(c) The rate of convergence of a first-order procedure can be increased by using Aitken's extrapolation formula which was discussed in a different connection in (67) above. We have

$$y - y_r \approx a_1(y - y_{r-1}) \quad ,$$

$$y - y_{r-1} \approx a_1(y - y_{r-2}) \quad .$$

If we eliminate a_1 from these equations and rearrange, we find that

$$(132) \qquad y \approx y_r - \frac{(y_r - y_{r-1})^2}{y_r - 2y_{r-1} + y_{r-2}} .$$

Once the elementary first-order procedure starts to converge, if we compute y_0, y_1, y_2 and then use (132) to estimate y, taking this value as a new y_0, and so on, the rate of convergence is second-order. In effect the first-order procedure is turned into a second-order one.

Although integral equations have been hardly mentioned so far in this section, the above summary of methods is directly relevant to the numerical solution of nonlinear Fredholm integral equations. Most of the methods used in practice to solve Fredholm equations are generalizations of those given above for algebraic equations. As a simple example, consider

$$(133) \qquad y(x) = \int_a^b k(x,t;y(t))\,dt + f(x) .$$

The analogue of the simple iterative procedure (i), equation (124), is given by

$$(134) \qquad y_{r+1}(x) = \int_a^b k(x,t;y_r(t))\,dt + f(x) .$$

Following the train of thought suggested by comment (a), if the dominant part of the kernel is given by an expression which is linear in y, say $m(x,t)\,y(t)$, then better convergence will be achieved by writing

$$y_{r+1}(x) - \int_a^b m(x,t)\,y_{r+1}(t)\,dt = \int_a^b \{k(x,t;y_r(t)) - m(x,t)\,y_r(t)\}\,dt + f(x) ,$$

and it may be worthwhile to do this, even though it is necessary to solve a Fredholm equation at each stage of the iteration. The method of interpolated iteration outlined in (b) above is applicable to the procedure (134) in an obvious way, and we need not go into detail.

The main formula for investigating the convergence of (134) is obtained by subtracting (134) from (133) which gives, approximately,

$$(135) \qquad y(x) - y_{r+1}(x) = \int_a^b \frac{\partial k(x,t;y(t))}{\partial y(t)} \{y(t) - y_r(t)\}\,dt .$$

If

$$|y(x) - y_r(x)| \leq \delta_r, \qquad |\partial k(x,t;y(t)/\partial y(t)| \leq N ,$$

then

$$\delta_{r+1} \leq (b-a) N \delta_r \leq \{(b-a) N\}^{r+1} \delta_0 ,$$

so that a sufficient condition for convergence is that $(b-a) N < 1$. However this is by no means a necessary condition, and for error estimation it is more satisfactory to proceed in the following way.

We assume that the kernel $\partial k(x,t;y(t))/\partial y(t)$ is such that an arbitrary function can be expanded in a series, in terms of the eigenfunctions ϕ_s defined by the equation

(136) $$\lambda_s \phi_s(x) = \int_a^b \frac{\partial k(x,t;y(t))}{\partial y(t)} \phi_s(t)\, dt ,$$

where λ_s is the eigenvalue corresponding to ϕ_s . Since the kernel is in general unsymmetric, the eigenvalues may be complex. We set

$$y(t) - y_0(t) = \sum_{s=1}^{\infty} a_s \phi_s(t) .$$

Repeated application of (135) gives

(137) $$y(t) - y_r(t) = \sum_{s=1}^{\infty} a_s \lambda_s^r \phi_s(t) .$$

If we define

$$\rho = \max_s |\lambda_s| ,$$

we see that the procedure is:

(138) convergent if $\rho < 1$, divergent if $\rho > 1$.

This result is the analogue of (128) for algebraic equations.

If there is a real eigenvalue λ_1 with maximum modulus, then (137) gives, for large r ,

(139) $$y(t) - y_r(t) \approx a_1 \lambda_1^r \phi_1(t) \approx \lambda_1 \{y(t) - y_{r-1}(t)\} .$$

The theory leading to (132) applies, and we can use Aitken's extrapolation formula. However in general if the original integral equation is nonlinear, the equation (136) will have complex conjugate eigenvalues of largest modulus. Instead of (139) we must write (assuming that $y(t)$ and $y_r(t)$ are real):

$$(140) \qquad \begin{cases} y(t) - y_{r-2}(t) \approx u(t) + \bar{u}(t) , \\ y(t) - y_{r-1}(t) \approx \lambda_1 u(t) + \bar{\lambda}_1 \bar{u}(t) , \\ y(t) - y_r(t) \approx \lambda_1^2 u(t) + \bar{\lambda}_1^2 \bar{u}(t) . \end{cases}$$

Suppose that λ_1 is the solution of the quadratic equation

$$\lambda^2 + \alpha\lambda + \beta = 0 ,$$

where α, β are real constants which we wish to determine. From (140), this gives

$$(141a) \qquad (y - y_r) + \alpha(y - y_{r-1}) + \beta(y - y_{r-2}) \approx 0 ,$$

i.e.

$$(141b) \qquad y \approx y_r - \frac{\alpha(y_r - y_{r-1}) + \beta(y_r - y_{r-2})}{1 + \alpha + \beta} .$$

In order to find α, β we note that, by writing down (141a) with $r+1$ in place of r, and subtracting the two equations, using the notation $\Delta y_r = y_{r+1} - y_r$,

$$\Delta y_r + \alpha\Delta y_{r-1} + \beta\Delta y_{r-2} \approx 0 .$$

Similarly

$$\Delta y_{r+1} + \alpha\Delta y_r + \beta\Delta y_{r-1} \approx 0 .$$

Hence

$$(142) \qquad \beta = \frac{D_r}{D_{r-1}} , \quad \text{where} \quad D_r = \Delta y_r^2 - \Delta y_{r+1}\, \Delta y_{r-1} ,$$

and, when β is known,

$$(143) \qquad \alpha = - (\Delta y_{r+1} + \beta\Delta y_{r-1}) / \Delta y_r .$$

The numerical procedure is therefore as follows: We form the quantities D_r/D_{r-1} for $r = 2, 3, \ldots$. If these are approximately constant then the assumptions underlying the analysis can be assumed to be valid. We can then compute α for $r = 2, 3, \ldots$, checking that these are also approximately constant. Finally, when α and β have been estimated, the extrapolated value of y is found from (141). A numerical example is given in §11. This extrapolation procedure is well-known in connection with the numerical determination of the complex eigenvalues of a matrix.

If we consider the equation

$$u = \lambda K u \tag{144}$$

where K is a nonlinear operator, and λ is a given parameter, the simple iterative procedure can be written

$$u_{r+1} = \lambda K u_r \ . \tag{145}$$

In general this will converge for small λ and diverge for large λ. Bueckner [44] has indicated that the following procedure may converge with satisfactory rapidity even though the simple iterative procedure diverges or converges very slowly:

$$u_{r+1} = \frac{(u_r, Ku_r)}{(Ku_r, Ku_r)} Ku_r \tag{146}$$

It is assumed that u is an element in a Hilbert space, with an inner product (u, v). The conditions required of the operator K are specified in detail in [44]. When using (146), we start off by choosing a suitable function for u_0, and then iterate until convergence is attained. The value of λ corresponding to the solution which has been obtained, is then deduced. If the solution corresponding to a given λ is required, it is necessary to find various solutions by the procedure just described, starting from different functions u_0, and then use inverse interpolation. The method (146) has been applied to Nekrasov's integral equation

$$\theta(x) = \lambda \int_0^{\pi} L(x,t) \frac{\sin \theta(t)}{1 + 3\lambda \int_0^{t} \sin\theta(s)\,ds}\, dt \ , \tag{147}$$

where

$$L(x,t) = \frac{2}{\pi} \sum_{n=1}^{\infty} \frac{1}{n} \sin nx \sin nt = \frac{1}{\pi} \log \left| \frac{\sin \frac{1}{2}(x+t)}{\sin \frac{1}{2}(x-t)} \right| \ .$$

This equation has been discussed from a general point of view in [81]. If we set

$$u(x) = \lambda \sin \theta(x) \ ,$$

then (147) becomes

$$u(x) = \lambda \sin \int_0^{\pi} L(x,t) \frac{u(t)}{1 + 3\int_0^t u(s)\,ds}\, dt .$$

If this is identified with (144) it is found that the operator K has the properties required for the iterative procedure (146). Numerical experiments were carried out, starting with $u_0 = \alpha \sin x$, for both positive and negative α. For small α it is clear that λ will be found to be nearly equal to unity. The iterative procedure (146) was satisfactory for $\lambda = 3$ which was the largest value of λ tried. The method (146) was much more satisfactory than the simple iteration (145).

If the obvious iterative methods fail, we can sometimes fall back on the old-fashioned method of false position: If we wish to solve

$$y = Ky + f ,$$

where K is a nonlinear integral operator, then choose two trial functions y_1 and y_2, and form

$$Y_1 = Ky_1 + f, \quad Y_2 = Ky_2 + f .$$

A new approximation Y to the exact solution is given by assuming that

(148) $$\frac{Y - Y_1}{Y - y_1} = \frac{Y - Y_2}{Y - y_2} ,$$

(149) $$Y = Y_2 - \frac{(Y_1 - Y_2)(y_2 - Y_2)}{(y_1 - Y_1) - (y_2 - Y_2)} .$$

If we take $y_2 = Y_1$, then y_1, Y_1, Y_2 give a sequence of successive iterates corresponding to y_{r-2}, y_{r-1}, y_r in our discussion of the iterative method (i), and (149) is Aitken's extrapolation formula (132). Equation (148) is effectively linear inverse interpolation, and the method can be improved by using more complicated inverse interpolation formulae.

We next consider the Newton-Raphson method for solving the integral equation (133). We set

$$y(x) = y_r(x) + h_{r+1}(x) .$$

Then (133) gives

$$y_r(x) + h_{r+1}(x) + \int_a^b k(x,t; y_r(t) + h_{r+1}(t))\, dt = f(x), \quad a \le x \le b .$$

On expanding by Taylor series, and neglecting second-order terms, we obtain the following equation for h_{r+1}, since y_r is assumed known:

$$h_{r+1}(x) + \int_a^b \frac{\partial k(x,t;y_r(t))}{\partial y_r(t)} h_{r+1}(t)\,dt$$

$$= f(x) - y_r(x) - \int_a^b k(x,t;y_r(t))\,dt .$$

This means that at each stage of the iteration it is necessary to solve a linear Fredholm integral equation, i.e. in practice, a set of simultaneous linear algebraic equations. The labor of doing this may be compensated by the rapid convergence of the Newton process, when one is near the required solution. Also the method always converges if the initial guess is sufficiently close to the required solution. Newton's method is treated in some detail in the paper by Dr. R. H. Moore in this volume, and will not be considered further here.

It is of course difficult to give any general rule concerning the 'best' iterative method, since so much depends on the specific form of the integral equation. The author's experience has been that a simple iterative procedure should not be dismissed merely because a first attempt produces divergent results. This remark is necessary because one is tempted to think that more sophisticated methods will necessarily be more effective in practice. The natural tendency is to try to devise clever methods before exploiting fully the possibilities of the obvious simple methods.

11. The numerical solution of the H-equation by simple iterative procedures

In order to illustrate some of the ideas outlined in the last section, we consider briefly some numerical aspects of a simple nonlinear integral equation which arises in radiative transfer. The paper of Dr. T. W. Mullikin, in this volume, is devoted to more general equations of this type. Dr. Mullikin makes some interesting comments on the numerical solution of these equations, especially in connection with the uniqueness of solutions.

The H-equation of Ambartsumian-Chandrasekhar is given by

$$H(x) = 1 + xH(x) \int_0^1 \frac{\Psi(t)\,H(t)}{x+t}\,dt , \tag{150}$$

where $\Psi(t)$ is a known real function, usually of simple form. It was the H-equation that prompted Chandrasekhar's remark that "fortunately the integral equation is nonlinear".

Equation (150) can be written in the form

$$H(x) = 1 + \tfrac{1}{2} H(x) \int_0^1 \Psi(t)\, H(t)\, dt + \tfrac{1}{2} H(x) \int_0^1 \frac{x-t}{x+t}\, \Psi(t)\, H(t)\, dt .$$

If we multiply by $\Psi(x)$ and integrate with respect to x, the last double integral vanishes identically, since the integrand is asymmetric in x and t, and we see that

$$X^2 - 2X + 2\lambda = 0 ,$$

where

$$X = \int_0^1 \Psi(x)\, H(x)\, dx, \quad \lambda = \int_0^1 \Psi(x)\, dx . \tag{151}$$

On solving the quadratic, choosing the solution which tends to zero as Ψ tends to zero, we find

$$\int_0^1 \Psi(x)\, H(x)\, dx = 1 - (1-2\lambda)^{1/2} . \tag{152}$$

This equation shows that a necessary condition for H to be real is $\lambda \leq \frac{1}{2}$. Also, on writing

$$\frac{x}{x+t} = 1 - \frac{t}{x+t}$$

in (150), and using (152), we see that an alternative form of the integral equation (150) is given by

$$(1-2\lambda)^{1/2} H(x) = 1 - H(x) \int_0^1 \frac{t\Psi(t)\, H(t)}{x+t}\, dt . \tag{153}$$

We proceed to examine straightforward iterative formulae for the solution of (150), (153), analogous to (124) for solution of the algebraic equation (123). As noted in the last section (for example, in connection with equations (129)) there are many possible iterative formulae, depending on the way in which the equation is arranged. To emphasize this point, we write out some of the possibilities. Denote the rth approximation to $H(x)$ by $H_r(x)$, and set

$$G_r(x) = x \int_0^1 \frac{\Psi(t)\, H_r(t)}{x+t}\, dt, \quad J_r(x) = \int_0^1 \frac{t\Psi(t)\, H_r(t)}{x+t}\, dt . \tag{154}$$

In order to solve (150) by an iterative procedure, we can replace H by either H_r or H_{r+1} in any way which seems convenient. It is natural to try first of all to obtain an algebraic expression giving H_{r+1} directly in terms of H_r. This means that we must not insert H_{r+1} under the integral sign since otherwise it is necessary to solve an integral equation for H_{r+1}. (It may be desirable to do this in more complicated cases, but this is not necessary here). We are left with six obvious possibilities which are listed below, using the notation (154). The equations on the left are derived from (150), and those on the right from (153):

(155a) $H_{r+1} = 1 + H_r G_r, \qquad (1-2\lambda)^{1/2} H_{r+1} = 1 - H_r J_r,$

(155b) $H_{r+1} = 1 + H_{r+1} G_r, \qquad (1-2\lambda)^{1/2} H_{r+1} = 1 - H_{r+1} J_r,$

(155c) $H_r = 1 + H_{r+1} G_r, \qquad (1-2\lambda)^{1/2} H_r = 1 - H_{r+1} J_r.$

In order to choose between these various possibilities, we first of all decide to ignore the second equation in (155a), and the first equation in (155c) since these are clearly not suitable for λ nearly equal to one-half, and x nearly equal to zero, respectively. There seems to be no very obvious reason for preferring any one of the four remaining procedures. We shall proceed empirically by trying one of these methods.

We present some numerical results obtained by using the second equation in (155b) with $\Psi(t)$ = constant = λ, where this λ is the same as the λ defined in (151). In view of (152) we must have $\lambda \leq \frac{1}{2}$. Empirically it is found that the most troublesome case is $\lambda = \frac{1}{2}$, as we should expect, and we give results only for this case. The second equation in (155b) then gives

(156)
$$H_{r+1}(x) = \left\{ \frac{1}{2} \int_0^1 \frac{t H_r(t)}{x+t} dt \right\}^{-1} .$$

Following the method discussed in §9, the integral is approximated by Simpson's rule, using $2n$ subdivisions of the range of integration. Although we know that $H(0) = 1$ (e.g. from (150)), this was not used during the calculation, since this provides a check on the numerical procedure, which should produce this result.

As an example of the convergence of the procedure, we give in Table 4 the values of $H_r(x)$ at $x = 1.0$ for two subdivisions of the interval ($\underline{n} = 1$), starting with $H_0(x) = 1$. The values of H_r do not vary regularly with r which suggests that the maximum eigenvalues of the error integral equation are complex conjugate, in which case the analysis given in connection with (140), (141) will apply. This is confirmed by computing the empirical values of β and α, defined in (142), (143). The results given in Table 4 show that the eigenvalues of largest modulus are dominant after about five iterations. They are given by the quadratic $\lambda^2 + 0.80\lambda + 0.23 = 0$ i.e. $\lambda = 0.40 \pm 0.26i$. The extrapolation formula (141b) could be used with confidence to reduce the number of iterations required for convergence.

Table 4. Illustration of convergence of iterative procedure

$$\Delta H_r = H_{r+1} - H_r, \quad D_r = (\Delta H_r)^2 - \Delta H_{r+1}\Delta H_{r-1},$$

$$\beta_r = D_r / D_{r-1}, \quad \alpha_r = -(\Delta H_{r+1} + \beta_r \Delta H_{r-1})/\Delta H_r .$$

r	H_r	ΔH_r	β_r	α_r
1	1.846			
		2979		
2	4.825			
		-2556		
3	2.269		0.047	0.377
		824		
4	3.093		0.390	1.442
		-191		
5	2.902		0.244	0.812
		-46		
6	2.856		0.242	0.821
		84		
7	2.940		0.250	0.827
		-58		
8	2.882		0.231	0.802
		27		
9	2.909		0.229	0.796
		-8		
10	2.901		0.232	0.806
		0		
11	2.901			

The iterative procedure is repeated until the maximum difference between successive iterates, for any value of x, is less than 10^{-8}. The final results are given in Table 5, for 2, 4, 8, 16, 32 subdivisions of the range, for $x = 0.0, 0.25, 0.50, 1.00$. These results are unsatisfactory from several points of view.

Table 5. Estimates of H(x) by a straightforward iterative procedure

Number of subdivisions	Number of iterations	x = 0.00		0.25	
2	30	1.003,515,12			
			224442		
4	19	1.000,870,70		1.548,914,39	
			65362		-149651
8	17	1.000,217,18		1.547,417,88	
			16492		- 9655
16	16	1.000,054,26		1.547,321,33	
			4070		+ 289
32	15	1.000,013,56		1.547,324,22	
Empirical t		4.1		?	
Extrapolated H		1.000,000		1.547,325	
Exact H		1.000,000		1.547,326	

Number of subdivisions	x = 0.50		1.00	
2	2.013,123,96		2.901,955,31	
		-73008		502162
4	2.012,393,88		2.906,976,93	
		29027		72699
8	2.012,684,15		2.907,703,92	
		7945		9331
16	2.012,763,60		2.907,797,23	
		1308		1164
32	2.012,776,68		2.907,808,87	
Empirical t	6.1		8.0	
Extrapolated H	2.012,779		2.907,810	
Exact H	2.012,778		2.907,809	

(i) Since we have used Simpson's rule which has an accuracy of h^4, where h is the size of the subdivision, the theoretical value of t defined in (68) is $2^4 = 16$. The empirical value of t is 4 when $x = 0$ and 8 when $x = 1$.

(ii) The estimates of H decrease with increasing number of subdivisions when $x = 0.0$, and increase for $x = 1.0$. For $x = 0.25$ and 0.50, the estimates first decrease and then increase. It is not possible to use the extrapolation formula (69) at $x = 0.25$.

In spite of these criticisms it is clear from the trend of the results that the estimate of H obtained by extrapolation should be correct to within about one unit in the sixth decimal place.

The fact that the empirical value of t is much less than the theoretical value indicates that the integrand of the integral cannot be approximated by parabolas over pairs of subintervals as required for the validity of the error formula for Simpson's rule. Inspection immediately indicates that the trouble arises from two causes:

(a) If we use the iteration given by the first formula in (155a), we see that the value of $H(x)$ near $x = 0$ is given by

$$H(x) \approx 1 + Cx \log x \,, \tag{157}$$

where C is a constant. The derivative of $H(x)$ is infinite at $x = 0$.

(b) The integrand in (156) is proportional to $t/(x+t)$ which has an awkward behavior when x and t are both near zero. If x is zero, this function is unity for all t, but if x is non-zero, the function tends to zero as t tends to zero.

Both of these sources of difficulty can be eliminated by a simple change of variable. In (156) set $x = z^2$, $t = u^2$. Then (156) becomes

$$H_{r+1}(z^2) = \left\{ \int_0^1 \frac{u^3 H_r(u^2)}{z^2 + u^2} du \right\}^{-1} .$$

The integrand tends to zero as u tends to zero, whatever the value of z. Also

$$H(u^2) \approx 1 + 2Cu^2 \log u$$

and the derivative of this expression with respect to u tends to zero as u tends to zero. Hence the change of variable minimizes both of the difficulties (a), (b), and the expected improvement in the numerical results is confirmed by the figures given in Table 6. The results for $x = 0$ are particularly satisfactory since the known result that $H(0) = 1$ was not used in the calculation. The empirical values of t are now close to the theoretical value of 16.

The moral of this example is that in numerical work one should always be alive to the possibility that an almost trivial change in the details of the calculation can considerably improve the numerical results.

Table 6. Estimates of $H(x)$ by iterative method with change of variable

Number of subdivisions	Number of iterations	x = 0.00	x = 0.25		x = 1.00	
2	32	1.000,000,00	1.550,510,26		2.898,979,49	
				198471		781337
4	25	1.000,000,00	1.548,525,55		2.906,793,86	
				114949		95824
8	18	1.000,000,00	1.547,376,06		2.907,752,10	
				4716		5492
16	17	1.000,000,00	1.547,328,90		2.907,807,02	
				250		329
32	16	1.000,000,00	1.547,326,40		2.907,810,31	
Expirical t		-	19		17	
Extrapolated H		1.000,000,00	1.547,326,3		2.907,810,5	

The H-equation is perhaps too simple to provide an altogether satisfactory test of a numerical method. A more awkward example of a similar type is given by the X-Y equations which provide a generalization of the H-equation:

$$X(\mu) = 1 + \tfrac{1}{2} k\mu \int_0^1 \{X(\mu) X(u) - Y(\mu) Y(u)\} \frac{du}{\mu+u} \tag{158a}$$

$$Y(\mu) = \exp(-\tfrac{\tau}{\mu}) + \tfrac{1}{2} k\mu \int_0^1 \{Y(\mu) X(u) - X(\mu) Y(u)\} \frac{du}{\mu-u} \tag{158b}$$

where k, τ are given constants. The second equation has the difficulty that the integrand has the indeterminate form $0/0$ when $\mu = u$ and some device has to be adopted, to represent the integrand numerically when $\mu \approx u$. The numerical solution of these equations has been considered in some detail by Mayers [95]. A straightforward iterative procedure is satisfactory for small k, but diverges for large k. Mayers considers that this is due to the factor $1/(\mu - u)$ in the integrand in the second equation. For large k he recommends the use of Newton's method (linearization of the error).

12. The solution of Fredholm equations by series representations

A wide class of methods for the solution of Fredholm equations can be summarized by saying that we try to solve the equation

$$y(x) + \int_a^b k(x,t;y(t))\,dt = f(x), \qquad (a \le x \le b), \tag{159}$$

by means of an approximate representation of the form

$$y(x) \approx Y(x) = \sum_{s=1}^{n} a_s v_s(x), \tag{160}$$

where the $v_s(x)$ are known functions, and the a_s are constants which are to be determined. This representation is substituted in (159), and we define the error residual $\epsilon(x)$ by the equation

$$\epsilon(x) = Y(x) + \int_a^b k(x,t;Y(t))\,dt - f(x).$$

Suitable values for the constants a_s can be determined by various criteria, all of which try to minimize $\epsilon(x)$ in some sense. We list the following:

(i) Collocation: We set $\epsilon(x) = 0$ for n suitably chosen values of x :

$$\epsilon(x_r) = 0, \qquad r = 1 \text{ to } n .$$

(ii) Least squares: We minimize

$$I = \int_a^b \epsilon^2(x)\, dx ,$$

by setting $\partial I/\partial a_r = 0$, $r = 1$ to n .

(iii) Galerkin's method: We set

$$\int_a^b \epsilon(x)\, u_r(x)\, dx = 0, \qquad r = 1 \text{ to } n ,$$

for n suitably chosen function $u_r(x)$ which may or may not be the same as the $v_s(x)$.

Each of these methods give n simultaneous nonlinear algebraic equations for the a_s . Some concrete examples can be found in [1]. These methods are not so universally and automatically applicable as the finite-difference methods of §9, but they are sometimes convenient.

The remainder of this section will be devoted to still another method for determining the constants a_s in the series (124), namely a variational method. We start from the functional

$$(161) \quad I(Y) = \int_a^b F(x, Y(x))\, dx + \int_a^b \int_a^b G(x, t; Y(x), Y(t))\, dx\, dt .$$

We set

$$(162) \qquad Y(x) = y(x) + \epsilon\, \eta(x) .$$

In the usual way the idea is that $\eta(x)$ is a function which is chosen arbitrarily at the beginning of the investigation. The parameter ϵ is then allowed to vary, so that I can be regarded as a function of ϵ . We wish to find the equation satisfied by y if I is stationary for variations of ϵ around zero. This condition can be written

$$(163) \qquad (\partial I/\partial \epsilon)_{\epsilon=0} = 0 .$$

A Taylor series expansion gives

$$G(x, t; Y(x), Y(t)) = G(x, t; y(x), y(t))$$

$$+ \epsilon\eta(x)\, G_3(x, t; y(x), y(t)) + \epsilon\, \eta(t)\, G_4(x, t; y(x), y(t)) + \ldots ,$$

where

$$G_3 = \frac{\partial G(x, t; y(x), y(t))}{\partial y(x)}, \quad G_4 = \frac{\partial G(x, t; y(x), y(t))}{\partial y(t)} .$$

The condition (163) applied to (161) therefore gives

$$\int_a^b \{F_y(x, y(x)) + \int_a^b [G_3(x, t; y(x), y(t)) + G_4(t, x; y(t), y(x))]\, dt\} \eta(x) dx = 0.$$

This is true for arbitrary $\eta(x)$. Hence $y(x)$ satisfies the integral equation

$$(164) \quad F_y(x, y(x)) + \int_a^b [G_3(x, t; y(x), y(t)) + G_4(t, x; y(t), y(x))]\, dt = 0 ,$$

$$(a \leq x \leq b) .$$

The principle that the stationary property of (161) leads to the integral equation (164) is apparently due to Volterra. It is described in [1].

In order to obtain a variational principle for a given integral equation we have to look for suitable functions F and G such that (164) is the required integral equation. A remark which is useful in practice is that if G is of the form

$$h(x, t)\; H(y(x),\; y(t)) ,$$

then the kernel of (164) is of the form

$$h(x, t) \frac{\partial H(y(x), y(t))}{\partial y(x)} + h(t, x) \frac{\partial H(y(t), y(x))}{\partial y(x)} .$$

This reduces to a simple form if $h(x, t) = h(t, x)$ and $H(u, v) = H(v, u)$, in which case the kernel of (164) becomes

$$2h(x, t) \frac{\partial H(y(x), y(t))}{\partial y(x)} .$$

If, also, $H(u, v) = J(u) J(v)$ then the kernel of (164) takes the form

$$(165) \qquad 2h(x, t) \frac{\partial J(y(x))}{\partial y(x)} J(y(t)) .$$

As an example, consider the equation

$$(166) \qquad \frac{P(x)}{y(x)} = Q(x) + \int_0^1 \frac{y(t)}{x+t}\, dt .$$

where P, Q are given functions. The H-equation (150) can be written in this form. The above theory gives, directly, the variational expression

$$(167) \quad I(Y) = 2\int_0^1 \{P(x) \log Y(x) - Q(x)\, Y(x)\}dx - \int_0^1\int_0^1 \frac{Y(x)\, Y(t)}{x+t}\, dx\, dt \ .$$

The variational principle can be applied in practice in the usual way, by substituting a series representation for $Y(x)$ of the form (160), where the constants a_s are determined by setting $\partial I/\partial a_r = 0$ for $r = 1$ to n. A difficulty immediately arises, namely that we have to evaluate integrals of the form

$$\int_0^1 \frac{P(x)\, v_r(x)}{\sum_{s=1}^{n} a_s v_s(x)}\, dx$$

where the a_s are unknown constants. This type of difficulty limits the utility of variational principles for nonlinear integral equations, especially since difference methods are more straightforward.

To determine the nature of the stationary property of I defined in (167), we examine the coefficient of ϵ^2 in the expansion

$$I(Y) = I(y) + \epsilon^2 C + \ldots \ .$$

We have

$$C = \tfrac{1}{2}\left(\frac{\partial^2 I}{\partial \epsilon^2}\right)_{\epsilon=0} = -\int_0^1 \frac{\eta^2(x)}{y^2(x)}\, dx - \int_0^1\int_0^1 \frac{\eta(x)\, \eta(t)}{x+t}\, dx\, dt \ .$$

On using an obvious replacement for $1/(x+t)$ we see that

$$\int_0^1\int_0^1 \frac{\eta(x)\, \eta(t)}{x+t}\, dt = \int_0^\infty z^2(u)\, du \geq 0 \ ,$$

where

$$z(u) = \int_0^1 e^{-ux}\, \eta(x)\, dx \ .$$

Hence $C \leq 0$ and

$$I(Y) \leq I(y) \ .$$

13. Conformal mapping by means of nonlinear integral equations

Consider the problem of calculating the flow of an incompressible, inviscid fluid round a two-dimensional body like an airfoil. The field is governed by Laplace's equation in two dimensions, so that conformal mapping is appropriate. It is standard practice to do this in two stages. If we denote a point in the physical plane by $z' = x' + iy'$, we first of all use a simple analytical mapping function such as the well-known transformation

$$z = z' + \frac{a^2}{z'}$$

to convert the airfoil into a curve in the z-plane which is nearly a circle, as in Figure 3. Various methods can then be used to map the z-plane into the ζ-plane (Figure 3(c)) in which the boundary curve is exactly a circle of unit radius. Most of the available methods are summarized in [61], [65], [72], [76]. The best known integral equation methods are those associated with the names of Lichtenstein-Gerschgorin and Theodorsen-Garrick. The former involves a linear singular integral equation. The latter leads to a nonlinear integral equation which we proceed to derive.

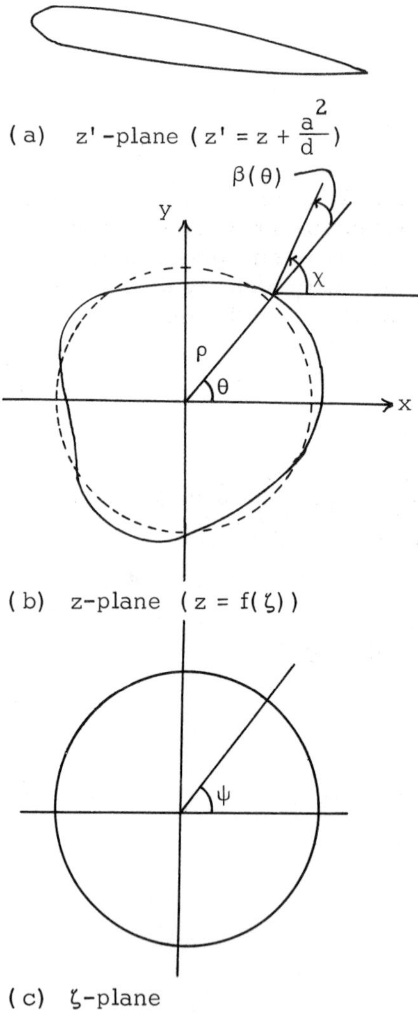

Figure 3

We require the following results on conjugate functions from complex-variable and potential theory. If $g(\zeta) = u(\zeta) + iv(\zeta)$ is analytic and bounded in the region $|\zeta| > 1$, then $g(\zeta)$ can be expanded in the form

$$g(\zeta) = c_0 + c_1\zeta^{-1} + c_2\zeta^{-2} + \dots . \tag{168}$$

If we set

$$\zeta = re^{i\psi}, \quad c_s = a_s + ib_s ,$$

then

(169a) $$u(\zeta) = a_0 + \sum_{s=1}^{\infty} (a_s \cos s\psi + b_s \sin s\psi) r^{-s} ,$$

(169b) $$v(\zeta) = b_0 + \sum_{s=1}^{\infty} (-a_s \sin s\psi + b_s \cos s\psi) r^{-s} .$$

The functions u and v are conjugate functions. If $u(\zeta)$ is known on $|\zeta| = 1$, then $v(\zeta)$ can be determined to within a constant b_0. The relation between u and v on $|\zeta| = 1$ can be expressed by the formula

(170) $$v(e^{i\psi}) = \frac{1}{2\pi} \int_0^{2\pi} v(e^{i\phi})\, d\phi + \frac{1}{2\pi} \int_0^{2\pi} u(e^{i\psi}) \cot \tfrac{1}{2} (\phi-\psi)\, d\phi .$$

The integral is to be interpreted as a Cauchy principal value. This formula can be verified, formally, by substituting the series for u, and evaluating the integrals by means of the following result, which is readily established by induction:

(171) $$\int_0^{\pi} \sin nt \cos \tfrac{1}{2}t\, dt = \pi, \qquad n = 1, 2, \ldots .$$

If $g(\zeta)$ is analytic for $|\zeta| < 1$, then the expansion in (168) is replaced by a similar expansion in powers of ζ, which means that r, ψ are replaced by r^{-1}, $-\psi$ in (169), and (170) is replaced by

(172) $$v(e^{i\psi}) = v(0) - \frac{1}{2\pi} \int_0^{2\pi} u(e^{i\phi}) \cot \tfrac{1}{2} (\phi-\psi)\, d\phi ,$$

where the term $v(0)$ is equivalent to the first integral on the right of (170), as can be seen by integrating the series form of v.

Suppose that C is a simple, closed, nearly-circular curve in the z-plane, represented in polar coordinates by specifying its radius vector ρ in terms of the polar angle θ, $\rho = \rho(\theta)$. From the theory of conformed mapping, we can find a function $f(\zeta)$ such that

(173) $$z = f(\zeta), \quad f(0) = 0, \quad f'(0) \text{ real and } > 0 ,$$

which maps the circle $|\zeta| < 1$ onto the interior of C. Suppose that the point $z = \rho \exp i\theta$ on the boundary of C in the z-plane corresponds to the point $\zeta = \exp i\psi$ on the circle of unit radius in the ζ-plane. If ψ is taken as an independent variable, then θ is a function of ψ, $\theta = \theta(\psi)$, and similarly $\rho(\theta)$ is also a function of ψ: $\rho = \rho(\theta(\psi))$. Consider the function

(174) $$g(\zeta) = \log \frac{f(\zeta)}{\zeta} .$$

On the circle $\zeta = \exp i\psi$ we have

(175) $$g(\zeta) = \log \rho + i(\theta - \psi) .$$

Because of the conditions on $f(0)$ and $f'(0)$ in (173), $f(\zeta)/\zeta$ is finite and real as ζ tends to zero. Hence $g(\zeta)$ is analytic for $|\zeta| < 1$, and the imaginary part of $g(\zeta)$ is zero when $\zeta = 0$. Hence the real and imaginary parts of $g(\zeta)$ satisfy (172), with $v(0) = 0$, i.e. from (175),

(176) $$\theta(\psi) - \psi = -\frac{1}{2\pi}\int_0^{2\pi} \{\log \rho(\theta(\phi))\} \cot\tfrac{1}{2}(\phi - \psi)\, d\phi, \quad 0 \le \psi \le 2\pi .$$

Consider next the problem of mapping the exterior of the circle $|\zeta| = 1$ onto the exterior of C. Suppose that the required mapping function is

$$z = f(\zeta) = c\zeta + c_0 + \sum_{s=1}^{\infty} c_s \zeta^{-s} ,$$

where c is real and positive. As before consider a function $g(\zeta)$ defined as in (174). From the assumed form of $f(\zeta)$ we see that $g(\zeta)$ tends to a real constant as ζ tends to infinity. In this case the real and imaginary parts of $g(\zeta)$ satisfy (170), the first integral on the right in (170) being zero. Hence

(177) $$\theta(\psi) - \psi = \frac{1}{2\pi}\int_0^{2\pi} \{\log \rho(\theta(\phi))\} \cot\tfrac{1}{2}(\phi - \psi)\, d\phi, \quad 0 \le \psi \le 2\pi .$$

Equation (176) is the Theodorsen-Garrick nonlinear integral equation for the unknown function $\theta(\psi)$ for the interior problem, and (177) is the corresponding equation for the exterior problem. Formally these differ only in the sign of the right-hand side. It is reasonable to expect that if the curve in the z-plane is nearly circular, these equations will be amenable to iterative numerical solution. For (176) we should write

(178) $$\theta^{(r+1)}(\psi) = \psi - \frac{1}{2\pi}\int_0^{2\pi} \{\log \rho(\theta^{(r)}(\phi))\} \cot\tfrac{1}{2}(\phi - \psi)\, d\phi .$$

The iteration can be started by choosing $\theta^{(0)} = \psi$. The integral on the right can be evaluated at any stage of the iteration, since ρ is a given function of θ . The problem of the numerical evaluation of the singular integral in (148) will be considered in the next section. It is reported in [61] that convergence of the iterative procedure is usually faster for the exterior than for the interior problem, when solving the Theodorsen-Garrick integral equation. This seems to be true also for the other nonlinear equations established below.

The Theodorsen-Garrick integral equation has been used extensively in the practical design of airfoils, both by direct numerical solution of the integral equation, and by developing approximate analytical solutions. In the latter category, we quote Goldstein's method, described in [64], [72]. The graphical comparison of exact and approximate solutions in these references is particularly interesting.

Several other integral equation formulations can be obtained for the above problem. At first sight these seem to be more complicated than the Theodorsen-Garrick integral equation, but they have the advantage that they can be generalized to deal with other problems, for instance free-boundary flow.

The integral equation which is obtained depends on the parameters used to characterize the curve. For the Theodorsen-Garrick equation, the curve C is specified in terms of polar coordinates ρ, θ . In order to use other specifications of the curve, we obtain some geometrical results. Denote by β the angle between the external normal to the curve C in the z-plane, and the radius vector at the point (ρ, θ) . Let χ be the angle between the outward normal in the z-plane, and the x-axis. Then (see Figure 3(b)):

(179) $$\chi = \theta + \beta .$$

Since $x = \rho \cos \theta$, $y = \rho \sin \theta$,

$$\tan(\beta + \theta + \tfrac{1}{2}\pi) = \frac{dy}{dx} = \frac{\rho \cos \theta \, d\theta + d\rho \sin \theta}{-\rho \sin \theta \, d\theta + d\rho \cos \theta} .$$

Simplification of this equation gives the result

(180) $$\tan \beta = -\frac{1}{\rho}\frac{d\rho}{d\theta} .$$

All the quantities ρ, θ, β, χ can be regarded as functions of the one independent variable ψ . From (180) we therefore have

(181) $$\frac{d\rho}{d\psi} = -\rho \tan \beta \frac{d\theta}{d\psi} .$$

If s denotes the distance along the curve C in the z-plane,

$$\left(\frac{ds}{d\psi}\right)^2 = \left(\frac{d\rho}{d\psi}\right)^2 + \rho^2\left(\frac{d\theta}{d\psi}\right)^2 .$$

Hence, on using (181),

$$(182) \qquad \frac{ds}{d\psi} = \frac{\rho}{\cos\beta}\,\frac{d\theta}{d\psi} \quad .$$

On the circumference of the circle of unit radius in the ζ-plane we have $\zeta = \exp i\psi$, so that

$$(183) \qquad \frac{df(\zeta)}{d\psi} = \frac{df}{d\zeta}\,\frac{d\zeta}{d\psi} = i\zeta\,\frac{df}{d\zeta} \quad .$$

If we differentiate the relation $f(\zeta) = \rho \exp i\theta$ with respect to ψ we obtain

$$i\zeta\,\frac{df}{d\zeta} = \frac{d\rho}{d\psi}\,e^{i\theta} + i\rho e^{i\theta}\,\frac{d\theta}{d\psi} \quad .$$

In using (181) this gives the fundamental relation

$$(184) \qquad f'(\zeta) = \frac{\rho}{\cos\beta}\,e^{i(\theta+\beta-\psi)}\,\frac{d\theta}{d\psi} \quad .$$

On the basis of these results we establish three different but related integral equations. Suppose first of all that the curve C in the z-plane is characterized by specifying β as a function of θ. From (184) we see that

$$\frac{\zeta f'(\zeta)}{f(\zeta)} = \frac{1}{\cos\beta}\,\frac{d\theta}{d\psi}\,e^{i\beta} \quad ,$$

so that

$$(185) \qquad i \log\left\{\frac{\zeta f'(\zeta)}{f(\zeta)}\right\} = i \log\left|\frac{1}{\cos\beta}\,\frac{d\theta}{d\psi}\right| - \beta \quad .$$

Consider the interior mapping problem. Since the limit of the term in brackets on the left is unity when ζ tends to zero, the imaginary part of the left-hand side of this equation is zero when ζ tends to zero. The expression on the left is an analytic function of ζ for $|\zeta| < 1$. Hence (172) can be applied, with $v(0) = 0$, and we find

$$(186) \qquad \frac{d\theta(\psi)}{d\psi} = \cos\beta(\theta(\psi))\exp\left\{\frac{1}{2\pi}\int_0^{2\pi} \beta(\theta(\phi))\,\cot\tfrac{1}{2}(\phi-\psi)\,d\phi\right\} .$$

This is the required integral equation. It seems to have been first established by M. S. Friberg [62]. A report of this work is given in

[76] (see also [65]). From the form of equation (186) it is reasonable to expect that it will be amenable to iterative calculation, provided that β is not too large, i.e. the curve C in the z-plane does not differ too much from a circle. If we start with $\beta = 0$, the equation gives $d\theta/d\psi = 0$, or $\theta = \psi$, and this can be improved in the usual way, since β is a known function of θ.

Next consider the following result, obtained from (149), (182), (184):

(187) $$i \log f'(\zeta) = i \log \frac{ds}{d\psi} - (\chi - \psi) ,$$

where we assume that the geometry of the curve is such that $ds/d\psi$ is always positive. Hence $ds/d\psi$ and $\chi - \psi$ are conjugate, and we can apply (170), (172):

(188) $$\log \frac{ds}{d\psi} = D \pm \frac{1}{2\pi} \int_0^{2\pi} \{\chi - \phi\} \cot \tfrac{1}{2} (\phi - \psi) \, d\phi .$$

where D is some constant, and the upper (lower) sign refers to the interior (exterior) problem. In the integral on the right, χ is regarded as a function of ϕ, $\chi = \chi(\phi)$. If we assume that χ is differentiable, then, on integrating (188) by parts, remembering that

(189) $$\chi(2\pi) - \chi(0) = 2\pi, \quad \int_0^{2\pi} \frac{d\chi(\phi)}{d\phi} \, d\phi = 2\pi ,$$

$$\int_0^{2\pi} \log |\sin \tfrac{1}{2} (\phi - \psi)| d\phi = -2\pi \log 2 ,$$

we see that

(190) $$\log \frac{ds}{d\psi} = D \mp \frac{1}{\pi} \int_0^{2\pi} \frac{d\chi}{d\phi} \log 2 |\sin \tfrac{1}{2} (\phi - \psi)| \, d\phi .$$

This last formula can be obtained independently by considering the limiting form of the Schwarz-Christoffel transformation for mapping a polygon into a circle, when the number of sides of the polygon tends to infinity in such a way that the polygon goes over into a smooth curve. If the vertices of the polygon are transformed into the points $\exp i\psi_s$ (s = 1 to n) on a circle of unit radius in the ζ-plane, then the Schwarz-Christoffel transformation $z = f(\zeta)$ gives the relation (see [65], pp. 153, 207):

(191) $$\frac{df}{d\psi} = K\{\sin\tfrac{1}{2}(\psi-\psi_1)\}^{\alpha_1-1}\{\sin\tfrac{1}{2}(\psi-\psi_2)\}^{\alpha_2-1}\ \dots\ ,$$

where the internal angles of the polygon in the z-plane are given by $\pi\alpha_s$, K is some constant, and

(192) $$\alpha_1 + \alpha_2 + \dots + \alpha_n = n - 2\ .$$

In the limiting case, as n tends to infinity, the α_s tend to zero and we can introduce a function $f(\psi)$ such that

$$1 - \alpha_s = (2\pi/n)\ f(\psi_s),\quad \psi_s = 2\pi s/n\ .$$

From (192)

(193) $$\int_0^{2\pi} f(\psi)\ d\psi = 2\ .$$

Taking logarithms of (191),

$$\log\frac{df}{d\psi} = \log K + \sum_{s=1}^{n}(\alpha_s - 1)\ \log\{\sin\tfrac{1}{2}(\psi-\psi_s)\}\ .$$

As n tends to infinity this can be replaced by

$$\log\frac{df}{d\psi} = \log K - \int_0^{2\pi} f(\phi)\ \log\{\sin\tfrac{1}{2}(\psi-\phi)\}\,d\phi\ .$$

We now separate real and imaginary parts. From (183), (184), the real and imaginary parts of the left-hand side are $\log ds/d\psi$ and χ. Hence

(194) $$\log\frac{ds}{d\psi} = P - \int_0^{2\pi} f(\phi)\ \log|\sin\tfrac{1}{2}(\phi-\psi)|\,d\phi\ ,$$

$$\chi(\psi) = Q - \pi\int_{\psi}^{2\pi} f(\phi)\ d\phi$$

where we have chosen the imaginary part of $\log x$ for $x < 0$ to be equal to $+\pi i$, so that $\chi(\psi)$ will increase by 2π when ψ increases by 2π (see (192)). The second equation gives $d\chi/d\psi = \pi f(\psi)$, and substitution of this result in (194) gives precisely (190) with the upper sign, corresponding to the inner problem. (From (189) the difference of a factor of 2 in the logarithm is equivalent to a different definition of the constants D, P.)

We now return to the formulation of the second of the three integral equations mentioned earlier. Assume that the curve C in the z-plane is characterized by specifying the normal direction χ as a function of arc-length s, $\chi = G(s)$. Then (188) gives directly an integral equation for s, regarded as a function of ψ (see [61], §12):

$$\frac{ds(\psi)}{d\psi} = A \exp\left\{\pm \frac{1}{2\pi} \int_0^{2\pi} \{G(s(\phi)) - \phi\} \cot \tfrac{1}{2}(\phi - \psi)\, d\phi\right\}, \tag{195}$$

where A is some constant. This is suitable for iterative solution. We start by guessing that $\chi = G = \phi$, so that $s(\psi) = A\psi + E$, where the constants A, E are determined by the conditions that $s(0) = 0$, and $s(2\pi) = \ell$, the known length of the curve. The iteration can be repeated, determining a new estimate of the constant A in a similar way, at each stage of the iteration.

The third integral equation is obtained by assuming that the curve C is characterized by specifying the curvature κ in terms of the normal direction χ, $\kappa = K(\chi)$. This is convenient since $\kappa = d\chi/ds$, so that

$$\frac{d\chi(\psi)}{d\psi} = K(\chi) \frac{ds}{d\psi},$$

and (190) gives the integral equation ([61], §11):

$$\frac{d\chi}{d\psi} = BK(\chi) \exp\left\{\mp \frac{1}{\pi} \int_0^{2\pi} \frac{d\chi(\phi)}{d\phi} \log 2\left|\sin \tfrac{1}{2}(\phi - \psi)\right| d\phi\right\}. \tag{196}$$

This is again a suitable equation for solution by an iterative procedure. The book [77] is based almost entirely on integral equations of this type. A remarkable variety of problems are treated, solutions being obtained both by approximate analytical methods, and by numerical methods. The simplest numerical iterative procedures seem to be adequate. This book provides a source of problems for testing more sophisticated methods for the solution of integral equations of the type considered in this section.

Free boundary problems involving cavities and wakes can be formulated in terms of integral equations similar to (195) and (196). Details can be found in [79] - [82], where references to previous work are given. The applications in [80], [82] are mentioned for historical reasons. The book [77] should also be quoted.

Nekrassov's integral equation (147) also fits into this context of ideas. If we set

$$F(t) = \log\left\{1 + \mu \int_0^t \sin z(\tau)\, d\tau\right\}$$

then (147) becomes (compare (196)):

$$\frac{dF}{dt} = \mu e^{-F(t)} \sin\left\{\frac{1}{3\pi}\int_0^{\pi} \log\left|\frac{\sin\frac{1}{2}(s+t)}{\sin\frac{1}{2}(s-t)}\right| \frac{dF(s)}{ds}\, ds\right\} .$$

14. The numerical evaluation of a singular integral

As indicated in the last section, the nonlinear integral equations for the conformal mapping of nearly circular regions onto a circle are usually solved by iteration. In aerodynamic applications it appears that one or two iterations, using the simple first-order procedure $\theta_{r+1} = F(\theta_r)$, give a sufficiently accurate solution of the Theodorsen-Garrick integral equations (176), (177). The convergence of the procedure has been examined theoretically in this case by Ostrowski [69], who gives references to previous work by Wittich and Warschawski. It is clear from the form of the equation that the iterative procedure should converge if the region in the z-plane is 'nearly' a circle. This implies that the tangent to the curve at any given point should not deviate too much from the tangent at the corresponding point on the circle. (See Figure 3(b)). Corresponding points are defined as points on the same radius vector.) More precisely Ostrowski establishes that if $\log \rho(\theta)$ has a uniformly bounded derivative:

$$|\rho'(\theta)/\rho(\theta)| \leq k, \quad k < 1 ,$$

where the bound of unity on k is sharp, then straightforward iterative solution of the Theodorsen-Garrick integral equation will converge, and

$$|\theta_r - \theta| < Ck^r ,$$

where C is a constant which is independent of θ and r, but, in the bound established by Ostrowski, C tends to infinity as k tends to unity.

The numerical solution of integral equations of the type considered in the last section involves the evaluation of certain singular integrals. Since this is a problem of some technical interest, and the techniques do not seem to be widely known, we sketch briefly the two commonly used methods, by considering the numerical evaluation of the Cauchy-principal-value integral:

$$(197) \qquad g(\psi) = \frac{1}{2\pi}\int_0^{2\pi} f(\phi) \cot\tfrac{1}{2}(\phi-\psi)\, d\phi .$$

In the first method, we divide the range 0 to 2π into $2n$ parts, and set

$$h = \pi/n, \qquad \phi_r = rh, \qquad f(\phi_r) = f_r, \qquad g(\phi_r) = g_r \; .$$

The functions f and g are both periodic, so that

$$f_r = f_{r-2n} \; ,$$

and there is no need to ensure that $0 \leq r \leq 2n$. From (197), on choosing $\psi = rh$, and setting $\phi = \psi + t$,

$$g_r = \frac{1}{2\pi} \int_{-\epsilon}^{\epsilon} f(rh+t) \cot \tfrac{1}{2} t \, dt + \frac{1}{2\pi} \int_{\epsilon}^{2\pi-\epsilon} f(rh+t) \cot \tfrac{1}{2} t \, dt$$

$$= g_{1r} + g_{2r}, \quad \text{say,}$$

where ϵ is a suitable constant, and the separation has been made in such a way that the integrand of g_{2r} does not possess a singularity, and can be evaluated by Simpson's rule. If we choose $\epsilon = \pi/n$ then

(198)
$$g_{2r} = \frac{1}{6n} \sum_{j=1}^{2n-1} a_j f_{r+j} \cot \tfrac{1}{2} jh$$
$$= \frac{1}{6n} \sum_{j=1}^{n-1} a_j (f_{r+j} - f_{r-j}) \cot \frac{j\pi}{2n} \; ,$$

where $a_1 = a_{2n-1} = 1$, and

$$a_j = 4, \; j = 2, 4, \ldots 2n-2, \qquad a_j = 2, \; j = 3, 5, \ldots 2n-3 \; .$$

The integral g_{1r} can be evaluated approximately as a series in even powers of ϵ by setting

$$f(rh+t) = f_r + tf'_r + \tfrac{1}{2} t^2 f''_r + \ldots \; ,$$

$$\cot \tfrac{1}{2} t = \frac{2}{t} - \frac{1}{6} t - \frac{1}{360} t^3 - \ldots \; .$$

The coefficients of ϵ involve odd-order derivatives of f_r . If these are approximated by standard finite-difference formulae, using up to fifth differences, the final result is (Naiman, [67]):

(199) $$g_{1r} = b_1(f_{r+1} - f_{r-1}) + b_2(f_{r+2} - f_{r-2}) + b_3(f_{r+3} - f_{r-3}) \; ,$$

where, to order ϵ^2,

$$(200) \quad 2\pi b_1 = \frac{239}{90} - \frac{167}{2520}\epsilon^2, \quad 2\pi b_2 = -\frac{88}{225} + \frac{2}{315}\epsilon^2, \quad 2\pi b_3 = \frac{19}{450} - \frac{1}{1512}\epsilon^2 .$$

Naiman states that evaluation of the integral (197) by (198)-(200) gives an accuracy of better than 1 in 1000 for $2n = 40$, $f(\phi) = \cos r\phi$, for small values of r, which are the most important in applications. It seems that no theoretical estimate is available for the optimum order of differences that should be retained in deriving (199), nor for the optimum choice of ϵ, which could be an integer multiple of π/n.

We next consider a second method for evaluation of integrals of the form (197), obtained by representing $f(\phi)$ approximately by means of a finite number of terms of its Fourier series:

$$(201) \qquad f(\phi) \approx a_0 + \sum_{s=1}^{n} (a_s \cos s\phi + b_s \sin s\phi) .$$

As usual, it is convenient to work in terms of the discrete set $f_r = f(\phi_r)$, where $\phi_r = rh$, $h = \pi/n$, $r = 0, 1, \ldots 2n-1$. Then

$$f_r = a_0 + \sum_{s=1}^{n-1} (a_s \cos srh + b_s \sin srh) + a_n \cos n\pi ,$$

$$(r = 0, 1, \ldots 2n-1) .$$

It is fortunate that the term in b_n drops out, because we now have $2n$ equations for $2n$ unknowns. This set of equations can be solved explicitly by means of the discrete analogue of the orthogonality properties of trignometric functions, and we find

$$(202a) \qquad a_0 = \frac{1}{2n} \sum_{r=0}^{2n-1} f_r, \quad a_s = \frac{1}{n} \sum_{r=0}^{2n-1} f_r \cos sr\frac{\pi}{n} ,$$

$$(202b) \qquad b_s = \frac{1}{n} \sum_{r=0}^{2n-1} f_r \sin sr\frac{\pi}{n} .$$

On substituting (201) in (197), and using the standard integral:

$$\frac{1}{\pi} \int_0^{\pi} \frac{\cos n\alpha}{\cos\alpha - \cos\beta} \, d\alpha = \frac{\sin n\beta}{\sin\beta} ,$$

we obtain the result:

$$g(\psi) \approx \sum_{j=1}^{n-1} (-a_j \sin_j \psi + b_j \cos j\psi) - a_n \sin n\psi \ .$$

If $g(\psi)$ is evaluated at $\psi = sh$, and the a_j, b_j are expressed in terms of f_r by means of (202), we find that

$$g_s = \frac{1}{n} \sum_{r=0}^{2n-1} f_r \sum_{j=1}^{n} \sin j(r-s)h \quad .$$

(203)

$$= \frac{1}{n} \sum_{k=1,3,5,\ldots} (f_{s+k} - f_{s-k}) \cot \frac{k\pi}{2n} \quad .$$

The summation over k goes up to $k = n-1$ if n is even, and $k=n-2$ if n is odd. This is the required integration formula. If s is odd (even) the formula involves values of f_m for only even (odd) values of m . A comparison of the forms of (197), (203) shows that (203) can be interpreted as the evaluation of the integral (197) by means of the ordinary rectangular rule, using intervals of width $2\pi/n$, and taking the value of the integrand at the mid-point of each interval, arranging that the singularity occurs at a point of subdivision of the range.

This second method for evaluating the integral (197) was described in [68] . It seems to have been developed and used in Europe, independently, at the end of the last war. (See references 9 and 10 in [64].) Other relevant references are [61], [63], [70], [76].

In aerodynamic applications it appears that results of a given accuracy are usually obtained with less labor when the second method of approximate integration is used, rather than the first.

15. The reduction of linear integral equations with difference kernels to nonlinear Fredholm equations

In this section we show that a nonlinear integral equation can be deduced from the following linear Fredholm integral equation with a difference kernel, or Wiener-Hopf equation with a finite range:

(204) $$\nu\phi(x) + \int_p^q k(x-t)\ \phi(t)\, dt = g(x), \qquad a \le x \le b \ ,$$

where k, g are given functions, and ν is a given constant. For simplicity we start by considering the corresponding equation with semi-infinite range:

$$(205) \qquad \nu\phi(x) + \int_0^\infty k(x-t)\,\phi(t)\,dt = g(x), \qquad 0 \le x < \infty .$$

Equation (205) can be solved exactly, and (204) can be solved approximately if the range of integration is large, by means of the Wiener-Hopf technique. However this may involve an awkward factorization in the complex plane, and it is of interest to have an alternative method for the numerical solution of these equations.

The connection between linear equations of the above type and nonlinear integral equations arose historically in the following way. An equation of type (205) with a special form of kernel (the Milne kernel (218) below) occurs in the theory of radiative transfer. The Wiener-Hopf technique was in fact invented to solve this particular equation. By means of another method of approach, namely by means of certain principles of invariance introduced by Ambartsumian and exploited by Ambartsumian and Chandrasekhar (see [90]), it was found that the same problem could also be formulated in terms of a nonlinear integral equation, the H-equation (150) below. Ambartsumian also showed that the H-equation could be deduced directly from the Wiener-Hopf equation with the Milne kernel (see for instance the exposition in [87], §28). Later K. M. Case [89] and V. V. Sobolev realized that this connection holds not only for the special integral equations of radiative transfer, but also for more general linear integral equations with difference kernels. The paper of K. M. Case applies the principle of translation-invariance directly to the integral equation (205) with semi-infinite range. We use a somewhat simple method related to (but not quite the same as) the second method invented by Ambartsumian.

If the function $g(x)$ in (205) is such that

$$|g(x)| < A\exp(-cx), \qquad \text{as } x \to +\infty ,$$

and we write

$$G(s) = \int_0^\infty g(x)\, e^{sx}\, dx, \qquad \operatorname{Re} s < c ,$$

where the sign of s is the opposite of that usually used in the Laplace transform, then

$$g(x) = \frac{1}{2\pi i}\int_{c-i\infty}^{c+i\infty} G(s)\, e^{-sx}\, ds .$$

To determine $g(x)$ from this integral, the contour must be closed in the right half-plane. The function $\phi(x)$ in (205) can therefore be found if we can solve

$$(206) \qquad \nu f(x;\beta) + \int_0^\infty k(x-t)\, f(t;\beta)\, dt = e^{-\beta x}, \quad \left\{\begin{matrix} 0 \le x < \infty \\ \operatorname{Re} \beta > c \end{matrix}\right\},$$

where the notation $f(x;\beta)$ is used to emphasize that f is a function of β. In fact

$$\phi(x) = \frac{1}{2\pi i} \int_{c-i\infty}^{c+i\infty} f(x;s)\, G(s)\, ds .$$

In addition to (206) we introduce the adjoint equation

$$(207) \qquad \nu f^*(x;\alpha) + \int_0^\infty k(t-x)\, f^*(t;\alpha)\, dt = e^{-\alpha x}, \quad \left\{\begin{matrix} 0 \le x < \infty \\ \operatorname{Re} \alpha > c \end{matrix}\right\}.$$

If $k(x-t)$ is a function of $|x-t|$ then the integral equation is self-adjoint, and $f^*(x;\alpha) = f(x;\alpha)$. This slightly simplifies the formulae which follow, but it is easier to see the structure of the manipulations if we distinguish the adjoint from the original equation.

Define

$$(208) \qquad F_+(\alpha,\beta) = \int_0^\infty f(x;\beta)\, e^{-\alpha x}\, dx, \quad F_+^*(\beta,\alpha) = \int_0^\infty f^*(x;\alpha)\, e^{-\beta x}\, dx .$$

It is easy to show that

$$(209) \qquad F_+(\alpha,\beta) = F_+^*(\beta,\alpha) ,$$

since we need only multiply (206) by $f^*(x;\alpha)$, (207) by $f(x;\beta)$, subtract, and integrate the result with respect to x from zero to infinity. The left-hand side of the resulting equation is identically zero, and (209) is obtained.

We next differentiate (206) with respect to x, using the result

$$\frac{d}{dx} \int_0^\infty k(x-\xi)\, f(\xi;\beta)\, d\xi = - \int_0^\infty \left\{ \frac{d}{d\xi} k(x-\xi) \right\} f(\xi;\beta)\, d\xi$$

$$= f(0;\beta)\, k(x) + \int_0^\infty k(x-\xi)\, \frac{df(\xi;\beta)}{d\xi}\, d\xi .$$

This gives

$$(210)\quad \nu \frac{df(x;\beta)}{dx} + f(0;\beta)\, k(x) + \int_0^\infty k(x-\xi) \frac{df(\xi;\beta)}{d\xi} d\xi = -\beta e^{-\beta x} , \qquad 0 \le x < \infty .$$

We now multiply this equation by $f^*(x;\alpha)$, (207) by $df(x;\beta)/dx$, subtract, and integrate with respect to x from 0 to ∞. We find:

$$(211)\quad \begin{aligned} f(0;\beta) \int_0^\infty k(x)\, f^*(x;\alpha)\, dx &= -\beta F_+^*(\beta,\alpha) - \int_0^\infty \frac{df(x,\beta)}{dx} e^{-\alpha x} dx \\ &= -(\beta+\alpha)\, F_+(\alpha,\beta) + f(0;\beta) , \end{aligned}$$

where, to obtain the last equation, we have integrated by parts and used (209). From (207)

$$\int_0^\infty k(t)\, f^*(t;\alpha)\, dt = 1 - \nu f^*(0;\alpha) .$$

Substitution in (211) gives

$$(212)\quad f_+(\alpha,\beta) = \frac{\nu f(0;\beta)\, f^*(0;\alpha)}{(\beta+\alpha)} .$$

This is a remarkable result since it expresses a function of two variables in terms of functions of a single variable.

An integral equation for $f(0;\beta)$ can now be derived by means of the following procedure. Inversion of the first equation in (208) gives

$$(213)\quad \frac{1}{2\pi i} \int_{a-i\infty}^{a+i\infty} F_+(\alpha,\beta)\, e^{\alpha x}\, d\alpha = \begin{cases} f(x;\beta), & x > 0 , \\ 0, & x < 0 . \end{cases}$$

By inserting this result in (206) with $x = 0$, we obtain,

$$(214)\quad \nu f(0;\beta) + \frac{1}{2\pi i} \int_{a-i\infty}^{a+i\infty} F_+(\alpha,\beta) \int_{-\infty}^{\infty} k(-t)\, e^{\alpha t}\, dt\, d\alpha = 1, \quad \mathrm{Re}\,\beta > c ,$$

where the limits of the inner integral can be taken as $(-\infty, \infty)$ because of (213). We introduce

$$(215)\quad K(\alpha) = \int_{-\infty}^{\infty} k(t)\, e^{-\alpha t}\, dt ,$$

and then (214) becomes

$$\nu f(0;\beta) = 1 - \frac{1}{2\pi i}\int_{a-i\infty}^{a+i\infty} F_+(\alpha,\beta)\, K(\alpha)\, d\alpha \ .$$

If this result is combined with (212) we obtain the following integral equation relating $f(0;\beta)$ and $f^*(0;\alpha)$:

$$(216) \qquad \nu f(0;\beta) = 1 - \frac{\nu f(0;\beta)}{2\pi i}\int_{a-i\infty}^{a+i\infty} \frac{K(\alpha)\ f^*(0;\alpha)}{\beta+\alpha}\, d\alpha \ .$$

If the roles of f and f^* are interchanged throughout the above analysis, we obtain a second integral equation

$$(217) \qquad \nu f^*(0;\beta) = 1 - \frac{\nu f^*(0;\beta)}{2\pi i}\int_{a-i\infty}^{a+i\infty} \frac{K(-\alpha)\ f(0;\alpha)}{\beta+\alpha}\, d\alpha \ .$$

The equations (216), (217) satisfied by f, f^* were first derived by K. M. Case [89], equation (14a,b), for the general kernel $k(x-t)$, by means of a different method depending on translation invariance. (Note that our α corresponds to $-p$ in Case's notation).

We apply the above analysis to the case of the Milne kernel:

$$(218) \qquad k(t) = -\int_1^{\infty} \Psi\left(\frac{1}{u}\right)\frac{1}{u}\, e^{-|t|u}\, du \ .$$

From the definition (215) we can show that

$$K(\alpha) = \int_1^{\infty} \Psi\left(\frac{1}{u}\right)\frac{1}{u}\left\{\frac{1}{\alpha-u} - \frac{1}{\alpha+u}\right\} du \ .$$

Since $k(t)$ is a function of $|t|$, the integral equation is self-adjoint, $f(0;\beta) = f^*(0;\beta)$, and (216), (217) give the single equation (taking $\nu = 1$):

$$(219) \qquad f(0;\beta) = 1 - f(0;\beta)\int_1^{\infty} \Psi\left(\frac{1}{u}\right)\frac{1}{u}\, L(\beta,u)\, du \ ,$$

where

$$(220) \qquad L(\beta,u) = \frac{1}{2\pi i}\int_{a-i\infty}^{a+i\infty} \frac{1}{(\beta+\alpha)}\left\{\frac{1}{\alpha-u} - \frac{1}{\alpha+u}\right\} f(0;\alpha)\, d\alpha$$

$$= -f(0;u) \ ,$$

where the integral has been evaluated by residues, by closing the contour in the right half-plane, using the fact that $f(0;\alpha)$ is analytic in this region. If we substitute this result in (219), suppose that β is a real number between 1 and infinity, and set

$$x = 1/\beta, \qquad t = 1/u \;, \qquad (221)$$
$$H(x) = f(0; 1/x) \;,$$

we obtain the generalized Ambartsumian-Chandrasekhar H-equation:

$$H(x) = 1 + xH(x) \int_0^1 \frac{\Psi(t)\, H(t)}{x+t} dt, \qquad 0 \le x \le 1 \;. \qquad (222)$$

The above analysis is easily extended to deal with certain more general equations. In the case of the finite-range equation (204) consider, instead of (206), (207),

$$\nu f(x;\beta) + \int_p^q k(x-t)\, f(t;\beta)\, dt = e^{-\beta x}, \qquad p \le x \le q \;, \qquad (223)$$

$$\nu f^*(x;\alpha) + \int_p^q k(t-x)\, f^*(t;\alpha)\, dt = e^{-\alpha x}, \qquad p \le x \le q \;.$$

Instead of (210) we now have, on differentiating (223):

$$\nu \frac{df(x;\beta)}{dx} + f(p;\beta)\, k(x-p) - f(q;\beta)\, k(x-q)$$
$$+ \int_p^q k(x-t) \frac{df(t;\beta)}{dt} dt = -\beta e^{-\beta x}, \qquad p \le x \le q \;,$$

the point being that integration by parts now introduces a contribution from the upper, as well as the lower, end-point. Proceeding exactly as before, we define

$$F(\alpha,\beta) = \int_p^q f(x;\beta)\, e^{-\alpha x}\, dx \;,$$

and we find, instead of (212),

$$F(\alpha,\beta) = \frac{\nu \{f(p;\beta)\, f^*(p;\alpha) - f(q;\beta)\, f^*(q;\alpha)\}}{\beta+\alpha} \;.$$

The equation (216) generalizes to a pair of integral equations, of which one is

$$(224)\quad \nu f(p;\beta) = 1 - \frac{\nu}{2\pi i}\int_{a-i\infty}^{a+i\infty} \frac{K(\alpha)\{f(p;\beta)\, f^{*}(p;\alpha) - f(q;\beta)\, f^{*}(q;\alpha)\}}{\beta+\alpha}\, d\alpha ,$$

with a similar equation for $f(q;\beta)$. We similarly define a quantity $F^{*}(\beta,\alpha)$, and derive another pair of integral equations, so that altogether there are four integral equations for the four unknown functions $f(p;\beta)$, $f(q;\beta)$, $f^{*}(p;\alpha)$, $f^{*}(q;\alpha)$. In the self-adjoint case these reduce to two equations involving two unknown functions. The X-Y equations (158) can be derived from this analysis in the same way as the H-equation (222) was derived above.

Consider next the equation

$$(225)\quad \nu f(x;\beta) + \int_0^{\infty} \{k(x-t) + m(x+t)\}\, f(t;\beta)\, dt = e^{-\beta x}, \quad 0 \le x < \infty .$$

If we try to repeat the analysis following (206), we see immediately that the correct adjoint equation is

$$\nu f^{*}(x;\alpha) + \int_0^{\infty} \{k(x-t) - m(x+t)\}\, f(t;\alpha)\, dt = e^{-\alpha x}, \quad 0 \le x < \infty .$$

These lead to the simultaneous nonlinear integral equations

$$\nu f(0;\beta) = 1 - \frac{\nu f(0;\beta)}{2\pi i}\int_{a-i\infty}^{a+i\infty} \frac{\{K(\alpha) + M(-\alpha)\}f^{*}(0;\alpha)}{\beta+\alpha}\, d\alpha ,$$

$$\nu f^{*}(0;\beta) = 1 - \frac{\nu f^{*}(0;\beta)}{2\pi i}\int_{a-i\infty}^{a+i\infty} \frac{\{K(\alpha) - M(-\alpha)\}f(0;\alpha)}{\beta+\alpha}\, d\alpha .$$

The method also generalizes to deal with systems of simultaneous linear integral equations with difference and sum kernels.

The linear integral equation (205) with difference kernel and semi-infinite range can be solved exactly by means of the Wiener-Hopf technique. The important step is a factorization of the form

$$(226)\quad K_{+}(s)\, K_{-}(s) = \lambda^2 + K(s) ,$$

where $K(s)$ is a known function of the complex variable s, and λ^2 is a constant which may be zero. In the case of (205), $\lambda^2 = \nu$, and $K(s)$ is the double-sided Laplace transform of the kernel $k(t)$, defined as in (215). It is assumed that $K(s)$ is regular in a strip parallel to the imaginary axis. For simplicity we shall assume that $k(t)$ is a function of $|t|$, so that $K(s)$ is an even function of s. We also assume that the strip of regularity can be taken to be $-c < \text{Re } s < c$. The functions K_+, K_- have to be determined so that $K_+(s)$ is regular in the right-half-plane $\text{Re } s > -c$, and $K_-(s)$ is regular in the left-half-plane $\text{Re } s < c$. We are assuming that $K(s)$ is an even function of s, and in this case it can be shown that

(227) $$K_-(-s) = K_+(s) .$$

Without going into detail, and without specifying conditions necessary for a rigorous treatment, we solve (206) by means of the Wiener-Hopf technique. The equation is extended to $x < 0$ by writing

(228) $$\int_0^\infty k(x-t)\ f(t;\beta)\ dt = h(x), \qquad -\infty < x \le 0 ,$$

where h is of course unknown. An application of a double-sided Laplace transform to (206), (228) then gives (remembering that we have set $\nu = \lambda^2$):

(229) $$\{\lambda^2 + K(s)\}\ F_+(s,\beta) = \frac{1}{s+\beta} + H_-(s)$$

where $F_+(s,\beta)$ has been defined in (208), and

$$H_-(s) = \int_{-\infty}^0 h(x)\ e^{-sx}\ dx .$$

Using (226), and rearranging, (229) becomes

(230) $$K_+(s)\ F_+(s,\beta) - \frac{1}{K_-(-\beta)\,(s+\beta)} = \frac{H_-(s)}{K_-(s)} + \left\{\frac{1}{K_-(s)} - \frac{1}{K_-(-\beta)}\right\}\frac{1}{s+\beta} .$$

It is necessary to impose conditions to ensure that the left side is regular and bounded in $\text{Re } s > -c$, the right side in $\text{Re } s < c$. There is a common strip of regularity so that this equation defines a function which is regular and bounded in the whole s-plane. By Liouville's theorem this function can only be a constant. We impose conditions to ensure that this constant is zero, and then (230) gives, on remembering (227),

$$F_+(s,\beta) = \frac{1}{K_+(s)\ K_+(\beta)\ (s+\beta)} .$$

A comparison of this equation with (212) shows that, since we are dealing with the self-adjoint case for which $f = f^*$,

$$K_+(s) = \{\nu^{1/2} f(0; s)\}^{-1} . \tag{231}$$

In particular, in the case of the Milne kernel (218), in conjunction with which we took $\nu = 1$, we see from (221) that

$$H(x) = 1/K_+(1/x) .$$

The unknown functions in the integral relations and integral equation; derived in the last two sections are directly related to the split-functions in the Wiener-Hopf technique.

It is of some interest to establish the integral relation for $K_+(s)$, corresponding to (216) for $f(0; \beta)$, directly. This can be done in the following way. Suppose that $K(s)$ tends to zero as s tends to infinity in the strip $-c < \operatorname{Re} s < c$, and that the factorization can be performed in such a way that $K_+(s)$, $K_-(s)$ tend to λ as s tends to infinity in the right and left half-planes, $\operatorname{Re} s > -c$, $\operatorname{Re} s < c$, respectively. Then, from Cauchy's theorem,

$$K_+(s) - \lambda = -\frac{1}{2\pi i} \int_{a-i\infty}^{a+i\infty} \frac{\{K_+(\zeta) - \lambda\}}{\zeta - s} d\zeta . \tag{232}$$

where $-c < a < c$, and $\operatorname{Re} s > -c$. On using (226), (228) we obtain

$$K_+(s) - \lambda - \frac{\lambda}{2\pi i} \int_{a-i\infty}^{a+i\infty} \left\{\frac{\lambda}{K_-(\zeta)} - 1\right\} \frac{d\zeta}{\zeta - s} - \frac{1}{2\pi i} \int_{a-i\infty}^{a+i\infty} \frac{K(\zeta)\, d\zeta}{K_-(\zeta)(\zeta - s)} . \tag{233}$$

The first integral is zero since the contour can be closed by a semi-circle at infinity in the left half-plane. On changing the sign of ζ in the last integral, (233) gives

$$K_+(s) - \lambda = \frac{1}{2\pi i} \int_{-a-i\infty}^{-a+i\infty} \frac{K(-\zeta)\, d\zeta}{K_-(-\zeta)(\zeta + s)}$$

i. e.

$$K_+(s) - \lambda = \frac{1}{2\pi i} \int_{b-i\infty}^{b+i\infty} \frac{K(\zeta)\, d\zeta}{K_+(\zeta)(\zeta + s)} , \quad -c < b < c , \tag{234}$$

where we have used (227). This is the required integral relation satisfied by $K_+(s)$. For specific forms of $K(\zeta)$ it can be reduced to an integral equation by deforming the contour along branch cuts.

The point of the procedure given in this section is that it converts singular integral equations with difference kernels into nonlinear integral equations with well-behaved kernels. We can regard these as generalizations of the H-equation, and we have seen in §11 that the H-equation is easy to solve numerically. The method given in this section therefore yields an alternative appraoch to the numerical solution of singular integral equations with difference kernels.

16. Additional comments

On reading this paper in typescript, it seems desirable to add the following comments.

We have been concerned mainly with finite difference methods, since in general it will be necessary to resort to an automatic computer to obtain numerical solutions of nonlinear integral equations. Nevertheless the reader should bear in mind that sometimes approximate analytical solutions can be obtained by exercising a certain amount of ingenuity. An interesting example is given by M. J. Lighthill [32a], who considers the Volterra equation

$$[F(z)]^4 = -\frac{1}{2z^{1/2}} \int_0^z \frac{dF(u)}{du} \frac{du}{(z^{3/2}-u^{3/2})^{1/3}}, \quad F(0) = 1 . \tag{235}$$

If we use Abel's inversion formula and integrate once, we obtain

$$F(z) = 1 - \frac{3\sqrt{3}}{\pi} \int_0^z \frac{u[F(u)]^4 \, du}{(z^{3/2} - u^{3/2})^{2/3}} .$$

It is clear from iterative solution of this last equation that $F(z)$ can be expanded as a power series in z, for small z. This gives:

$$F(z) = 1 - 1.461z + 7.252z^2 - 46.46z^3 + 332.9z^4 - 2538z^5 + 20120z^6 - \ldots . \tag{236}$$

If the general term of this series is denoted by $a_n z^n$, it is found that a_{n-1}/a_n is almost constant for large n, and this ratio tends to -0.106, as n tends to infinity. This indicates that there is a singularity at $z = -0.106$. If it is assumed that (235) is true for negative z, and that the solution near the singularity is of the form $A(z+k)^\lambda$ where A, λ, k are constants, it is easy to prove that $\lambda = -1/9$. There are several ways of estimating A, k. Lighthill assumes that $k = -0.106$ from the series, and deduces $A = 0.852$. The method is extended to give

(237) $$F(z) \approx 0.852\,(z + 0.106)^{-1/9} - 0.198\,(z + 0.106)^{1/3} \; .$$

To obtain the asymptotic behavior of $F(z)$ for large z, suppose that $F(z) \sim Bz^{-\lambda}$ as z tends to infinity. We split the range $(0, z)$ into $(0, w)$, (w, z) where we shall later choose $w = z^p$, $0 < p < 1$. Then, retaining only the dominant terms,

$$\int_0^w \frac{dF(u)}{du} \frac{du}{(z^{3/2}-u^{3/2})^{1/3}} \sim \frac{1}{z^{1/2}} \int_0^w \frac{dF(u)}{du}\, du \sim -\frac{F(0)}{z^{1/2}} \; .$$

$$\int_w^z \frac{dF(u)}{du} \frac{du}{(z^{3/2}-u^{3/2})^{1/3}} \sim -\lambda B \int_w^z \frac{u^{-\lambda-1}du}{(z^{3/2}-u^{3/2})^{1/3}}$$

$$= -\frac{\lambda B}{z^{\frac{1}{2}+\lambda}} \int_{w/z}^1 \frac{v^{-\lambda-1}dv}{(1-v^{3/2})^{1/3}} \sim \frac{B}{z^{1/2}w^{\lambda}} \; .$$

Hence (235) gives, retaining only the dominant terms,

$$B^4 z^{-4\lambda} = \frac{1}{2z} \; ,$$

or $\lambda = \frac{1}{4}$, $B^4 = \frac{1}{2}$, and $F(z) \sim 0.8409 z^{-\frac{1}{4}}$, for large z . Lighthill gives the following further terms in the expansion:

(238) $$F(z) \sim 0.8409\, z^{-\frac{1}{4}} - 0.1524\, z^{-\frac{1}{2}} - 0.0195\, z^{-\frac{3}{4}} - 0.0038\, z^{-1} - \dots \; .$$

The result (236) is used for $0 < z < 0.1$, (238) for $z > 0.5$, and (237) is used as a guide to the shape of the curve of $F(z)$ in $0.1 < z < 0.5$. In this way it is possible to estimate $F(z)$ to within one or two percent over the whole range of z .

Another comment which should be added is the following. We have made no mention of an application of numerical integration by means of which Chandrasekhar ([90], pp. 110-114) has obtained an explicit approximate solution of the H-equation (150). Equation (150) is replaced by:

$$H_n(x) = 1 + xH_n(x) \sum_{j=1}^{n} \frac{a_j \Psi(x_j)}{x + x_j} H_n(x_j) \; ,$$

where the $a_{\pm j}$ ($j = 1, \ldots n$, $a_{-j} = a_j$), and $x_{\pm j}$ ($j = 1, \ldots n$, $x_{-j} = -x_j$) are the weights and subdivisions appropriate to a quadrature formula in the interval $(-1, 1)$. Then Chandrasekhar shows that the solution of this equation which is regular and non-zero in $x \geq 0$ is given by

$$H_n(x) = \frac{1}{x_1 \ldots x_n} \frac{(x_1+x) \ldots (x_n+x)}{(1+k_1x) \ldots (1+k_nx)},$$

where the k_i ($i = 1, \ldots n$) are the non-negative roots of the associated characteristic equation

$$1 = 2 \sum_{j=1}^{n} \frac{a_j \Psi(x_j)}{1-k^2 x_j^2}.$$

Dr. P. M. Anselone has pointed out to me that it can be proved that $H_n(x)$ tends to $H(x)$, uniformly in x, as n tends to infinity, by means of the arguments in his interesting papers [85], [86]. These papers refer to the solution by Gaussian quadrature of the linear integro-differential equations of radiative transfer, but the method can be extended to more general quadrature formulae.

As a final comment, the reader's attention is drawn to references like [45], [46], [48], [51] which obtain results for general operator equations which have immediate numerical applications to nonlinear integral equations. A section on this topic might well have been included in the present paper. However this subject is represented in other papers in this volume, and it was decided that a better overall balance would be obtained by concentrating attention in this paper on finite difference methods on the one hand, and nonlinear integral equations which arise in physical applications, on the other.

17. Acknowledgements

The numerical work in §4 was carried out as a result of conversations with Dr. Bill Jameson of Collins Radio, Cedar Rapids, in connection with heat loss from satellites. Dr. J. Nohel has also encouraged this work.

I am indebted to Mrs. S. C. Wu who carried out the computations summarized in the tables in this paper. I am also indebted to Drs. P. M. Anselone and L. B. Rall for various references.

REFERENCES

I The numerical solution of nonlinear integral equations - general references

[1] L. Collatz, The Numerical Treatment of Differential Equations, 3rd Edn., Springer (1960).

[2] L. Fox (editor), Numerical Solution of Ordinary and Partial Differential Equations, Pergamon (1962).

[3] Symposium on the Numerical Treatment of Ordinary Differential Equations, Integral and Integro-differential Equations, Birkhauser-Verlag (1960). Survey paper by A. Walther and B. Dejon, General report on the numerical treatment of integral and integro-differential equations, 645-671.

II The numerical solution of linear integral equations (see also above references)

[4] H. Bueckner, Die praktische Behandlung von Intergralgleichungen Springer (1952).

[5] H. Edels, K. Hearne, and A. Young, Numerical solution of the Abel integral equation, J. Math. Phys. 41 (1962), 62-75.

[6] L. Fox and E. T. Goodwin, The numerical solution of non-singular linear integral equations, Phil. Trans. Roy. Soc. 245 (1953), 501-534.

[7] J. G. Jones, On the numerical solution of convolution integral equations, and systems of such equations, Math. Comp. 15 (1961), 131-142.

[8] A. Young, The application of product integration to the numerical solution of integral equations, Proc. Roy. Soc. A 224 (1954), 561-573.

III Miscellaneous references on numerical methods

[9] P. Henrici, Discrete Variable Methods in Ordinary Differential Equations, Wiley (1962).

[10] J. Todd (editor), Survey of Numerical Analysis, McGraw-Hill (1962).

IV Solution by analogue computer

[11] J. Crank, The Differential Analyzer, Longmans (1947).

[12] R. Gawronski, The application of the analogue computer to solutions of some nonlinear integral and integro-differential equations, Arch. Mech. Stos. 2 (1959), 37-42.

[13] H. Wallman, An electronic integral transform computer and the practical solution of integral equations, J. Franklin Inst. 250 (1950), 45-61.

V Step-by-step methods for the numerical solution of nonlinear Volterra equations

(See also papers in [3] by M. Laudet and H. Oules, R. Pennachi, P. Pouzet, and M. A. Sneider, and references given in these papers.)

[14] E. Aparo, Sulla resoluzione numerica delle equazione integrali di Volterra di seconda specie, Alti Acad. Naz. Lincei Rend. Cl. Sci. Fiz. Mat. Nat. (8) 26 (1959), 183-188.

[15] J. Douglas and B. F. Jones, Numerical methods for integro-differential equations of parabolic and hyperbolic types, Num. Math. 4 (1962), 96-102.

[16] G. F. Miller, A note on the numerical solution of certain nonlinear integral equations, Proc. Roy. Soc. A 236 (1956), 529-534.

[17] H. Oules, Une methode de resolution numerique de l' equation integrale du type de Volterra, Chiffres 3 (1960), 137-142.

[18] P. Pouzet, Evaluation des erreurs de troncature pour les formules de Runge-Kutta relatives au traitement numerique des equations integrales de type Volterra, Comptes Rendus Acad. Sci. Paris 252 (1961), 1901-1903.

VI Relevant finite difference methods for hyperbolic and parabolic partial differential equations

[19] J. B. Diaz, On an analogue of the Euler-Cauchy polygon method for the numerical solution of $u_{xy} = f(x, y, u, u_x, u_y)$, Archive for Rat. Mech. Anal. 1 (1958), 357-390.

[20] J. Douglas, A survey of numerical methods for parabolic differential equations, Advances in Computers, Vol. II, Ed. L. Alt, Academic Press (1961).

[21] R. H. Moore, A Runge-Kutta procedure for the Gousat problem in hyperbolic partial differential equations, Archive for Rat. Mech. Anal. 1(1961), 37-63.

VII Miscellaneous references on nonlinear Volterra integral equations

[22] H.T. Davis, Introduction to nonlinear differential and integral equations, Dover (1962).

[22a] B. F. Jones, The determination of a coefficient in a parabolic differential equation, I. J. Math. Mech. 11 (1962), 907-918 II (with J. Douglas) ibid. 919-926.

[23] E. G. Keller, Mathematics of Modern Engineering, Vol. II, Wiley (1942)

[24] J. Lennertz Beitrag zur Frage nach der Wirkung eines Querstosses auf einen Stab, Ing. Arch. 8 (1935), 37-46.

[25] V. Volterra, Lecons sur la theorie mathematique de la lutte pour la vie, Paris (1931).

[26] V. Volterra, Theory of functionals and of integral and integro-differential equations, Dover (1959).

VIII The boundary-layer equations

[27] D. Meksyn, New Methods in Laminar Boundary-layer Theory, Pergamon (1961).

[28] J. Siekmann, The laminar boundary-layer along a flat plate, Zeits. F. Flugwiss. 10 (1962), 278-281.

[29] J. Siekmann, Note on an integral equation occurring in stagnation point flow, ZAMP 13 (1962), 182-186.

[30] H. Weyl, On the differential equations of the simplest boundary layer problem, Ann. Math. 43 (1942), 381-407.

IX Nonlinear Volterra equations and heat conduction (a) Nonlinear boundary conditions

[31] P.L. Chambré, Nonlinear heat transfer problem, J. Appl. Phys. 30 (1959), 1683-8.

[32] N. Levinson, A nonlinear Volterra equation arising in the theory of superfluidity, J. Math. Anal. & Applic. 1 (1960), 1-11. (See C.C. Lin, Phys. Rev. Letters, 2 (1959), 245-246).

[32a] M. J. Lighthill, Contributions to the theory of heat transfer through a laminar boundary layer, Proc. Roy. Soc. 202A (1950), 359-377.

[33] W. R. Mann and F. Wolf, Heat transfer between solids and gases under nonlinear boundary conditions, Quart. Appl. Math. 9 (1951), 163-184.

[34] K. Padmavally, On a nonlinear integral equation, J. Math. Mech. 7 (1958), 533-555.

[35] J. H. Roberts and W. R. Mann, A nonlinear integral equation of Volterra type, Pacific J. Math. 1 (1951), 431-445.

X Nonlinear Volterra equations and heat conduction (b) Moving boundaries

[36] B. A. Boley, A method of heat conduction analysis of melting and solidification problems, J. Math. Phys. 40 (1961), 300-313.

[37] G. W. Evans, E. Isaacson and J. K. L. MacDonald, Stefan-like problems, Quart. Appl. Math. 8 (1950), 312-319.

[38] I. I. Kolodner, Free boundary problem for the heat equation with applications to problems of change of phase, Comm. Pure Appl. Math. 9 (1956), 1-31.

[39] N. M. H. Lightfoot, The solidification of molten steel, Proc. Lond. Math. Soc. 31 (1930), 97-116.

XI Miscellaneous references on nonlinear heat-conduction and diffusion

[40] J. Crank, The Mathematics of Diffusion, Oxford Univ. Press (1956).

[41] M. R. Hopkins, Heat conduction in a medium having thermal properties depending on the temperature, Proc. Phys. Soc. 50 (1938), 703-706.

XII Topics related to the numerical solution of nonlinear Fredholm integral equations

[42] C. M. Alblow and C. L. Perry, Iterative solutions of the Dirichlet problem for $\Delta u = u^2$, J. Soc. Industr. Appl. Math. 7 (1959), 459-467.

[43] A. N. Baluev, On the approximate solution of nonlinear integral equations, Gos. Univ. Uc. Zap. Ser. Mat. Nauk. 33 (1958), 28-31.

[44] H. F. Bueckner, An iterative method for solving nonlinear integral equations, See Rome Symposium [3] above, 613-643. This was originally issued as M. R. C. report 207, Dec. 1960.

[45] L. Collatz and J. Schroeder, Einschliessen der Losungen von Randwertaufgaben, Num. Math. 1 (1959), 61-72.

[46] L. V. Kantorovich, Functional analysis and applied mathematics, Uspekhi Mat. Nauk 3 (1948), 89-185. (Nat. Bur. Stand. translation by C. D. Benster, March, 1952).

[47] M. Lotkin, The solution by iteration of nonlinear integral equations, J. Math. Phys. 33 (1955), 346-355.

[48] K. Nickel, Fehlerabschatzungs-und Eindeutigkeitssatze fur Integro-differentialgleichungen, Archive for Rat. Mech. Anal. 8 (1961), 159-180.

[49] E. J. Nystrom, Zur numerische Lösung von Randwertaufgaben bei gewöhnlichen differentialgleichungen, Acta Math. 76 (1944), 157-184.

[50] L. B. Rall, An application of Newton's method to the solution of a nonlinear integral equation, Tech. Rep. No. 7, Dept. of Math., Oregon State College, (1955).

[51] J. Schroeder, Funktionanalytische Herleitung von Fehlerabschatzungen und ihre praktische Durchfuhrung auf Rechenanlagen, Zeits. Ang. Math. Mech. 40 (1960), T27-37.

XIII Nonlinear bending of shells

[52] H. B. Keller and E. L. Reiss, Iterative solutions for the nonlinear bending of circular plates, Comm. Pure Appl. Math. 11 (1958), 273-292.

[53] M. Stippes and R. E. Beckett, Symmetrically loaded circular plates, J. Franklin Inst. 257 (1954), 465-479.

XIV Nonlinear elasticity, plasticity, and creep

[54] A. A. Il'yushin, Some problems in the theory of plastic deformations, Prikl. Mat. Mekh. 7 (1943), 245-272.

[55] M. A. Jaswon and A. J. E. Foreman, The non-Hookean interaction of a dislocation with a lattice inhomogeneity, Phil. Mag. 43 (1952), 201-220.

[56] A. Mendelson, M. H. Hirschberg and S. S. Manson, A general approach to the practical solution of creep problems, Trans. A.S.M.E. 81, Journal of Basic Eng. (1959), 585-594.

[57] A. Mendelson and S. S. Manson, Practical solution of plastic deformation problems in the elastic-plastic range, NACA Tech. Rep. R-28(1959).

[58] V. M. Panferov, On the convergence of a method of elastic solutions for the problem of elasto-plastic bending of a plate, Prikl. Mat. Mekh. 16 (1952), 195-212.

[59] V. M. Panferov, A general method of solution of boundary problems in the theory of elasto-plastic deformations for the simple loadings of A.A. Il'yusin, Vestnik Moscow Univ. (1952), No. 2, 41-62.

[60] M. I. Rozovskii On nonlinear integral equations of creep for a cylindrical shell, subjected to external pressure, Izv. Akad. Nauk SSSR, Otd Tekh. Nauk No. 9 (1958), 139-142.

XV The Theodorsen-Garrick method for conformal mapping (This is a selection from an extensive literature.)

[61] G. Birkhoff, D. M. Young and E. H. Zarantonello, Numerical methods in conformal mapping, Proc. Symp. Appl. Math. IV, McGraw-Hill (1953), 117-140, (A preliminary version appeared in: Proc. Nat. Acad. Sci. U.S.A., 37(1951), 411-414.)

[62] M. S. Friberg, A new method for the effective determination of conformal maps, University of Minnesota thesis (1951). (See also [65], [76].)

[63] I. E. Garrick, Conformal mapping in aerodynamics, with emphasis on the method of successive conjugates, Nat. Bur. Stand., Applied Math. Series 18 (1952), 137-147.

[64] S. Goldstein, Low-drag and suction airfoils, J. Aero. Sci. 15(1948), 189-214 (See also: A theory of aerofoils of small thickness, Parts 1-6, Current papers Aero. Res. Council, London, Nos. 68-73, issued (1956).)

[65] C. Gram (Editor), Selected Numerical Methods, Regnecentralen, Copenhagen (1962).

[66] C. Kaplan, On a new method for calculating the potential flow past a body of revolution, NACA Rep. No. 752 (1943).

[67] I. Naiman, Numerical evaluation of the ϵ-integral occuring in the Theodorsen arbitrary airfoil potential theory, NACA Wartime Report, Langley Field, L-136 (1944).

[68] I. Naiman, Numerical evaluation by harmonic analysis of the ϵ-function of the Theodorsen arbitrary-airfoil potential theory, NACA Wartime Report, Langley Field, L-153 (1945).

[69] A. M. Ostrowski, On the convergence of Theodorsen's and Garrick's method of conformal mapping, Nat. Bur. Stand., Applied Math. Ser. 18 (1952), 149-163.

[70] A. M. Ostrowski, On a discontinuous analogue of Theodorsen's and Garrick's method, Nat. Bur. Stand., Appl. Math. Sec. 18 (1952), 165-174.

[71] A. M. Ostrowski, Theodorsen's and Garrick's method for conformal mapping of a unit circle on to an ellipse, Nat. Bur. Stand., Appl. Math. Ser. 42 (1955), 3-5.

[72] A. Robinson and J. A. Laurmann, Wing Theory, Cambridge Univ. Press (1956).

[73] E. Study, Vorlesungen uber ausgewahlte Gegenstande der Geometrie, Zweites Heft, Konforme Abbildung Einfach-zusammenhangender Bereiche, Teubner (1913).

[74] T. Theodorsen, Theory of wing sections of arbitrary shape, NACA Report No. 411 (1931).

[75] T. Theodorsen and I. E. Garrick, General potential theory of arbitrary wing sections, NACA Report No. 452 (1933).

[76] S. E. Warschawski, Numerical methods of conformal mapping, Proc. Symp. Appl. Math. VI, McGraw-Hill (1956), 219-250.

[77] L. C. Woods, The Theory of Subsonic Plane Flow, Cambridge Univ. Press (1961).

XVI Fluid flows with free boundaries (See also [61])

[78] G. Birkhoff and E. H. Zarantonello, Jets, Wakes and Cavities, Academic Press (1957).

[78a] G. Birkhoff, H. H. Goldstine, and E. H. Zarantonello, Rend. Sem. Mat. Torino, 13 (1954), 205-223.

[79] S. Brodetsky, Discontinuous flow past circular and elliptic cylinders, Proc. Roy. Soc. A 102 (1923), 542-553.

[80] A. Lauck, Die Überfall über ein Wehr, Zeits. Ang. Math. Mech. 5 (1925), 1-16.

[81] L. M. Milne-Thomson, Theoretical Hydrodynamics, 4th ed., Macmillan (1961).

[82] E. Trefftz, Uber die Kontraktion kreisformiger Flussigkeitsstrahlen, Zeits. Math. Phys. 64 (1916), 34-61.

XVII Transonic fluid flow

[83] J. R. Spreiter, Aerodynamics of wings and bodies at transonic speeds, J. Aero/Space Sci. 26 (1959), 465-486.

[84] J. R. Spreiter, A. Y. Alksne and B. J. Hyett, Theoretical pressure distributions for several nonlifting airfoils at high subsonic speeds, NACA Tech. Note 4148 (1958).

XVIII Radiative transfer (The Ambartzumian-Chandrasekhar equations)

[85] P. M. Anselone, Convergence of Chandrasekhar's method for the problem of diffuse reflection, Monthly Notices Roy. Astr. Soc. 120 (1960), 498-503.

[86] P. M. Anselone, Convergence of the Wick-Chandrasekhar approximation technique in radiative transfer, Astrophys. J. 128 (1958), 124-129. (See also Astrophys. J. 130 (1959), 881-883.)

[87] I. W. Busbridge, The Mathematics of Radiative Transfer, Cambridge Univ. Press (1960).

[88] I. W. Busbridge and D. W. N. Stibbs, On the intensities of interlocked multiplet lines in the Milne-Eddington model, Monthly Notices, Roy. Astr. Soc. 114 (1954), 2-16.

[89] K. M. Case, On Wiener-Hopf equations, Annals of Physics 2 (1957), 384-405.

[90] S. Chandrasekhar, Radiative Transfer, Dover reprint (1960).

[91] S. Chandrasekhar and F. H. Breen, On the radiative equilibrium of a stellar atmosphere, XVI, Astrophys. J. 105 (1947), 435-440: XIX ibid. 106 (1947), 143-144.

[92] S. Chandrasekhar, D. Elbert and A. Franklin, The X- and Y-functions for isotropic scattering, Astrophys. J. 115 (1952), 244-268, 269-278.

[93] K. I. Gross, Discussion of an iterative solution to an equation of radiative transfer, J. Math. Phys. 41 (1962), 53-61.

[94] D. L. Harris, Diffuse reflection from planetary atmospheres, Astrophys. J. 126 (1957), 408-412.

[95] D. F. Mayers, Calculation of Chandrasekhar's X- and Y-functions for isotropic scattering, Monthly Notices Roy. Astr. Soc. 123 (1962), 471-484.

[96] T. W. Mullikin, Radiative transfer in homogeneous plane-parallel atmospheres, Rand Corporation RM-3209-NASA, August, 1962.

[97] V. V. Sobolev, Diffuse radiation in a medium with mirror-reflecting boundaries, Soviet Physics Doklady (translation) 6 (1961), 21-23.

[98] V. V. Sobolev, A Treatise on Radiative Transfer, Van Nostrand (1963).

[99] D. W. N. Stibbs and R. E. Weir, On the H-functions for isotropic scattering, Monthly Notices, Roy. Astr. Soc. 119 (1959), 512-525.

[99a] G. M. Wing, An Introduction to Transport Theory, Wiley (1962).

XIX Radiative transfer (other references)

[100] V. Baumann, Eine nichtlineare Integro-differentialgleichung der Warmeubertragung bei Warmeleitung und-strahlung, Math. Zeits 64 (1956), 353-384.

[101] R. E. Bellman, R. E. Kalaba and M. C. Prestrud, Invariant Imbedding and Radiative Transfer in Slabs of Finite Thickness, Elsevier (1963).

[102] R. Bellman, R. Kalaba and G. M. Wing, On the principle of invariant bedding and neutron transport theory, II Functional equations, J. Math. Mech. 7 (1958), 741-756.

[103] A. Walther, J. Dorr and E. Eller, Mathematische Berechnung der Temperaturverteilung in der Glasschmelze mit Beruck-sichtigung von Warmeleitung und Warmestrahlung, Glastech. Ber. 26 (1953), 133-140.

[104] G. M. Wing, Solution of a time-dependent one-dimensional neutron transport problem, J. Math. Mech. 7 (1958), 757-766.

XX Electron beams and plasmas. Simplified forms of the Boltzmann equation

[105] M. Born and H. S. Green, A General Kinetic Theory of Liquids, Cambridge Univ. Press (1949).

[106] A. Caruso and A. Cavalière, The structure of the collionless plasma-sheath transition, Il Nuovo Cimento, 26 (1962), 1389-1404.

[107] O. P. Gandhi and J. E. Rowe, Nonlinear theory of injected-beam crossed-field devices, Article in: Crossed-field Microwave devices, Vol. I, Academic Press (1961).

[108] H. W. Liepmann, R. Narasimha and M. T. Chaline, Structure of a plane shock layer, Physics of Fluids, 5 (1962), 1313-1324.

[109] F. M. Nekrasov, Nonlinear theory of oscillations in an electron-ion plasma, Z. Tehn. Fiz. 30 (1960), 774-780. (Transl.: Tech. Phys. USSR, 5 (1961), 727-733).

(110] F. M. Nekrasov, On the nonlinear theory of stationary processes in an electron plasma, Z. Eksper. Teor. Fiz. 38 (1960), 233-238. (Transl.: Soviet Phys. JETP, 11 (1961), 170-173.)

D. H. HYERS

Some Nonlinear Integral Equations of Hydrodynamics

1. Introduction

We shall deal principally with two classical problems from the mathematical theory of water waves. The first problem is that of the existence of periodic surface waves of permanent type, under the assumptions that the flow is incompressible, irrotational, and two-dimensional. The designation "of permanent type" refers to the hypothesis that the wave profile (air-water interface) moves down the channel without change of form, or more exactly, that the flow appears stationary when viewed from a coordinate system attached to the wave profile.

The second problem concerns the existence of the (non-periodic) solitary wave, and will be discussed below in section 4. Recent results and some generalizations of these problems will be considered briefly in sections 3, 5, and 6.

There are two characteristic difficulties in such problems. First, they are free boundary problems, so that the region of flow in the geometric plane is unknown. Of course, in the cases considered here (stationary flows) one can get around this difficulty by mapping the flow region onto some other plane, e.g., the plane of the complex potential function. (See, for example, Stoker [IV]).

The second difficulty still remains. This is the nonlinear character of the boundary condition to be satisfied at the free boundary. Since the pressure is constant at this air-water interface, it follows from Bernoulli's law that

$$|w|^2 + 2gY = \text{const.} \tag{1.1}$$

along the profile, where $w = u - iv$ is the complex conjugate of the velocity vector, g is the acceleration of gravity, and Y is the (vertical) ordinate of the profile.

Another point that should be mentioned here is that these problems have the character of bifurcation problems. For in the case of a flat, or infinitely distant bottom, there is always the trivial solution present, in which the flow is merely that with $w = 0$ and with constant Y. Thus, non-trivial solutions for small amplitudes must "branch off" from this trivial solution.

The first problem referred to above was solved in the small by A. I. Nekrasov in Russia, and by T. Levi-Civita in Italy [28,23]. Both authors, assuming infinite depth, mapped the portion of the geometric plane below the profile and between two vertical lines one wave-length apart onto the unit disc in another complex plane, with the origin in the new plane corresponding to the infinitely deep points of the geometric plane (see Figure 1). Levi-Civita then proved the existence of the solution by the use of a rather complicated procedure involving approximations by (nonlinear) trigonometric expressions, the method of majorants, etc.

Nekrasov, on the other hand, attacked the problem by using a known Green's function to reduce the problem to that of solving the following system of nonlinear integral equations:

$$\theta(\varphi) = \mu \int_{-\pi}^{\pi} K(\varphi, s) [\Upsilon(s)]^{-1} \sin\theta(s)\, ds ,$$

(1.2)

$$\Upsilon(\varphi) = 1 + \mu \int_{0}^{\varphi} \sin\theta(s)\, ds .$$

Let λ denote the wave length and c the velocity of propagation of the wave; then the parameter μ occurring in (1.2) is defined by:

(1.3)
$$\mu = \frac{3g\lambda}{2\pi c^2 |w_t|^3} .$$

Here $c|w_t|$ is the particle speed at the trough T (with the understanding, already mentioned, that the coordinate system is attached to the wave profile). The kernel is defined by:

(1.4)
$$K(\varphi, s) = \sum_{n=1}^{\infty} \frac{\sin n\varphi \sin ns}{3n\pi} ;$$

the unknown function $\theta(\varphi)$ is the angle of inclination of the velocity vector along the free boundary (F. B. in Figure 1). The independent variable φ is also shown in Figure 1. It is the angle of $\zeta = \exp[\frac{2\pi i}{\lambda c}F]$, where $F(z)$ is the complex velocity potential.

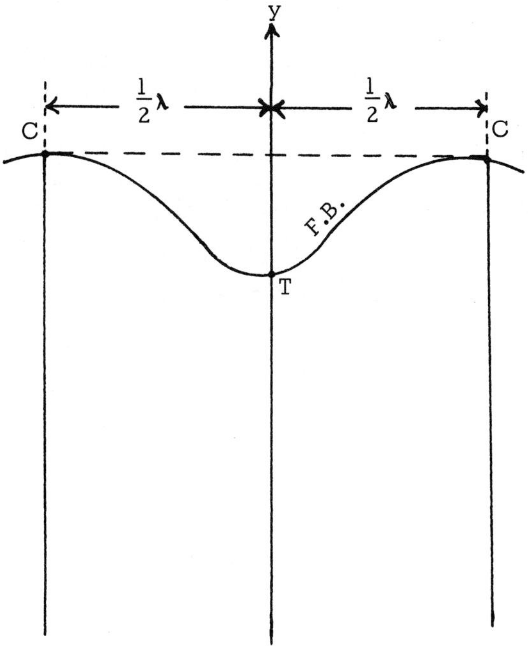

Geometric Plane

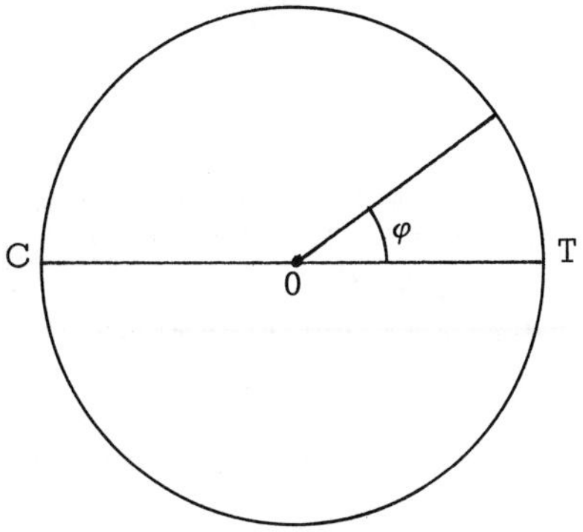

ζ - Plane

Figure 1

2. Solution of The First Problem By The Method of Liapunov-Schmidt

A classical method of investigation of the system (1.2) is to make use of the theory of Schmidt-Liapunov [26], [33]. E. Schmidt's method, and the particular application to this problem, are both given in Lichtenstein's book [III]. Other variants of the same general approach may be found, for example, in [I] and [17b]. In all these versions of the theorem for (1.2), the results hold only in the small, i.e., the amplitude of the wave is severely restricted in size.

In order to sketch the Liapunov-Schmidt approach as applied to our problem, we write the system (1.2) in the abbreviated form:

$$\theta = \mu K F[\mu, \theta] \quad , \tag{2.1}$$

where K stands for the linear integral operator

$$Kf = \int_{-\pi}^{\pi} K(\varphi, s)\, f(s)\, ds \quad , \tag{2.2}$$

and where

$$F[\mu, \theta] = \frac{\sin \theta(\varphi)}{1 + \mu \int_{0}^{\varphi} \sin \theta(s)\, ds} \quad . \tag{2.3}$$

We may regard (2.1) as a nonlinear functional equation for the unknown element θ of the Banach space B of all continuous functions on the closed interval $[-\pi, \pi]$ which vanish at the end points of this interval, with the usual maximum norm.

Taking the Fréchet differential of both sides of (2.1) and evaluating it at the point $\theta = 0$, we obtain the homogeneous "variational equation:"

$$\delta\theta - \mu K \delta\theta = 0 \quad . \tag{2.4}$$

The eigenvalues and eigenfunctions of this linear integral equation are displayed by the formula (1.4). For example, the first eigenvalue is $\mu_1 = 3\pi$, corresponding to the eigenfunction $\theta_1 = \sin \varphi$. Incidentally, this first eigenfunction corresponds to the linearized solution of the problem, ascribed to Airy (cf. H. Lamb [viii]).

In order to solve (2.1) for small θ, and with μ in the neighborhood of μ_1, we rewrite the equation in the form:

$$\theta - \mu_1 K\theta = \mu K \{F[\mu, \theta] - \theta\} + \alpha K\theta \quad , \tag{2.5}$$

in which

$$\alpha = \mu - \mu_1 \quad . \tag{2.6}$$

By a well known theorem from the theory of linear integral equations with symmetric kernels (Fredholm alternative), the equation

$$\theta - \mu_1 K\theta = \rho \qquad (\rho \in B) \tag{2.7}$$

will have a solution if and only if the right member ρ is orthogonal to the solution θ_1 of (2.4). Thus a necessary condition for the solution of (2.5) is that:

$$L[\mu K\{F[\mu, \theta] - \theta\} + \alpha K\theta] = 0 \quad , \tag{2.8}$$

where L is the linear functional:

$$L[\rho] = \int_{-\pi}^{\pi} \theta_1(\varphi)\, \rho(\varphi)\, d\varphi \quad . \tag{2.9}$$

Following Liapunov's method, we consider the modified equation:

$$\theta - \mu_1 K\theta = \rho - \pi^{-1} L[\rho]\,\theta_1 \quad , \tag{2.10}$$

The right member of which is constructed so that it is orthogonal to θ_1; ρ is now to be regarded as an abbreviation for the right member of (2.5):

$$\rho = \mu K\{F[\mu, \theta] - \theta\} + \alpha K\theta \quad . \tag{2.11}$$

(Note that (2.10) coincides with (2.7) when ρ and θ_1 are orthogonal.) According to the Fredholm alternative, already mentioned, eq. (2.10) may be "solved" in the form:

$$\theta = M[\rho - \pi^{-1} L[\rho]\,\theta_1] + \beta\theta_1 \quad , \tag{2.12}$$

where β is an arbitrary real constant. Here M is a bounded linear operator on B to B; in Friedrichs' terminology, it is a "pseudo-inverse" of $I - \mu_1 K$ (see [I], p. 144, ff.), and has the property that $(I - \mu_1 K)\, M(I - \mu_1 K) = I - \mu_1 K$.

Next, by restricting the quantities $\|\theta\|$, $|\alpha|$, and $|\beta|$ to be sufficiently small, we see from (2.6), (2.11), and (2.12) that the right member of (2.12) can be made small. Thus we can solve (2.12) by the standard procedure of iteration (here it is convenient to take $\beta\theta_1$ as the starting element). The resulting sequence of successive approximations will converge to a limit in B; this limit will be designated by $\theta(\alpha, \beta)$, since it depends on the values of the two parameters exhibited.

The resulting two parameter family of solutions of (2.12) is now inserted into (2.8); the resulting equation:

$$\Lambda(\alpha, \beta) \equiv L[(\mu_1 + \alpha) K \{F[\mu_1 + \alpha, \theta(\alpha, \beta)] - \theta(\alpha, \beta)\}] + \alpha LK[\theta(\alpha,\beta)] = 0 \tag{2.13}$$

is known as the <u>bifurcation equation</u> for the problem. Fortunately, in this particular case, it is not difficult to show that corresponding to each sufficiently small value of the parameter β, a value $\alpha = \alpha(\beta)$ of α can be found which will satisfy (2.13). Moreover, $\alpha(\beta)$ is continuously differentiable* in the neighborhood of $\beta = 0$.

It follows immediately that for each (small) β, $\theta(\beta) = \theta(\alpha(\beta), \beta)$ is the required solution of (2.1), with $\mu = \mu_1 + \alpha(\beta)$.

3. <u>Recent Results on the First Problem</u>

Several authors have used Nekrasov's equation as an example of general theories of nonlinear functional equations in Banach spaces, during the past ten years. In particular, M. A. Krasnosel'skii (in Russia) has written on this subject [17 (b)].

Using the theory of topological degree together with the theory of bifurcation, etc., as developed by Schauder and Leray [22] and by E. Rothe [30], Jane Cronin [4], R. Bartle [1], and various others as a foundation, Krasnosel'skii [V], [17(a)] and his Russian colleagues have established a fairly comprehensive "nonlinear spectral theory."

However, until recently, no really significant progress was made in extending the results of Nekrasov and Levi-Civita.

In [17 (b)], Krasnosel'skii analysed the solutions of Nekrasov's equation in detail, as an illustration of a general theory. He showed that various local solutions exist, near each eigenvalue μ_n. However, from the physical point of view, it turns out that all but one of these solutions are essentially "extraneous." In Levi-Civita's classical paper, it was indicated, heuristically, that the local solutions, for μ in the neighborhood of $\mu_n (n = 1, 2, 3, 4, \ldots)$ should correspond to multiples of the basic period, and thus should be simply different mathematical descriptions of the same physical

---

* Actually there are two branches of the function; each branch is continuously differentiable. See Friedrichs [I] p. 132; cf., also Hyers-Ferling [13], p. 72.

problem. The rigorous proof of this heuristic argument, together with a local uniqueness theorem for the physical problem, may be found in Hyers-Ferling [13]. The result is:

Theorem 3.1. There exist positive numbers δ and ϵ such that, for every value of the wave length λ and the propagation velocity c satisfying the inequality:

$$0 < 1 - g\lambda/2\pi c^2 < \delta ,$$

there exists a unique non-trivial wave of permanent type in an infinitely deep channel whose (actual) particle velocity vector (U, V) satisfies $U^2 + V^2 < \epsilon^2$. There are no such waves satisfying this restriction on the velocity together with the inequality:

$$0 \leqq g\lambda/2\pi c^2 - 1 < \delta ,$$

except the trivial one for which $U = V = 0$.

H. F. Bueckner has investigated Nekrasov's equation from a slightly different view point [2]. He developed an iteration scheme suitable for numerical calculations, and numerical experiments were carried out on an I.B.M. 704 computer, here at the M.R.C.

It remained for a Russian mathematician, Yu. P. Krasovskii, to make the big step forward [18 (a)]. Krasovskii attacked the problem by using the "method of cones" (Krasnosel'skii [V, chapter V) and succeeded in establishing an existence theorem for Nekrasov's equation in the large. His method will now be indicated. A look at Figure 1 reveals that if one confines the investigation of the physical problem to symmetric waves (so that $\theta(\varphi)$ is required to be an odd function), then he may deal with the class of continuous, non-negative functions on the interval $[0,\pi]$ which vanish at the end-points of this interval; moreover, the kernel $K(\varphi, s)$ is non-negative on the square: $0 \leq \varphi \leq \pi$, $0 \leq s \leq \pi$. It follows that the linear integral operator (2.2) is a positive operator (if we change the lower limit in the integral to zero instead of $-\pi$). These remarks suggest the attack on the problem by the method of cones.

Let B_0 denote the space of all continuous functions defined on the closed interval $[0, \pi]$ which vanish at the end points of the interval, with the usual maximum norm. The set of such functions which are non-negative form a cone C in B_0. For the present purpose, the operator K is to be defined by:

$$Kf = \int_0^\pi K(\varphi, s) f(s) ds , \tag{3.1}$$

where $f \in B_0$.

Following Krasovskii, we rewrite Nekrasov's equation in the form:

(3.2) $$\theta(\varphi) = \frac{g\lambda}{2\pi c^2} \int_0^{\pi} K(\varphi, s)\, e^{-3C\sigma\theta} \sin\theta\, ds \quad ,$$

where $C\sigma\theta$ is the "harmonic conjugate" of θ satisfying the condition:

(3.3) $$\int_0^{\pi} C\sigma\theta\, ds = 0 \quad .$$

Put

(3.4) $$A\theta = \int_0^{\pi} K(\varphi, s)\, e^{-3C\sigma\theta} \sin\theta\, ds \quad .$$

The problem is then to find θ in the cone $C(\theta \neq 0)$ which satisfies

(3.5) $$\theta = \nu A \theta$$

For some $\nu > 0$. It is not difficult to show that to each solution of this problem there corresponds a fluid flow with the parameters of the flow related by:

(3.6) $$\nu = g\lambda/2\pi c^2 \quad .$$

The operator A is defined in the ball with center at the origin and radius $r < \pi/6$ lying in the space B_0; A is a nonlinear, continuous, and compact operator. Basic to the proof of the existence theorem in the large is the inequality:

(3.7) $$\int_0^{2\pi} e^{\lambda C\sigma\theta}\, ds \leqq \max \frac{2\pi}{\cos\lambda\theta} \, ,$$

where $|\lambda\theta| < \pi/2$.

If one restricts the nonlinear operator A to the inter-section C_r of the cone C and the ball of radius r mentioned above, then A is a positive operator on C_r . Moreover, it can be shown that the operator A has a "monotone minorant" in C_r, in the sense of Krasnosel'skii. Thus, by theorem (2.4), chapter V, p. 269 of [V] , it follows that the positive eigenfunctions of the nonlinear operator A form a continuous branch in C of length r . By applying standard methods of the theory of positive operators, one can show that the whole positive spectrum of A is contained in a certain finite interval $a < \nu < b$, where a and b are positive. Moreover, the quantities a and b do not depend on the norm of θ . Hence, even if there should be waves with the slope of the tangent of their profile greater than $\pi/6$, the corresponding values of ν belong to the interval (a, b) . In particular, it is clear that in a fluid of infinite depth and bounded velocity, waves of arbitrarily large wave length cannot exist.

To summarize, Krasovskii has proved that, for a fluid of infinite depth, there exist periodic symmetric waves for which the maximum slope* of the profile can have any value between 0 and $\pi/6$. In the same paper he also states an existence theorem in the large for the case of finite depth.

4. The Solitary Wave

Another type of steady, two-dimensional flow with a free boundary, and with only gravity acting in addition to the pressure forces, is the solitary wave (see Figure 2). This is distinguished from the periodic type of wave discussed above by the fact that it can only exist when the depth is finite, and by the boundary conditions far upstream and downstream. As indicated in Figure 2, the profile of the free boundary has a horizontal asymptote located at a distance ℓ above the bottom, which, for the present, will assumed to be horizontal and flat.

An interesting discussion of the long history of the problem of the solitary wave will be found in Lamb [VIII] and Stoker [IV].

The first existence proof for such a flow was given by M. A. Lavrent'ev [21]. He started with the known results for periodic waves, with certain modifications, and then used a limiting procedure, with the wave length tending to infinity, in order to obtain the existence of the solitary wave.

Several years later, another (more direct) proof of existence was given by K. O. Friedrichs and D. H. Hyers [9]. The approach is described on pp. 342-351 of Stoker [IV], and will be briefly indicated below.

Recently, several mathematicians have used the methods of the Friedrichs-Hyers paper to obtain results in various other related problems. Some of these recent applications will be outlined briefly in a later section of the present paper.

First, however, it will be necessary to describe the application of the "higher order" shallow water theory of Friedrichs to the

---

* This result is probably the best possible, since the angle of $\pi/6$ corresponds to the limiting case of Stokes's peaked wave (cf., Lamb [VIII], p. 418).

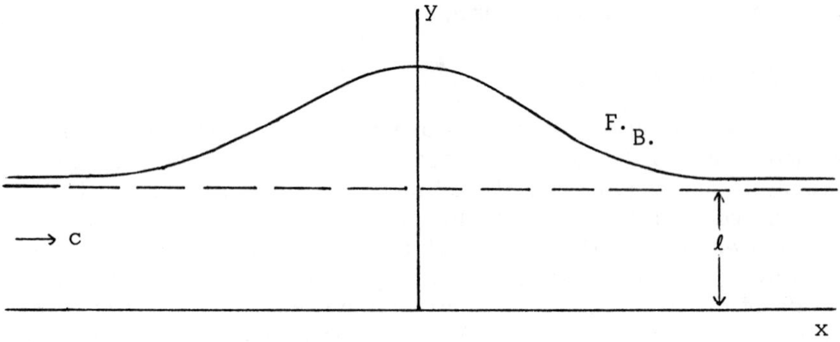

Figure 2

problem of the solitary wave (for a description of Friedrichs's method, see [8(a)].

An interesting aspect of the problem of the solitary wave, is that the "standard operating procedure" of linearization fails ignobly. In fact, if one linearizes the problem, he ends up with only the flows with uniform velocity and horizontal free surfaces.

Even more shocking to the sensibilities is the further fact that the same result occurs if one uses the standard, first-order, non-linear shallow water theory (in analogy with gas dynamics; see Stoker [IV], p. 327). Thus, the perturbation theory of Friedrichs, involving higher order approximations in the shallow water theory is essential to this approach to the problem.

Using essentially the same dependent variables as those employed by Levi-Civita in his classical papers on waves of permanent type, we define the following quantities. The basic flow parameter is:

$$\gamma = g\ell/c^2 \ , \tag{4.1}$$

where, as in section 1, c denotes the velocity of propagation of the profile. As before, the coordinate system is attached to the profile, and the motion is assumed to be steady when viewed from this reference frame. In the case of the solitary wave, we must have (and we assume that):

$$\gamma < 1 \text{ (i.e., the flow is supercritical).} \tag{4.2}$$

It is convenient to introduce another parameter "a" which will replace γ in our formulas; it is defined by:

$$\gamma = \exp[-3a^2] \ , \qquad (a > 0) \ . \tag{4.3}$$

Our dependent variables θ and τ are defined by:

$$w = \mu - iv = \exp\{\tau - a^2 - i\theta\} \ . \tag{4.4}$$

Thus, as in the previous problem, along the free-boundary, θ represents the slope of the profile (F.B. in Figure 2).

The independent variables are the velocity potential φ and the stream function ψ (made dimensionless quantities).

The problem is to find an analytic function $\omega = \theta + i\tau$ of the complex variable $\chi = \varphi + i\psi$ which is holomorphic in the strip $0 \leq \psi \leq 1$ of the χ-plane, and which satisfies the following boundary conditions.

(4.5) $$\frac{\partial\theta}{\partial\psi} = e^{-3\tau} \sin\theta \qquad \text{along } \psi = 1 \ ;$$

(4.6) $$\theta = 0 \qquad \text{along } \psi = 0 \ ;$$

(4.7) $$\theta \to 0, \ \tau \to a^2 \ \text{as} \ |\varphi| \to \infty \ .$$

The perturbation method of Friedrichs for the shallow water theory is somewhat reminiscent of Prandtl's boundary-layer theory. We use the parameter "a" defined by (4.3) as a "stretching" parameter, as follows.

Put:

(4.8) $$\bar{\varphi} = a\,\varphi \ ,$$

leaving the other independent variable ψ unchanged. The dependent variables θ and τ will then be functions of a, $\bar{\varphi}$, and ψ, and are expanded in powers of a :

(4.9) $$\begin{aligned} \tau &= a^2\tau_1(\bar{\varphi}, \psi) + a^4\tau_2(\bar{\varphi}, \psi) + \ldots \\ &\qquad \ldots \\ \theta &= a^3\theta_1(\bar{\varphi}, \psi) + a^5\theta_2(\bar{\varphi}, \psi) + \ldots \quad . \end{aligned}$$

The Cauchy-Riemann equations for θ and τ transform into

(4.10) $$\partial\theta/\partial\psi = -a\partial\tau/\partial\bar{\varphi}; \ \partial\tau/\partial\psi = a\partial\theta/\partial\bar{\varphi} \quad .$$

An application of the boundary conditions together with (4.9) and (4.10) lead to the fact that τ_1 is independent of ψ, and to the following differential equation for the function $\tau_1(\bar{\varphi})$:

(4.11) $$\tau_1''' - 9\tau_1\tau_1' = 0, \ -\infty < \bar{\varphi} < +\infty \ .$$

Appropriate boundary conditions are taken to be:

(4.12) $$\tau_1'(0) = 0, \ \tau_1(\infty) = 1, \ \tau_1''(\infty) = 0 \ ,$$

which are in accordance with (4.7) . The solution of (4.11) and (4.12) is:

(4.13) $$\tau_1 = 1 - 3\,\text{sech}^2(3\bar{\varphi}/2) \ .$$

Remark. It seems probable that the series (4.9) are not convergent, but rather furnish an asymptotic development, as $a \to 0$.

In the existence proof, no use is made of the "representation" (4.9), but extensive use is made of the differential equation (4.11) and its solution (4.13). No details will be entered into here. Instead we give a very brief indication of the over-all method used in the existence proof.

By using an appropriate Green's function (similar to those developed in F. John [15a]), the problem can be reformulated in terms of a system of nonlinear integral equations, with the range of integration being the interval $-\infty < \varphi < \infty$. Next, the change of variable (4.8) is used, and the system takes the form:

$$(4.14) \qquad \bar{\theta}(\bar{\varphi}) = [-S_1 + a\Theta]\, F(\bar{\theta}, \bar{\tau}, a) \; .$$

$$\bar{\tau}(\bar{\varphi}) = 1 + [S_0 - a^2 S_2 + a^2 T]\, F(\bar{\theta}, \bar{\tau}, a) \; .$$

Here the S_j are the integral operators:

$$S_0 f = \frac{3}{4} \int_{-\infty}^{\infty} \operatorname{sgn}(\varphi - \varphi')(\varphi - \varphi')^2 f(\varphi')\, d\varphi' \; ;$$

$$(4.15) \qquad S_1 f = \frac{3}{2} \int_{-\infty}^{\infty} |\varphi - \varphi'|\, f(\varphi')\, d\varphi' \; ;$$

$$S_2 f = \frac{3}{5} \int_{-\infty}^{\infty} \operatorname{sgn}(\varphi - \varphi')\, f(\varphi')\, d\varphi' \; .$$

The symbols Θ and T are also linear integral operators, depending on the parameter a, whose definitions are too complicated to be given here. The nonlinearity occurs in the function F, which is given by

$$(4.16) \qquad \begin{aligned} F(\bar{\theta}, \bar{\tau}, a) &= a^{-5} [\exp\{-3a^2 \bar{\varphi}\} \sin a^3 \bar{\theta} - a^3 \bar{\theta}] \\ &= -3\bar{\tau}\bar{\theta} + 0[a^2] \; . \end{aligned}$$

The bar over the two dependent variables refers to the fact that we have made the following change of dependent variables:

$$\theta(\varphi, 1) = a^3 \bar{\theta}(\bar{\varphi}), \; \tau(\varphi, 1) = a^2 \bar{\tau}(\bar{\varphi}) \; .$$

The operators $S_j (j = 0, 1, 2)$ given by (4.15) will be defined, providing that $f(\varphi)$ is an odd continuous function with the properties that the integral

$$\int_{-\infty}^{\infty} \varphi^2 |f(\varphi)| \, d\varphi$$

exists, and that the auxiliary condition

$$L[f] \equiv \int_{-\infty}^{\infty} \varphi f(\varphi) \, d\varphi = 0 \tag{4.17}$$

holds. In a sense, the condition (4.17) plays the same role as the orthogonality condition did in the solution of Nekrasov's equation (see eqs. (2.7) - (2.9) . In the present problem, with the approach we are using, the idea (of Liapunov) of introducing a modified equation, for which the auxiliary condition is automatically satisfied, seems to be essential.

Thus, we introduce a function $\eta(\bar{\varphi})$ satisfying

$$\int_{-\infty}^{\infty} \bar{\varphi} \eta(\bar{\varphi}) \, d\bar{\varphi} = 1 \ ; \tag{4.18}$$

specifically, we may take:

$$\eta(\bar{\varphi}) = \frac{1}{4} \tau_1'(\bar{\varphi}) = \frac{9}{2} \frac{\sinh 3\bar{\varphi}}{(1 + \cosh 3\bar{\varphi})^2} \ . \tag{4.19}$$

It also seems essential to restrict ourselves to the case where the unknown functions $\theta(\varphi)$ and $\tau(\varphi)$ are odd and even, respectively; this means that we are restricting the profile of the free surface to being symmetric about its crest.

The modified system is obtained from (4.14) by replacing the function F by:

$$E(\bar{\theta}, \bar{\tau}, a) = F(\bar{\theta}, \bar{\tau}, a) - L[F(\bar{\theta}, \bar{\tau}, a)] \ . \tag{4.20}$$

If the parameter a is set equal to zero in the modified system, it turns out that the solution to this reduced system is simply

$$\bar{\theta} = -\tau_1'(\bar{\varphi}), \ \bar{\tau} = \tau_1(\bar{\varphi}) \ , \tag{4.21}$$

where τ_1 is given by (4.13) .

It is convenient in continuing the discussion to drop the "bars" from all our variables; only the stretched variables will be used. In order to prove an existence theorem, we introduce the following function spaces. Let B_1 denote the Banach space of all odd, continuous functions on $-\infty < \varphi < \infty$ for which the quantity $e^{2\varphi}\theta(\varphi)$ remains bounded for all $\varphi \geqq 0$, with the norm:

$$(4.22) \qquad \|\theta\| = \sup e^{2\varphi}|\theta(\varphi)| \ , \qquad (0 \leq \varphi < \infty) \ .$$

Similarly, B_2 will denote the Banach space of all even, continuous functions $t(\varphi)$ for which $e^{2\varphi}t(\varphi)$ remains bounded for all positive values of φ, where t now replaces $\tau - 1$ and the norm is defined in the same way as in (4.22). The symbol B will then denote the Banach space which is the Cartesian product of B_1 and B_2.

The modified system then takes the abbreviated form:

$$(4.23) \qquad G(\omega, a) = 0 \ ,$$

and the problem is to find a solution ω to this equation for positive values of a, given the solution $\omega = \omega_1$ when $a = 0$. After proving the necessary lemmas, and obtaining the pseudo-inverse of the Fréchet derivative of $G(\omega, a)$ at the point where $\omega = \omega_1$ and $a = 0$, we were able to apply the implicit function theorem of Hildebrandt and Graves [11] to obtain the existence of a two-parameter family of solutions $\omega = \omega(a, b)$ of (4.23), valid for small values of the parameters a and b. By inserting this family of solutions into the "auxiliary condition" (4.17) in which f is replaced by $F(\theta, \tau, a)$, we obtained the bifurcation equation for our problem:

$$(4.24) \qquad \Lambda(a, b) \equiv L[F(\theta(a, b), \tau(a, b), a)] = 0 \ .$$

It is now an easy matter to apply the ordinary implicit function theorem to the equation (4.24) and to thus demonstrate the existence of a numerically valued function $b = b(a)$ which satisfies (4.24) and is continuously differentiable in the interval $0 \leq a \leq a_0$, providing that a_0 is sufficiently small. This leads at once to the solution of the system (4.14) which satisfies (4.17) for each sufficiently small positive value of the parameter a. This ends our brief outline of the proof of the existence of the solitary wave.

5. Summary of Results on the Two Classical Problems

Although for the purposes of quick exposition we have restricted ourselves to the case of infinite depth in the first mentioned problem of periodic waves, the case of finite depth has been thoroughly treated in the literature, using the same general methods as those discussed in sections 2 and 3 . For example, the methods of Levi-Civita were employed by D. J. Struik [34] to establish an existence theorem in the small. W. Littman used the approach of Friedrichs-Hyers [9] to establish the existence (in the small) of periodic waves for a liquid of finite depth in the case where the basic dimensionless parameter (see (4.1)) is close to its critical value of unity. Moreover, as already indicated above in section 3, Krasovskii succeeded in establishing the existence of periodic waves in the large for the case of finite depth.

Some other results [18(b)] of Krasovskii are of interest here. By proving two "non-existence" theorems, he showed that no solitary wave can exist when the depth is infinite, nor can any exist when the depth is finite, while the Froude number $\Gamma = c^2/gh$ is less than the critical value of unity.

The results on these classical problems may be visualized by means of a schematic diagram (Figure 3). As indicated in this diagram, the solutions (especially in the near critical range) are not unique, by any means. From the physical point of view, this is not surprising. For, all these steady-state flows are presumably the result of various initial value problems as the time tends to infinity (see Stoker [IV]).

6. Some Generalizations of the Theory of the Solitary Wave

In a recent paper [20], W. T. Kyner has given approximate solutions for the problem of steady flows of a heavy liquid over a small obstacle placed in the bed of the stream, at near-critical velocities. This work was reported briefly in a paper given here last year at the Symposium on Nonlinear Problems [XII] . Using the Friedrichs shallow water theory expansion scheme, in analogy with eq. (4.9), Kyner showed how the coefficients of the powers of the stretching parameter "a" could be determined. The first coefficient (of a^2) in the expansion satisfies a nonlinear differential equation of the form:

$$j''' = 9\, jj' + 3f \quad . \tag{6.1}$$

Under the assumptions that the particle velocity upstream at infinity is the constant c, and that the height of the profile there is ℓ , the appropriate conditions for the solution j as the (dimensionless) velocity potential φ approaches negative infinity are:

$$j \to 1,\ j' \to 0,\ j'' \to 0 \quad \text{as} \quad \varphi \to -\infty \ . \tag{6.2}$$

The function f appears in (6.1) because of the presence of the obstacle. It is assumed that $f = 0$ for $\varphi < 0$, so that the flow

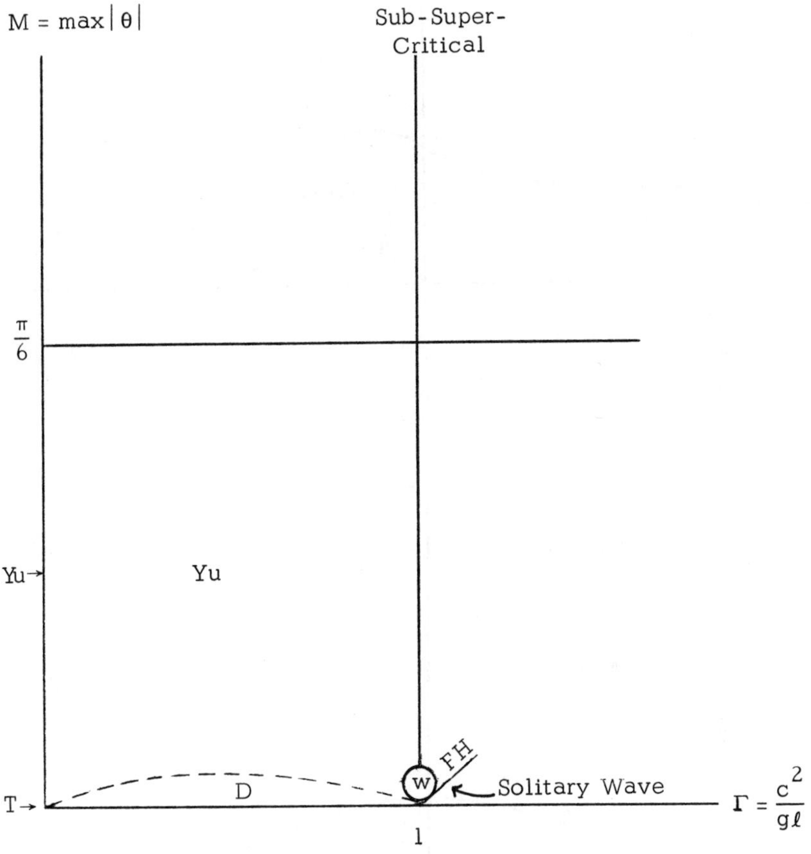

M = max|θ|
Sub-Super-
Critical
π/6
Yu→
Yu
T→
D
W
FH
Solitary Wave
Γ = c²/gℓ
1

Figure 3

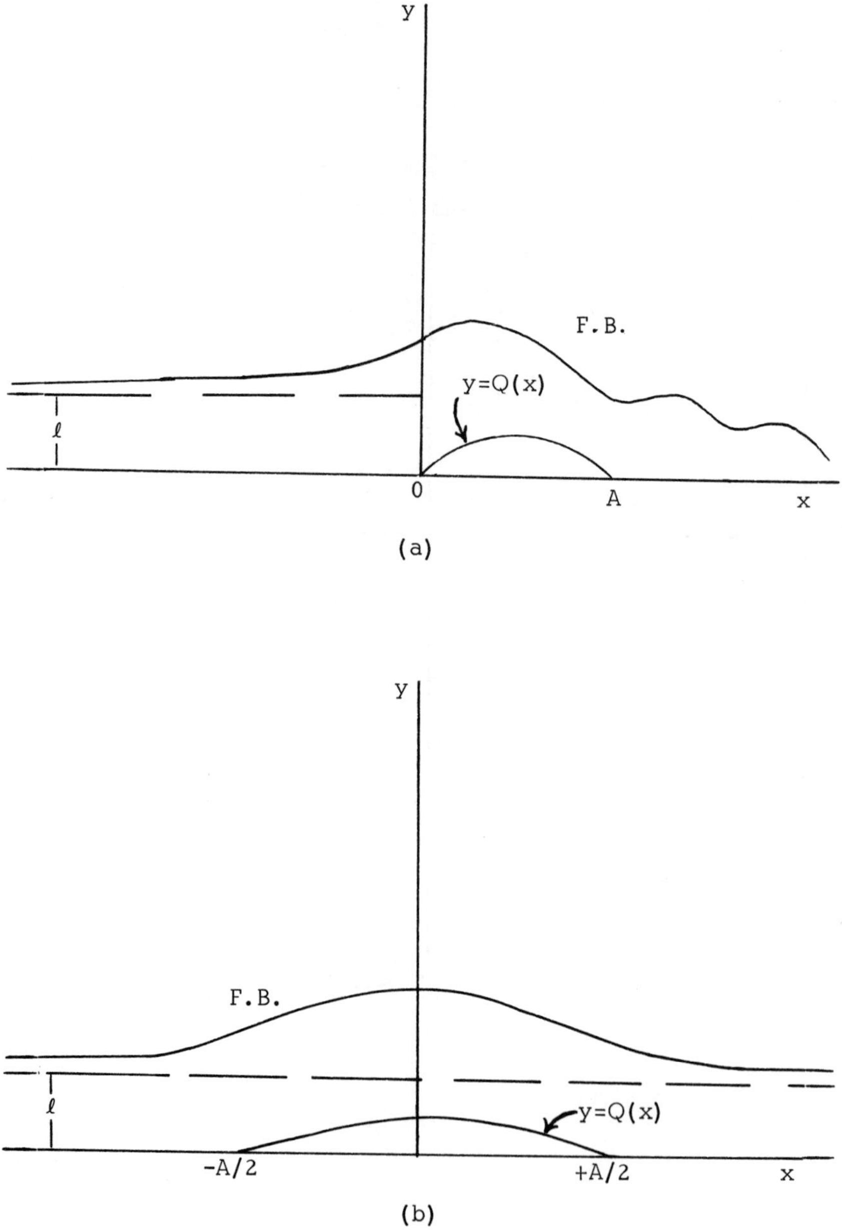

Figure 4

upstream is essentially the "left portion" of a solitary wave (see Figure 4). For $0 < \varphi < A$, f is non-zero, and for $\varphi > A$, $f = 0$, where A is a constant depending on the extent of the obstacle. By a careful study of the differential equation (6.1), Kyner found that there are three different cases, depending on the nature of the "bump," i.e., depending on the properties of the function f . Let b be a "positioning parameter" for the solitary wave portion of the solution, thus:

$$j(\varphi) = 1 - 3\,\mathrm{sech}^2(3\varphi/2 - b). \quad \varphi < 0$$

(6.3) $$j'(\varphi) = 9\,\mathrm{sech}^2(3\varphi/2 - b)\,\mathrm{tank}(3\varphi/2 - b), \quad \varphi < 0 .$$

With suitable restrictions on the indefinite integral F of the function f, the following result was proved.

Theorem 6.1. If $b > 0$, then there exist constants $A(b)$ and $C(b)$ such that, for any continuous function F with its support in $[0, A(b)]$ and with $0 \leq F(\varphi) \leqq C(b)$, there is a unique solution of (6.1) and (6.2) which is bounded and nonperiodic for $\varphi < 0$, and periodic for $\varphi > A$.

On the other hand, a "piecewise solitary wave", which is aperiodic downstream as well, will be produced if

(6.4) $$\int_0^A j'(s)F(s)\,ds = 0 \quad \text{and} \quad -2 \leqq j(A) < 1 .$$

This can be achieved by fixing the value of the positioning parameter b and then increasing the size of the bump until (6.4) is just satisfied. Or, the same result can be obtained by keeping F fixed and reducing b to its critical value. In either case, the perturbation of the left-hand portion (6.3) of the solitary wave will take place near its crest.

In a paper [14] just completed, Kyner and I have proved the following existence theorem for the symmetric piecewise solitary wave.

Theorem 6.2. Let $Q(x)$ be an even function* of class $C^{(2)}$ on the real axis, and let Q have compact support. Then, for values of the Froude number $\Gamma = c^2/g\ell$ greater than, but sufficiently close to unity, there exists a two-dimensional incompressible, irrotational, and steady flow over the bottom surface of profile $y = Q(x)$. The profile of the free boundary is symmetric about the y-axis, and has

* Certain additional restrictions on the derivative $Q'(x)$ of Q are also required in the proof. E. g., the function $F(\varphi)$, which is related to Q', must be chosen in accordance with Theorem 6.1 and the conditions (6.4) above.

$y = \ell$ as its horizontal asymptote. The particle velocity at infinity has the value c . Moreover, as the function $Q(x)$ tends to zero, this flow tends to the ordinary solitary wave.

The proof of this theorem is much too complicated to be given here. Suffice it to say that the method outlined in section 4 above was extended, with variations, to the present case. The main new difficulty to be overcome was in the connection between the boundary value problem for the analytic function defined in the plane of the complex potential and the original problem.

Other generalizations of the solitary wave have been investigated by I. G. Filippov [6] and by A. M. Ter-Krikorov [35(b)]. Filippov studied the problem of a vortex below the surface of a heavy liquid at nearly critical speeds. Using the approach outlined above in section 4, he demonstrated the existence of a solution which approaches the solitary wave as the strength of the vortex approaches zero. Previously, another solution to the same problem had been found [35(a)] which approached the (trivial) uniform flow when the vortex strength went to zero.

In [35(b)], Ter-Krikorov proved an existence theorem for the case of "rotational" flows of the solitary wave type. He assumed that the vorticity Ω was a function of the stream function ψ only, but otherwise allowed $\Omega(\psi)$ to be quite arbitrary. The problem was reduced first to that of a nonlinear boundary value problem for an elliptic system of partial differential equations, and then to a system of integro-differential equations, by the construction of an appropriate Green's function. The solution of the latter system was then investigated, again by methods based on that of section 4 of the present paper.

7. Concluding Remarks

R. Gerber [10] has studied the existence of steady flows of a heavy fluid over various types of bottom configurations. His method is based on Leray-Schauder [22(c)] and on Leray [22(b)] . However, these flows apparently do not reduce to those discussed in section 1-3 when the bottom becomes flat, but rather to the uniform flow. Mathematically speaking, they represent a "branch" of the manifold of solutions, different from those represented by the classical waves.

The subject of nonlinear integral equations in hydrodynamical problems is a large one. There are many examples of their use in a wide variety of problems in fluid dynamics in the literature of the present century. The present writer has neither the time nor the temerity to venture further into this vast field. As samples indicating something of the diversity of such applications, we cite the references [3], [5], [7], [8b], [19], [22], [36], and [37].

BIBLIOGRAPHY

A. Books and Lecture Notes

I K. O. Friedrichs, "Lectures on Functional Analysis", N.Y.U. Lecture Notes (1950) (Notes by F. A. Ficken).

II "Gravity Waves", Proceedings of a National Bureau of Standards Semicentennial Symposium Held June 18-20, 1951, N.B.S. Circular 521.

III L. Lichtenstein, (a) "Vorlesungen uber enige Klassen nichtlinearer Integralgleichungen und Integro-differentialgleichungen", J. Springer, Berlin (1931). (b) Grundlagen der Hydromechanik, J. Springer, Berlin (1929).

IV J. J. Stoker, "Water Waves", Interscience Publ., N. Y. (1957).
Note This book contains an extensive bibliography.

V M. A. Krasnosel'skii, "Topological Methods in the Theory of Nonlinear Integral Equations", Moscow-Leningrad (1956) (in Russian).

VI S. Banach, "Operations Lineaires", Monografje Matematyczne, Tom I, Warsaw (1932).

VII A. I. Nekrasov, "The Exact Theory of Steady Waves in the Surface of a Heavy Fluid", Izdat. Akad. Nauk, SSR, Moscow (1951).

VIII H. Lamb, "Hydrodynamics", 6th Ed. (1932); Dover Publ., New York, (1945).

IX G. Birkhoff, "Hydrodynamics, a Study in Logic, Fact, and Similitude", Princeton U. Press (1950).

X J. B. Serrin and G. È. Latta, "Notes on Hydrodynamics", Princeton University (1951-52).

XI A. D. Michal, "Le Calcul Differentiel dans les Espaces de Banach", v. 1, Gauthier-Villars, Paris (1958).

XII R. E. Langer (Ed.), "Nonlinear Problems", M.R.C., University of Wisconsin Press, Madison (1963).

XIII Proceedings of Symposia in Applied Math., v. 1. Amer. Math. Soc., New York (1949).

XIV Handbuch der Physik, v. VIII/1, Springer Verlag, Berlin (1959).

B. Articles

1. R. G. Bartle, Singular points of functional equations, Trans. Amer. Math. Soc., v. 75 (1953), 366-384.

2. H. F. Bueckner, An iterative method for solving nonlinear integral equations, M.R.C. Technical Summary Report No. 207, December 1960.

3. D. S. Carter, (a) Local behavior of plane gravity flows at the confluence of free boundaries and analytic fixed boundaries, Jour. Math. and Mech., v. 10 (1961), 441-450. (b) Asymptotic behavior of infinite fluid jets under gravity, Tech. Report No. 16, Feb., 1963, Dept. of Math., O.S.C. (c) Existence of a class of steady plane gravity flows, Pacific Jour. Math., v. 11 (1961), 803-819.

4. J. Cronin, Branch points of solutions of equations in Banach space, Trans. Amer. Math. Soc. v. 69 (1950), 208-231, and v. 76 (1954), 207-222.

5. D. Dumitrescu, V. Ionescu and C. Craciun, Die Stromung schwerer Flussigkeiten mit freier Oberflache in senkrechter Ebene, Rev. Mec. Appl., v. 5 (1960), 457-482.

6. I. G. Filippov, Solution of the problem of a vortex below the surface of a liquid at Froude numbers close to unity, Prikl. Mat. Meh., v. 24 (1960), 698-716 (in Russian).

7. R. Finn, (a) On the steady-state solutions of the Navier-Stokes equations, III, Acta Math. (Stockholm), v. 105 (1961), 197-244. (b) On the Stokes Paradox and related questions, See [XII], pp. 99-116.

8. K. O. Friedrichs, (a) On the derivation of the shallow water theory, Comm. Pure and Appl. Math., v. 1 (1948), 81-85. (b) Pinch Buckling. Revs. Modern Physics, v. 32 (1960), 889-897.

9. K. O. Friedrichs and D. H. Hyers, The Existence of solitary waves, Comm. Pure and Appl. Math., v. 7 (1954), 517-550.

10. R. Gerber (a) Sur les solutions exactes des equations du mouvement avec surface libre d'un liquide pesant, Jour. de Math Pures et Appl. 34 (1955), 23-299. (b) Sur une classe de solutions des equations du mouvement avec wurface libre d'un liquide pesant, C. R. Acad. Sci. Paris 242 (1956) 1260-1262.

11. T. H. Hildebrandt and L. M. Graves, Implicit functions and their differentials in general analysis, Trans. Amer. Math. Soc., v. 29 (1927), 127-153.

12. D. H. Hyers, Linear topological spaces, Bull. Amer. Math. Soc., v. 51 (1945), 1-21, and p. 1001.

13. D. H. Hyers and J. A. Ferling, On the local uniqueness problem for periodic surface waves of permanent type in a channel of infinite depth, Math. Magazine, v. 31 (1957), 61-74.

14. D. H. Hyers and W. T. Kyner, Existence of symmetric steady flows near critical speed. (submitted to Archive for Rat. Mech. and Anal.)

15. F. John, (a) On the motion of floating bodies I, II, Comm. Pure and Appl. Math., v. 2 (1949), 13-57, and v. 3 (1950), 45-100. (b) Two-dimensional potential flows with a free boundary, Same Comm., v. 6 (1953), 497-503.

16. Th. Von Karman, The engineer grapples with nonlinear problems, Josiah Willard Gibbs Lecture. Bull. Amer. Math. Soc., v. 46 (1940), 615-683.

17. M. A. Krasnosel'skii, (a) Some problems of nonlinear analysis, Amer. Math. Soc. Translations, Ser. 2, v. 10 (1958), 345-409.
<u>Note</u>. This reference contains an extensive bibliography on nonlinear operators and integral equations up to the year 1954. (b) On Nekrasov's equation in the theory of waves on the surface of a heavy fluid, Dokl. Akad. Nauk SSSR, v. 109 (1956), 456-459 (in Russian).

18. Yu P. Krasovskii, (a) Theory of steady-state waves of large amplitude, Soviet Physics-Doklady, v. 5 (1960), 62-65; Ž. Vyčisl. Mat. i Mat. Fiz., v. 1 (1961), 836-855 (in Russian). (b) Existence of aperiodic flows with free boundaries, Soviet Physics - Doklady, v. 5 (1960), 684-686.

19. M. J. Kravtchenko, Sur le probleme de representation conforme de Helmholtz; theorie des sillages et des proues, Jour. Math. Pures et appl., v. 20 (1941), 35-301.

20. W. T. Kyner, Steady flows near critical speed, Jour. Fluid Mech., v. 14 (1962), 517-528.

21. M. A. Lavrent'ev. (a) On the theory of long waves; (b) A contribution to the theory of long waves, Amer. Math. Soc. Translation No. 102 (1954).

22. J. Leray, (a) Etude de diverses equations integrales non lineaires et quelques problemes que pose l'Hydrodynamique, Jour. Math. Pures et Appl., v. 9 (1933), 1-82. (b) Les Problemes de representation conforme d'Helmholtz; theorie des sillages et des proues, Comm. Math. Helvitici, v. 8 (1936) 149-180 and 250-253.
J. Leray and J. Schauder, (c) Topologie et equations fonctionelles, Ann. Ec. Norm. Sup., v. 51 (1934), 45-78.

23. T. Levi-Civita, Determination rigoureuse des ondes permanentes d'ampleur finie, Math. Annalen, v. 93 (1925), 264-314.

24. H. Lewy, (a) A note on harmonic functions and a hydrodynamical application, Proc. Amer. Math. Soc., v. 3 (1952), 111-113. (b) On steady free surface flows in a gravity field, Comm. Pure Appl. Math., v. 5 (1952), 413-414.

25. W. Littman, On the existence of periodic waves near critical speed, Comm. Pure Appl. Math., v. 10 (1957), 241-269.

26. A. Liapunov, Sur les figures d'equilibre peu differentes des ellipsoides d'une masse liquide homogene douee d'un mouvement de rotation, Acad. Imp. Sci., St.-Petersbourg (1906).

27. N. N. Moiseev, Nonuniqueness of the possible form of steady flow of a heavy liquid for Froude numbers close to unity, Prikl. Mat. Meh. v. 21, No. 6 (1957), 860-864 (in Russian).

28. A. I. Nekrasov, On stationary waves, Bulletin of the Polytechnic Institute of Ivanovo-Vognesenskii, v. 3 (1921), 52-65, and v. 6 (1922), 155-171 (in Russian).

29. L. Nirenberg, Waves of Finite Amplitude, (Unpublished ms.) New York Univ.

30. E. Rothe, (a) On non-negative functional transformations, Amer. Jour. Math., v. 66 (1944), 245-254. (b) Mapping degree in Banach spaces and spectral theory, Math. Zeit., v. 63 (1955), 195-218. (c) See [XII], pp. 233-256. Note. Prof. Rothe has contributed many articles over a period of more than a quarter of a century to the theory of nonlinear functional equations in Banach spaces. See, e.g., the bibliography following the article by Dolph and Minty in this book.

31. J. B. Serrin, (a) On the stability of viscous fluid motions, Arch. Rat. Mech. Anal., v. 3 (1959), 1-13. (b) See [XII]. (c) See [XIV].

32. J. Schauder, Der Fixpunktsatz in Functionalraumen, Studia Math., v. 2 (1930), 171-180.

33. E. Schmidt, Zur Theorie der linearen und nichtlinearen Integralgleichungen, III, Math. Annalen 65 (1908), 370-399.

34. D. J. Struik, Determination rigoureuse des ondes irrotationelles periodiques dans un canal a profondeur finie, Math. Annalen, v. 95 (1926), 595-634.

35. A. M. Ter-Krikorov, (a) Exact solutions for the motion of a vortex on the surface of a liquid, Isv. Akad. Nauk, SSSR, ser. mat., v. 22 (1958), 177-200 (in Russian). (b) A solitary wave on the surface of a turbulent liquid, Ž. Vyčisl. Mat. i Mat. Fiz., v. 1 (1961), 1077-1088 (in Russian).

36. H. Villat, Sur l'ecoulement des fluides pesants, Ann. Ec. Norm. Sup., v, 32 (1915), 177-214.

37. A. Weinstein, (a) Sur un probleme aux limites dans une bande indefinie, C. R. Paris, v. 184 (1927), 497-499. (b) Sur la vitesse de propagation de l'onde solitaire, Rend. dei Lincei (6) v. 3 (1926), p. 463ff. (c) See [XIII], pp. 1-18. (d) On surface waves, Canadian Jour. Math., v. 1 (1949), 271-278.

38. G. B. Whitham, (a) The effect of hydraulic resistance in the dam-break problem, Proc. Royal Soc., ser. A, v. 227 (1955), 399-407. (b) Mass, momentum and energy flux in water waves, Jour. Fluid Mech., v. 12 (1962), 135-147.

Some of the work reported on here was supported by the Office of Naval Research.

T. W. MULLIKIN

Nonlinear Integral Equations of Radiative Transfer

1. Introduction

The area of mathematical physics which we shall discuss is somewhat unique compared to the others discussed in this seminar. A peculiar feature of this subject is the fact that within the mathematical model of certain radiative transfer problems there are both linear and nonlinear equations which determine desired functions. As opposed to the usual situation, the linear equations are exact and not merely linear approximations to the nonlinear equations. This fortunate situation permits us to obtain many exact results about the nonlinear equations by a study of the linear equations.

We shall discuss one of the relatively simple problems in the theory of radiative transfer; that of determining quantitatively the intensity of radiation (neglecting polarization and redistribution of absorbed radiation) in a homogeneous, plane-parallel atmosphere that is of finite thickness and infinite lateral extent, and that is exposed to monochromatic radiation impinging on one side of the atmosphere from a given direction. This also describes the transport of monoenergetic neutrons in a sub-critical slab reactor.

The mathematical formulation of this problem as a scalar linear integro-differential equation dates back to Schwarzchild [64, 65] and has been extensively studied [cf. 16, 21, 30, 33, 34, 36, 38, 39, 46, 47, 78]. If a steady state prevails, boundary conditions on the face of the atmosphere allow the conversion to a linear integral equation. This equation is solved uniquely by a series, the n-th term of which gives the contribution of radiation which has been scattered n times [cf. 34].

In theory then this problem is completely solved. The actual computation of quantities by means of the series is practical, however, only if either the atmosphere is thin or absorption is strong for each scattering. It is in an attempt to find more practical methods of computation that various authors have formulated nonlinear equations.

Most astronomical observations give only radiation reflected from or transmitted through an atmosphere, whereas the above mentioned solution to the transport equation gives a solution throughout the atmosphere. This led Ambartsumian first to the formulation of nonlinear integral equations for the intensity of radiation reflected from a semi-infinite atmosphere [1]. These equations were derived by observing that the problem for a semi-infinite atmosphere is invariant under the addition of a slab of finite thickness. This idea has been exploited by Ambartsumian [4] and Sobolev [68, 69], by Chandrasekhar [22, 23] under the name of "Principles of Invariance," and by Preisendorfer [58-60], Bellman, Kalaba, and Wing [11-13], Redheffer [62, 63], Ueno [75, 76], and others under the title of "Invariant Imbedding." Many of the derivations of these equations have been heuristic and are similar to the standard heuristic method for deriving equations in mathematical physics by particle counting, being novel in that the physical parameter of atmospheric thickness is varied.

It is easily shown that these nonlinear equations can be derived rigorously from the transport equation [8, 9, 16, 36, 49]. For more complicated geometries this seems preferable since the heuristic particle counting has lead to errors [9].

We shall sketch below the derivation of some of these nonlinear equations from the transport equation. We shall also show that the same functions can be obtained as solutions to linear singular integral equations. With these linear equations it is possible to do precise existence and uniqueness studies.

For the sake of simplicity we shall restrict ourselves to the case of isotropic scattering. In this case some of the derivations are deceptively simple. The results which we shall give can be extended to anisotropic scattering, and we shall give references where appropriate. For certain well known results, which are derived in a new manner, the method of derivation is given since it is the one most easily extended to anisotropic scattering.

We do not attempt to give any part of the theories of polarization [22], of inhomogeneous media [13, 19, 49, 74] or of other geometries [8, 13, 22, 59] and other boundary value problems [23]. We do not touch on the problems of neutron reactor theory, which fit naturally into this subject matter, but in which one often asks different questions than those considered here. Neither do we consider various numerical methods obtained by replacing the linear transport equation by a system of approximate equations [4, 6, 7, 20, 22, 71].

In summary then our objective is to take the simplest problem which is of physical significance and which will serve to display the derivations and useful role of certain formulations other than the transport equation. Of particular importance are the questions of existence, uniqueness, and practicality for computational purposes.

We give a list of references which is extensive but by no means exhaustive. Additional references can be found in many of the papers and books cited, and no slight is meant here by the omission of references to any particular author or work.

2. The Transport Equation

We shall consider a homogeneous plane-parallel atmosphere of finite optical thickness τ . Optical depth into the medium is measured by a variable x, $0 \leq x \leq \tau$, in a direction normal to a face of the atmosphere. We let $I(x, \mu, \phi)$ denote intensity of radiation at depth x in a direction specified by θ , the inclination to the positive x axis, and by ϕ, the azimuth referred to a fixed axis normal to the x axis. Here $\mu = \cos\theta$.

The notion of homogeneity should perhaps be clarified. An actual atmosphere can have variations in the density and in the mass absorption and scattering coefficients [22]. The optical depth is introduced as a variable to remove these variations from the equation. If after this transformation of variables the law of local scattering is constant, the medium is said to be homogeneous.

The interaction of radiation with the medium results in absorption as well as the scattering of some of this energy into other directions. We shall assume that radiation fields do not interact with each other, that the frequency of the radiation is unchanged upon scattering, and that absorbed radiation is not reemitted.

We consider a monochromatic parallel beam of radiation of unit average intensity per unit time falling on the entire face of the atmosphere at $x = 0$ from some direction (ν, ϕ) . We suppose that a steady state exists. Rather than formulate the incident field as a boundary condition in the form of a δ-function in direction, we consider the reduced incident field as a source throughout the medium. If we consider isotropic scattering, the transport equation for the intensity of diffuse radiation is independent of ϕ and is given by [22, 34] ,

$$\mu \frac{\partial I}{\partial x}(x, \mu, \nu) + I(x, \mu, \nu) = J(x, \nu) \quad , \qquad (2.1)$$

where the source function J is given by

$$(2.2) \qquad J(x, \nu) = \exp[-x/\nu] + \frac{\omega}{2} \int_{-1}^{1} I(x, \sigma, \nu)\, d\sigma \quad ,$$

$$0 \leq \omega \leq 1 \, , \quad -1 \leq \mu \leq 1 \, , \quad 0 \leq \nu \leq 1 \; .$$

If we consider the medium surrounding the atmosphere as a vacuum, then no diffuse radiation enters the faces of the atmosphere. This gives the boundary conditions

$$(2.3) \qquad I(0, \mu, \nu) = I(\tau, -\mu, \nu) = 0 \, , \quad 0 \leq \mu \leq 1 \; .$$

We have given the transport equation for isotropic scattering. The results to be given below have extensions to the case of anisotropic scattering where ω in (2.2) is replaced under the integral by a phase function which is usually assumed to be given by a finite expansion in Legendre polynomials of the cosine of the angle between incident and observational directions [cf. 22, 34].

Using the boundary conditions (2.3), we have from (2.1)

$$(2.4) \qquad I(x, \mu, \nu) = \frac{1}{\mu} \int_0^x \exp[y - x)/\mu]\, J(y, \nu)\, dy$$

for $0 < \mu \leq 1$, and

$$(2.5) \qquad I(x, \mu, \nu) = \frac{1}{|\mu|} \int_x^\tau \exp[(y - x)/\mu]\, J(y, \nu)\, dy$$

for $-1 \leq \mu < 0$.

If these relations are inserted in (2.2) we obtain the familiar linear integral equation [22, 34]

$$(2.6)\qquad J(x, \nu) = \exp[-x/\nu] + \frac{\omega}{2}\int_0^1\int_0^\tau \exp[-|x-y|/\mu]\,J(y,\nu)\,dy\,\frac{d\mu}{\mu} .$$

The integral operator without ω is known as the truncated Hopf operator Λ and it has been intensively studied [20, 30, 34, 38, 39, 50, 78] . This operator is usually written in terms of the exponential integral $E_1(x)$, but for later computational purposes we prefer the above form.

For the physical application it is the solution of (2.6) for ν in the interval $0 \leq \nu \leq 1$ that is of importance. For the mathematical analysis that follows it is important to consider solutions for all nonzero complex values of ν . We shall state the following well-known theorem [16, 34, 36] which has an appropriate extension to anisotropic scattering.

<u>Theorem 1.</u> <u>For</u> $0 \leq \omega \leq 1$ <u>and</u> $0 \leq \tau < \infty$ <u>the equation</u>

$$(2.7)\qquad J - \omega\,\Lambda(J) = B$$

<u>has a unique solution for any bounded function</u> B <u>given by</u>

$$(2.8)\qquad J = \sum_{n=0}^{\infty} \omega^n \Lambda^n(B) .$$

<u>If for</u> $|\nu| > 0$, <u>we take</u>

$$(2.9)\qquad B = \exp[-x/\nu] ,$$

<u>then</u> J <u>is analytic in the extended domain</u> $|\nu| > 0$ <u>and real valued and nonnegative for real</u> $\nu \neq 0$.

This is the basic existence and uniqueness result which expresses the solution in familiar terms as the sum of contributions from n-th order scatterings. The series (2.8) converges geometrically with a ratio equal to ω times the maximum eigenvalue $\lambda(\tau)$ of Λ . Many estimates of λ as a function of τ have been made [cf. 20, 50] . Since λ is asymptotic to 1 as τ goes to infinity, e.g.,

$\lambda(4) = .9$, the series computation is practical only for small τ or for small ω.

Our objective below is to discuss other formulations that replace (2.7) by other equations and replace (2.8) by a computation which is practical for all $0 \le \tau < \infty$ and $0 \le \omega \le 1$.

3. Nonlinear Equations

We now derive certain nonlinear equations for determining I and J on the faces of the atmosphere. One motivation for this is that the computation of I throughout the atmosphere represents unnecessary work for many applications since it is only the reflected or transmitted intensities that are observed (p. 555 of [3]). Another motivation is the fact that the outward intensities on the faces of the atmosphere represent missing boundary conditions for the transport equation. If these boundary conditions can be determined then it is a simple matter to compute intensities interior.

Many of the derivations of nonlinear equations are heuristic arguments based on "Principles of Invariance" [3, 22] or the "Principle of Invariant Imbedding" [13, 76]. We shall not state any of these principles but instead sketch a derivation of the nonlinear equations from the transport equation.

We first define certain standard functions. The scattering function S and the transmission function T are defined by [22]

$$S(\mu, \nu) = \mu I(0, -\mu, \nu) ,$$
(3.1)
$$T(\mu, \nu) = \mu I(\tau, \mu, \nu), \qquad 0 \le \mu \le 1 .$$

By (2.4) and (2.5) these are merely Laplace transforms of the function J which is defined to be zero outside the interval $0 \le x \le \tau$, that is

$$S(\mu, \nu) = \int_0^\tau \exp[-y/\mu]\, J(y, \nu)\, dy ,$$
(3.2)
$$T(\mu, \nu) = \int_0^\tau \exp[-(\tau - y)/\mu]\, J(y, \nu)\, dy .$$

These functions are well defined in the complex μ-plane, $|\mu| > 0$, as entire functions of the variable μ^{-1}. In this setting they are dependent since

$$S(\mu, \nu) = \exp[-\tau/\mu]\, T(-\mu, \nu) \quad . \tag{3.3}$$

In view of our previous comment on analyticity of J in ν, S and T are analytic in μ and ν for all $|\mu| > 0$ and $|\nu| > 0$.

Following Busbridge [16], we define X and Y functions by

$$\begin{aligned} X(\mu) &= J(0, \mu) \quad , \\ Y(\mu) &= J(\tau, \mu) \quad . \end{aligned} \tag{3.4}$$

From (2.6) it is obvious that

$$J(\tau - x, \mu) = \exp[-\tau/\mu]\, J(x, -\mu) \tag{3.5}$$

so that

$$Y(\mu) = \exp[-\tau/\mu]\, X(-\mu) \quad . \tag{3.6}$$

Using (3.2) and (3.4) in (2.6) we see also that

$$\begin{aligned} X(\mu) &= 1 + \frac{\omega}{2} \int_0^1 S(\sigma, \mu) \frac{d\sigma}{\sigma} \quad , \\ Y(\mu) &= \exp[-\tau/\mu] + \frac{\omega}{2} \int_0^1 T(\sigma, \mu) \frac{d\sigma}{\sigma} \quad . \end{aligned} \tag{3.7}$$

By the definition of S and T and the self-adjointness of the operator Λ, we have

$$\begin{aligned} S(\mu, \nu) &= S(\nu, \mu) \quad , \\ T(\mu, \nu) &= T(\nu, \mu) \quad . \end{aligned} \tag{3.8}$$

This fact is also true for anisotropic scattering [3, 22, 52], but the proof is more complicated since the operator replacing Λ in general is not self-adjoint [52].

A differentiation of equation (2.6) gives by Theorem 1 the following theorem [16, 22].

Theorem 2. Let J satisfy (2.6). Then for $0 < x < \tau$ we have

$$\frac{\partial J}{\partial x}(x, \mu) + \mu^{-1} J(x, \mu) = \frac{\omega X(\mu)}{2} \int_0^1 J(x, \sigma) \frac{d\sigma}{\sigma} - \frac{\omega Y(\mu)}{2} \int_0^1 J(\tau - x, \sigma) \frac{d\sigma}{\sigma} . \tag{3.9}$$

For $0 \leq x < \tau$, the onesided derivative $\frac{\partial J}{\partial \tau}$ is given by

$$\frac{\partial J}{\partial \tau}(x, \mu) = \frac{\omega}{2} Y(\mu) \int_0^1 J(\tau - x, \sigma) \frac{d\sigma}{\sigma} . \tag{3.10}$$

This theorem has an appropriate extension to anisotropic scattering [52].

If we multiply (3.9) by $\exp(-x/\nu)$ and $\exp[-(\tau - x)/\nu]$ and integrate, we obtain the familiar equations [16, 22]

$$\begin{aligned} \left(\frac{1}{\mu} + \frac{1}{\nu}\right) S(\mu, \nu) &= X(\mu) X(\nu) - Y(\mu) Y(\nu) , \\ \left(\frac{1}{\mu} - \frac{1}{\nu}\right) T(\mu, \nu) &= X(\mu) Y(\nu) - Y(\mu) X(\nu) . \end{aligned} \tag{3.11}$$

If these are inserted in (3.7) we obtain Chandrasekhar's equations for $0 \leq \mu \leq 1$,

$$\begin{aligned} X(\mu) &= 1 + \frac{\mu\omega}{2} \int_0^1 \frac{X(\mu) X(\nu) - Y(\mu) Y(\nu)}{\mu + \nu} d\nu , \\ Y(\mu) &= \exp[-\tau/\mu] + \frac{\mu\omega}{2} \int_0^1 \frac{Y(\mu) X(\nu) - X(\mu) Y(\lambda)}{\mu - \nu} d\nu . \end{aligned} \tag{3.12}$$

If (3.10) is substituted in (3.9) and the Laplace transforms taken, we obtain the familiar equations [22]

$$(3.13)\quad \begin{aligned} &(\frac{1}{\mu}+\frac{1}{\nu})\, S(\mu,\nu) + \frac{\partial S}{\partial \tau}(\mu,\nu) \\ &= [1+\frac{\omega}{2}\int_0^1 S(\mu,\sigma)\frac{d\sigma}{\sigma}][1+\frac{\omega}{2}\int_0^1 S(\nu,\sigma)\frac{d\sigma}{\sigma}]\ , \\ &\frac{1}{\mu}\, T(\mu,\nu) + \frac{\partial T}{\partial \tau}(\mu,\nu) \\ &= [1+\frac{\omega}{2}\int_0^1 S(\mu,\sigma)\frac{d\sigma}{\sigma}]\,[e^{-\tau/\nu}+\frac{\omega}{2}\int_0^1 T(\nu,\sigma)\frac{d\sigma}{\sigma}]\ . \end{aligned}$$

Equation (3.10) is also useful in obtaining an instability result discussed in Sec. 6. Setting $x = 0$ we obtain [22]

$$(3.14)\quad \frac{\partial X}{\partial \tau}(\mu,\tau) = Y(\mu,\tau)\frac{\omega}{2}\int_0^1 Y(\sigma,\tau)\frac{d\sigma}{\sigma}\ , \quad \tau > 0\ .$$

Using this and (3.6) we get [22]

$$(3.15)\quad \frac{\partial Y}{\partial \tau}(\mu,\tau) + \frac{1}{\mu}\, Y(\mu,\tau) = X(\mu,\tau)\frac{\omega}{2}\int_0^1 Y(\sigma,\tau)\frac{d\sigma}{\sigma}\ , \quad \tau > 0\ .$$

Analogous definitions and results have been given for anisotropic scattering [22, 52]. For isotropic scattering problems in other geometries, Bailey [8] and Bailey and Wing [9] have given similar rigorous derivations of invariance principles from the transport equation. One interesting feature of this work is the disclosure of an error in previous heuristic derivations [9].

Equations (3.12) and (3.13) are the nonlinear equations which have been most used for numerical calculations [14, 24, 25, 26, 27, 28, 41]. They represent necessary conditions only on the solution J to (2.6) [22]. Before considering the important questions of uniqueness and stability, we turn in the next section to the derivation of certain linear equations which are also necessary conditions on S, T, X, and Y.

4. Linear Singular Equations

We want now to derive certain linear equations as necessary conditions on the unique solution J to equation (2.6). For the isotropic case a derivation of these equations from the nonlinear X and Y equations is due to Busbridge [16, 36]. (See also Crum [29].) Busbridge's approach has never been extended to similar equations for anisotropic scattering. For this reason we give a different derivation for the isotropic case which does readily extend to the anisotropic case [54].

We apply the operator Λ to equation (2.6). With Λ expressed as in (2.6), it is an easy computation to show that for ν replaced by any complex number z outside the interval [-1, 1] we have the equation for $\Lambda(J)$

$$(4.1) \qquad \omega\Lambda(J)(x, z) - (\omega\Lambda)^2(J)(x, z) = \frac{z\omega}{2}\exp[-x/z]\int_{-1}^{1}\frac{d\sigma}{z-\sigma} - \frac{z\omega}{2}\int_0^1 \frac{\exp[-x/\sigma]}{z-\sigma}\,d\sigma - \frac{z\omega}{2}\exp[-\tau/z]\int_0^1 \frac{\exp[-(\tau-x)/\sigma]}{z+\sigma}\,d\sigma \; .$$

By the uniqueness result of Theorem 1, we obtain the solution

$$(4.2) \qquad \omega\Lambda(J)(x, z) = J(x, z)\frac{z\omega}{2}\int_{-1}^{1}\frac{d\sigma}{z-\sigma} - \frac{z\omega}{2}\int_0^1\frac{J(x,\sigma)}{z-\sigma}\,d\sigma - \frac{z\omega}{2}\exp[-\tau/z]\int_0^1\frac{J(\tau-x,\sigma)}{z+\sigma}\,d\sigma \; .$$

The last term follows from (3.5).

Combining this with (2.6) we obtain linear conditions on J.

<u>Theorem 3.</u> <u>For complex</u> z <u>outside the interval</u> [-1, 1] <u>the unique solution to</u> (2.6) <u>also satisfies the equation</u>

$$(4.3) \qquad \lambda(z)\,J(x, z) = \exp[-x/z] - \frac{z\omega}{2}\int_0^1\frac{J(x,\sigma)}{z-\sigma}\,d\sigma - \frac{z\omega}{2}\exp(-\tau/z)\int_0^1\frac{J(\tau-x,\sigma)}{z+\sigma}\,d\sigma \; .$$

<u>The function</u> λ <u>is defined by</u>

$$\lambda(z) = 1 - \frac{z\omega}{2} \int_{-1}^{1} \frac{d\sigma}{z-\sigma} , \tag{4.4}$$

<u>and</u> x <u>is merely a parameter satisfying</u> $0 \leq x \leq \tau$.

If $J(x, \mu)$ and $J(\tau - x, \mu)$ are known for $0 \leq \mu \leq 1$, then (4.3) defines their meromorphic extension to complex z outside $[-1, 1]$. If J is to satisfy (2.6), it must be analytic in all z for $|z| > 0$. This means that the right hand side of (4.3) must vanish at the zeros of λ .

The function λ is even and has only two real roots. For $0 \leq \omega < 1$ these are given by $\pm 1/k$ where k is the nonzero root of

$$2k = \omega \ln \frac{1+k}{1-k} . \tag{4.5}$$

For $\omega = 1$, λ has a double root at infinity.

We demand that the right hand side of (4.3) vanish to the same order as λ . For $0 \leq \omega < 1$ we obtain the conditions

$$\exp[\pm kx] = \frac{\omega}{2} \int_0^1 \frac{J(x, \sigma)\, d\sigma}{1 \pm k\sigma} + \frac{\omega}{2} \exp[\pm k\tau] \int_0^1 \frac{J(\tau - x, \sigma)}{1 \pm k\sigma} d\sigma . \tag{4.6}$$

For $\omega = 1$, we have

$$\begin{aligned} 2 &= \int_0^1 [J(x, \sigma) + J(\tau - x, \sigma)]\, d\sigma , \\ \tau \int_0^1 J(\tau - x, \sigma)\, d\sigma &= 2x + \int_0^1 \sigma\, [J(x, \sigma) - J(\tau - x, \sigma)]\, d\sigma . \end{aligned} \tag{4.7}$$

We have therefore obtained two linear constraints on J for each x by demanding analyticity in the variable z .

Now we can use Plemelj's formula [57] to obtain singular equations for determining $J(x, \mu)$ and $J(\tau - x, \mu)$ on $0 \leq \mu \leq 1$. For μ in $0 < \mu < 1$ we take limits of (4.3) in the complex plane as z tends to μ first with $\mathrm{Im}(z) > 0$ and then with $\mathrm{Im}(z) < 0$.

Adding these limits and using analyticity of J, we obtain the singular equation [54]

$$(4.8)\qquad \lambda_0(\mu)\, J(x,\mu) = \exp[-x/\mu] - \frac{\mu\omega}{2}\int_0^1 \frac{J(x,\sigma)}{\mu-\sigma}\,d\sigma - \frac{\mu\omega}{2}\exp[-\tau/\mu]\int_0^1 \frac{J(\tau-x,\sigma)}{\mu+\sigma}\,d\sigma \; .$$

The singular integrals are computed as Cauchy principle values. The function λ_0 is given by

$$(4.9)\qquad \lambda_0(\mu) = 1 + \frac{\mu\omega}{2}\,\ln\frac{1-\mu}{1+\mu} \; .$$

If we evaluate (4.8) at $x = 0$ and at $x = \tau$ and recall (3.4) we obtain the equations [16, 29, 31, 53]

$$(4.10)\qquad \begin{aligned} \lambda_0(\mu)\, X(\mu) &= 1 - \frac{\mu\omega}{2}\int_0^1 \frac{X(\sigma)\,d\sigma}{\mu-\sigma} - \frac{\mu\omega}{2}\exp[-\tau/\mu]\int_0^1 \frac{Y(\sigma)\,d\sigma}{\mu+\sigma} \\ \lambda_0(\mu)\, Y(\mu) &= \exp[-\tau/\mu]\left[1 - \frac{\mu\omega}{2}\int_0^1 \frac{X(\sigma)\,d\sigma}{\mu+\sigma}\right] - \frac{\mu\omega}{2}\int_0^1 \frac{Y(\sigma)\,d\sigma}{\mu-\sigma} \end{aligned} \; .$$

If equation (4.3) is multiplied by $\exp[-x/\nu]$ and by $\exp[-(\tau-x)/\nu]$ and integrated on x, we obtain the following analogous equations for S and T functions [52]. The linear singular equations are

$$(4.11)\qquad \begin{aligned} \lambda_0(\mu)\, S(\nu,\mu) &= \frac{\mu\nu}{\mu+\nu}\left(1 - \exp\left[-\tau\left(\frac{1}{\nu}+\frac{1}{\mu}\right)\right]\right) - \frac{\mu\omega}{2}\int_0^1 \frac{S(\nu,\sigma)\,d\sigma}{\mu-\sigma} \\ &\quad - \frac{\mu\omega}{2}\exp[-\tau/\mu]\int_0^1 \frac{T(\nu,\sigma)\,d\sigma}{\mu+\sigma} \\ \lambda_0(\mu)\, T(\nu,\mu) &= \frac{\mu\nu}{\mu-\nu}\Big(\exp[-\tau/\mu] - \exp[-\tau/\nu]\Big) - \frac{\mu\omega}{2}\int_0^1 \frac{T(\nu,\sigma)\,d\sigma}{\mu-\sigma} \\ &\quad - \frac{\mu\omega}{2}\exp[-\tau/\mu]\int_0^1 \frac{S(\nu,\sigma)\,d\sigma}{\mu+\sigma} \end{aligned} \; .$$

For $0 \leq \omega < 1$ the linear constraints are

$$(4.12) \qquad \frac{\nu}{1 \pm k\nu}\left(1 - \exp\left[-\tau\left(\frac{1}{\nu} \pm k\right)\right]\right) = \frac{\omega}{2}\int_0^1 \frac{S(\nu,\sigma)\,d\sigma}{1 \mp k\sigma}$$

$$+ \frac{\omega}{2}\exp\left[\mp k\tau\right]\int_0^1 \frac{T(\nu,\sigma)\,d\sigma}{1 \pm k\sigma} .$$

For $\omega = 1$, the linear constraints are

$$2\nu(1 - \exp[-\tau/\nu]) = \int_0^1 [S(\nu,\sigma) + T(\nu,\sigma)]\,d\sigma$$

$$(4.13) \qquad \tau\int_0^1 T(\nu,\sigma)\,d\sigma = 2\nu^2\,(1 - (1 + \tau/\nu)\exp[-\tau/\nu]) \quad .$$

$$+ \int_0^1 \sigma[S(\nu,\sigma) - T(\nu,\sigma)]\,d\sigma$$

In view of (3.11) we expect solutions to (4.11) to be given simply by solutions to (4.10) .

Even though (4.10) is important in its relation to scattering and transmission functions, (4.8) for x and $\tau - x$ are equally important since they determine the source function J at any symmetric depths in the slab. Any numerical method for treating (4.10) applies equally well to (4.8) . This is of particular significance in reactor criticality problems [37] . In a paper currently being written with Dr. Leonard, we are showing that a study of (4.8) leads both to the criticality condition for slabs and spheres, i.e., the functional relation between τ and the average neutron production per fission, and to Fredholm equations for the neutron density in these critical reactors. This is related to, but simpler than, some current work in neutron transport [21, 45, 48, 80] .

Although (4.3) and the resulting equations have been derived from the transport equation, they express some physical principle of duality. The transport equation, which expresses differential changes in I interior to the slab, has been replaced by an equation which relates J, and hence also I, at x and $\tau - x$ by means of the functional dependence of J on variations of the angle of incident radiation on the face of the atmosphere. We refrain from designating this as a new principle.

5. The Uniqueness Problem

Before considering the merits of various equations for numerical computations it is imperative to determine whether or not each set of equations has a unique solution. For some reason this problem is often confused with the problem of uniqueness in the physical problem supposedly represented by the mathematical model.

We illustrate with a quote from Ambartsumian [3, p. 559], where he is discussing the symmetry of the function S (ρ in his notation) for a semi-infinite atmosphere "... However, since equation (33.24) can have, from its physical significance, only one solution, the function $\rho(\eta, \xi)$ must be symmetrical: ...".

The conclusion about symmetry reached by this argument is correct. However, the reasoning is incorrect since, except in the conservative case of $\omega = 1$, the equation he is discussing has two symmetric solutions expressed in terms of the two solutions [16] to Ambartsumian's equation (eqn. (33.28) on p. 559 of [3]) or, what is the same thing, Chandrasekhar's H equation.

We quote from Chandrasekhar [22, p. 208] as an illustration of a more appropriate viewpoint. "The reference to the question of uniqueness of the solution in the preceding paragraph draws attention to a fact which we have so far ignored, namely, that there are, indeed, no grounds for believing that the principles of invariance, by themselves, can lead to determine solutions of the various problems. The invariances and the equations they lead to are only necessary conditions; it is by no means obvious that they are also sufficient ....".

The confusion of physical models with mathematical models often causes the mathematician's query to be termed "academic" when he asks, "But do the equations have a unique solution?" With regard to some of the equations given in previous sections we shall see just how relevant is this question.

Let us consider first the nonlinear equations (3.12) for X and Y functions. Chandrasekhar realized the importance of the uniqueness problem for these equations, and, in fact, he shows [22] that these equations have a one parameter family of solutions for $\omega = 1$. The uniqueness problem is also considered by Busbridge [16]. We [51] recently gave a complete discussion of the solutions to equations similar to (3.12) but with ω replaced under the integral by a nonnegative "characteristic function" whose integral is bounded by $1/2$. We have also studied the uniqueness question for similar equations in anisotropic scattering [52].

For isotropic scattering we show in [51] that for $\omega = 1$ Chandrasekhar found only half of the solutions to (3.12). We designate by X_0 and Y_0 the functions (3.4). Then all solutions to (3.12) for $\omega = 1$ are given by

$$X(\mu) = (1+b\gamma\mu)X_0(\mu) + \mu(a+b\mu)[X_0(\mu) + Y_0(\mu)] ,$$

(5.1)

$$Y(\mu) = (1-b\gamma\mu)Y_0(\mu) - \mu(a-b\mu)[X_0(\mu) + Y_0(\mu)] .$$

The constant γ is given by

(5.2) $$\gamma = \frac{x_1 + y_1}{y_0}$$

with

(5.3) $$x_i = \frac{1}{2}\int_0^1 X_0(\nu)\nu^i\,d\nu, \quad y_i = \frac{1}{2}\int_0^1 Y_0(\nu)\nu^i\,d\nu .$$

The parameters a and b are arbitrary solutions to

(5.4) $$b(b\gamma^2 + 2a\gamma - 2) = 0 .$$

The solutions with $b = 0$ are given by Chandrasekhar [22].

For $0 \leq \omega < 1$ the solutions to (3.12) are given by

$$X(\mu) = \left[1 + \frac{(f\alpha - g\beta)\mu + k\mu^2(f\alpha + g\beta)}{1-(k\mu)^2}\right]X_0(\mu) + \frac{(f\beta - g\alpha)\mu + k\mu^2(f\beta + g\alpha)}{1-(k\mu)^2}Y_0(\mu) ,$$

(5.5)

$$Y(\mu) = \left[1 - \frac{(f\alpha - g\beta)\mu - k\mu^2(f\alpha + g\beta)}{1-(k\mu)^2}\right]Y_0(\mu) - \frac{(f\beta - g\alpha)\mu - k\mu^2(f\beta + g\alpha)}{1-(k\mu)^2}X_0(\mu) .$$

The constant k is given by (4.5) and constants α and β are given by

$$\alpha = 1 - \frac{\omega}{2} \int_0^1 \frac{X_0(\nu)}{1+k\nu}\, d\nu \,,$$

(5.6)

$$\beta = \frac{\omega}{2} \int_0^1 \frac{Y_0(\nu)}{1+k\nu}\, d\nu \,.$$

The parameters f and g are arbitrary points on the hyperbola

(5.7) $$(f^2 - g^2)(\alpha^2 - \beta^2) = 2k(f\alpha + g\beta) \,.$$

These results were easily obtained by first describing all solutions to the linear equations (4.10). The totality of such solutions is given either by (5.1) and with arbitrary parameters a and b or by (5.5) and arbitrary parameters f and g . The constraints (5.3) on a and b and (5.6) on f and g are the only additional restriction imposed by the nonlinear equations (3.12) .

So we have a set of equations (3.12) which were first derived from heuristic "Invariance Principles". If the variable μ is restricted to the values $0 \le \mu \le 1$ of physical interest, these equations alone do not specify a unique solution. It is easily shown that the linear constraints (4.6), evaluated at $x = 0$, are additional equations needed to select the desired functionals, X and Y, of the solution J to (2.6) . But it is hardly likely that these constraints would be derived by a heuristic particle counting. They come from the mathematical condition of analyticity in a variable which is usually restricted to the interval $0 \le \mu \le 1$ as the cosine of an angle in the interval $[0, \frac{\pi}{2}]$.

The fact that equations (3.12) do not have a unique solution does not mean that they are wrong. It just means that they do not constitute a complete set of equations. Without a mathematical investigation of uniqueness of solution to a set of equations it is not always possible to say that the some needed equations may not have been overlooked.

As we have already remarked, the linear equations (4.10) have a two parameter family of solutions. We know, however, that the constraints (4.6) are also necessary conditions. These constraints and equations (4.10) are a complete set of equations with a unique solution. We shall see in Section 7 that these equations can be transformed to a form ideal for numerical computation.

We have not discussed the uniqueness problem for the nonlinear integro-differential equations (3.13). We shall do this along with other considerations in the next section.

6. Instability Results

In this section we wish to discuss the appropriateness of the various nonlinear equations for numerical computations. We are particularly interested in the problem of stability. Since solutions to equations are usually approximated by numerical solutions to approximate equations, it is helpful, in bounding errors, to know properties of solutions to the perturbed equations, in particular, their degree of approximation to the solution to the exact equations.

We wish first of all to consider the nonlinear X and Y equations (3.12). To understand the importance for numerical computations of the multiplicity of solutions given in Sec. 5 we need a result about the function J.

Theorem 4. *Let* $e(\tau)$ *denote the maximum eigenvalue of the operator* Λ. *Then* $e(\tau) < 1$ *for* $0 \leq \tau < \infty$, *and the solution* J *to* (2.6) *is an analytic function of* ω *for all complex* ω *in the domain* $|\omega| < 1/e(\tau)$.

This theorem is easily established by standard spectral theory arguments about the inverse $(I - \omega\Lambda)^{-1}$ for the compact, positive definite, self-adjoint operator Λ.

This result shows that the functions X_0 and Y_0 have power series expansions in ω which converge in the circle $|\omega| < 1/e(\tau)$. We now show that this fails to be true for all solutions (5.1) and (5.5) to (3.12) other than X_0 and Y_0.

The function (5.5) contain the constant k. As a function of ω, k is determined by (4.5), which we rewrite as

$$\frac{1-\omega}{\omega} = k^2\left[\frac{1}{3} + \frac{k^2}{5} + \dots + \frac{k^{2n-2}}{2n+1}\dots\right], \quad |k| < 1. \tag{6.1}$$

It is easily seen that $k = 1$ at $\omega = 0$, but that k as a function of complex ω has a singularity at $\omega = 0$ and a branch point of order 2 at $\omega = 1$. Therefore k in (5.5) is not an analytic function of ω even in the domain $|\omega| < 1$. The functions given in (5.1) are appropriate limits of those given in (5.5) as ω tends to 1 and k tends to 0, where k has a branch point as a function of ω.

We obtain then another characterization of the functions X_0 and Y_0.

Theorem 5. There is a unique solution to equations (3.12) which is analytic in ω for $|\omega| < 1/e(\tau)$, namely the functions X_0 and Y_0.

A standard numerical technique for solving functional equations such as (3.12) is by iteration [3, 20, 26, 27, 32, 61]. Let the iterations be defined by

$$X_{n+1}(\mu) = 1 + \frac{\mu\omega}{2}\int_0^1 \frac{X_n(\mu)X_n(\nu) - Y_n(\mu)Y_n(\nu)}{\mu+\nu}\,d\nu ,$$

(6.2)
$$Y_{n+1}(\mu) = \exp[-\tau/\mu] + \frac{\mu\omega}{2}\int_0^1 \frac{Y_n(\mu)X_n(\nu) - X_n(\mu)Y_n(\nu)}{\mu-\nu}\,d\nu ,$$

$$X_1 = Y_1 = 0 .$$

This generates the n-th partial sums in the power series expansion of the solutions X_0 and Y_0. This procedure is also equivalent to introducing in (3.12) the power series expansions in powers of ω and equating coefficients, a standard perturbation analysis.

By Theorem 5 this iterative method, if computed with absolute precision, leads to the desired solution X_0 and Y_0 to (3.12) by reason of the analyticity. But what of the many solutions (5.1) or (5.5)? These are solutions to (3.12) which are not analytic in ω and in theory will not be reached by the iterative method as long as the initial functions in the iteration are not chosen to be one of these extraneous solutions.

There are, however, extraneous solutions to (3.12) which are arbitrarily close to the desired solution (X_0, Y_0). It is to be expected, as has been observed, that as the iterations seem to be converging, numerical errors introduce the influence of the extraneous solutions and cause oscillations. So in theory the iterative methods will converge to a unique solution, but in practice the presence of extraneous solutions arbitrarily near the limit introduces instability in the calculations. Only by extreme accuracy can this instability be avoided in treating the X and Y equations (3.12) .

The nonlinear equations (3.12) are obtained from (3.9) without any use of (3.10) . This results in nonuniqueness of solutions. Rather than consider (3.9) and (3.10) we now consider the equation (3.13) for the function S . This is a nonlinear integro-differential equation for determining S as a function of the total optical thickness τ of the atmosphere. The initial condition on S for $\tau = 0$, i.e., no atmosphere, is naturally

$$S(\mu, \mu_0, 0) = 0 \quad . \tag{6.3}$$

Equations (3.13) and (6.3) represent the conversion of a boundary value problem for linear equations (2.1) and (2.3) to an initial value problem for Ricatti type equations. The computational advantage of such a formulation is obvious and has been much emphasized [13, 63]. Computations with these equations have been performed for isotropic scattering [14] .

If we specify an initial function for S at $\tau = \tau_0$ by

$$S(\mu, \nu, \tau_0) = s(\mu, \nu) \quad , \tag{6.4}$$

we can readily convert (3.13) to a nonlinear integral equation of Volterra type

$$\begin{aligned} S(\mu, \nu, \tau) = \exp\left[\frac{-\mu\nu(\tau - \tau_0)}{\mu + \nu}\right] s(\mu, \nu) + \int_{\tau_0}^{\tau} \exp\left[\frac{-\mu\nu(\tau - t)}{\mu + \nu}\right] \times \\ \times \left[1 + \frac{\omega}{2}\int_0^1 S(\mu, \sigma, t)\frac{d\sigma}{\sigma}\right]\left[1 + \frac{\omega}{2}\int_0^1 S(\nu, \sigma, t)\frac{d\sigma}{\sigma}\right] dt \; . \end{aligned} \tag{6.5}$$

One can show that for sufficiently small $\tau - \tau_0$ and s the right hand side of (6.5) is a contracting operator and, hence, that the equation has a unique solution. This solution can be continued for larger values of τ .

In recent reports [55, 56] we have studied solutions to (3.13) and a family of initial conditions (6.4). This is actually equivalent to studying equations (3.14) and (3.15). Of particular interest are a family of singular solutions, i.e., infinite for finite τ, and their nearness of approach to the desired solution for increasing τ.

We designate the solution to (3.13) and (6.3) by S_0. It can be shown that

$$\lim_{\tau \to \infty} S_0(\mu, \nu, \tau) = \frac{\mu\nu}{\mu+\nu} H(\mu) H(\nu) , \tag{6.6}$$

where H is Chandrasekhar's notation (see also Ambarzumian [3]) for the limiting value of the function X_0 as τ tends to infinity.

We consider first the conservative case, i.e., $\omega = 1$. It can be shown [51, 53, 55] that as τ tends to infinity

$$S_0(\mu, \nu, \tau) = \frac{\mu\nu}{\mu+\nu} H(\mu) H(\nu) + 0(\frac{1}{\tau}) . \tag{6.7}$$

So S_0 approaches the limit, given in (6.6), only as $1/\tau$.

By use of (3.14) and (3.15) and (5.1) - (5.3) it is possible to exhibit solutions to (3.13) and initial conditions

$$S(\mu, \nu, 0) = 4(1+2B\mu\nu)\mu\nu . \tag{6.8}$$

We have given explicit solutions for (6.8) [55], but we only give them here in the form

$$S(\mu, \nu, \tau) = S_0(\mu, \nu, \tau) + 0(\frac{1}{\tau})$$

$$+ \frac{B}{1 - 2B \int_0^\tau (x_1(t) + y_1(t))^2 dt} 0(1) .$$

For any $B > 0$ these solutions are infinite for some finite value of τ. By choosing B sufficiently small and positive and τ sufficiently large it is possible to find a singular solution which comes arbitrarily close to the solution S_0 before it becomes infinite.

For $0 \leq \omega < 1$ there are also singular solutions to (3.13), but then these can come within a distance of S_0 proportional to the constant k and no closer. Since the initial conditions and solutions are more complicated in this case, we merely refer to [56] for details.

The nonlinear integrodifferential equations with initial conditions are attractive from the numerical viewpoint. The above results show, however, that there is a limit to the accuracy which can be achieved for large values of τ, at least in the conservative and near-conservative cases.

7. Linear Fredholm Equations

We conclude with a quick survey of some results obtained from the linear singular equations (4.10) and linear constraints (4.6) or (4.7). The method for treating these equations is to invert the singular operator to obtain linear Fredholm equations; a procedure previously applied by Busbridge [18]. By analytic continuation the transformed equations can then be transformed to Fredholm equations with continuous kernels, which are much simpler than those obtained by Busbridge. The same program has been carried out for anisotropic scattering [54], but in less complete form.

For simplicity we merely give here the results for $\omega = 1$. Complete details are given in [53] for X and Y equations with a characteristic function ψ instead of the constant ω, and in [54] for anisotropic scattering. The equations for X and Y functions have been programmed.

By consistent use of the theory of singular integral equations and analytic function theory, we have obtained the following formulae.

We designate by H the limit of the X_0 function as τ tends to infinity. Then H is given on $0 \leq \mu \leq 1$ by the formula [53]

$$H(\mu) = (1+\mu) \exp\left[\mu \int_0^1 \frac{\theta(t)}{t(t+\mu)}\, dt\right]. \tag{7.1}$$

The function λ_0 is given by (4.9) for $\omega = 1$, and θ is defined by

$$\theta(\mu) = \frac{1}{\pi} \tan^{-1}\left[\frac{\pi\mu}{2\lambda_0(\mu)}\right], \qquad 0 \leq \theta \leq 1 . \tag{7.2}$$

The formula (7.1) is not given in [53] but is obtained from the formula given there by analytic continuation.

For finite values of τ we obtain X_0 and Y_0 functions as corrections to (7.1). We have [53]

$$(7.3)\qquad X_0(\mu) = H(\mu)\left\{f(\mu) - \mu \exp\left[\int_0^1 \frac{\theta(t)}{t}\,dt\right] A + \frac{\mu}{2}\int_0^1 \frac{f(t)-f(\mu)}{t-\mu}\,\frac{dt}{H(t)\left([\lambda_0(t)]^2 + [\frac{\pi t}{2}]^2\right)}\right\},$$

and

$$(7.4)\qquad Y_0(\mu) = H(\mu)\left\{g(\mu) + \mu \exp\left[\int_0^1 \frac{\theta(t)}{t}\,dt\right](A-1) + \frac{\mu}{2}\int_0^1 \frac{g(t)-g(\mu)}{t-\mu}\,\frac{dt}{H(t)\left([\lambda_0(t)]^2 + [\frac{\pi t}{2}]^2\right)}\right\},$$

with

$$A = \frac{1 - \int_0^1 \theta(t)\,dt}{\tau + 2\left(1 - \int_0^1 \theta(t)\,dt\right)} .$$

The functions f and g are given by

$$(7.5)\qquad f = \frac{P+Q}{2}, \qquad g = \frac{P-Q}{2},$$

where P and Q satisfy the Fredholm equations

$$(7.6)\qquad P = -L(P) + 1 + \exp[-\tau/\mu](1-\mu N(-\mu)),$$

$$Q = L(Q) + 1 - \exp[-\tau/\mu]\left[1 - \frac{\mu\tau N(-\mu)}{\tau + 2\left(1 - \int_0^1 \theta(t)\,dt\right)}\right],$$

with

$$(7.7)\qquad N(-\mu) = \frac{\exp\left[\int_0^1 \frac{\theta(t)}{t+\mu}\,dt\right]}{1+\mu}$$

The linear integral operator L, which we shall not display, has a continuous nonnegative kernel. The equations (7.6) can be solved by iteration to converge uniformly, since, in this norm, we have shown [53] that

$$(7.8) \qquad ||L|| \leq \left(1 - \exp\left[-\int_0^1 \frac{\theta(t)}{t}\,dt\right]\right) e^{-\tau} .$$

The convergence is <u>very</u> rapid except for τ near 0 .

A numerical program for computing X_0 and Y_0 from these formulae has a natural check. For $\tau = 0$ the computations are no different than for $\tau > 0$ and must generate X_0 and Y_0 to be identically 1. This amounts to computing H by (7.1) and then generating $1/H$ by the formula

$$(7.9) \qquad H^{-1}(\mu) = f(\mu) - \frac{\mu}{2} \exp\left[\int_0^1 \frac{\theta(t)}{t}\,dt\right] + \frac{\mu}{2}\int_0^1 \frac{f(t) - f(\mu)}{t - \mu} \frac{dt}{H(t)\left([\lambda_0(t)]^2 + [\frac{\pi t}{2}]^2\right)} ,$$

where now

$$(7.10) \qquad f = - L(f) + 1 - \frac{\mu}{2(1+\mu)} \exp\left[\int_0^1 \frac{\theta(t)}{t+\mu}\,dt\right] .$$

We see then that the linear equations and linear constraints have a unique solution. By the use of analytic function theory these are reduced to quadratures and rapidly convergent Fredholm equations.

8. Conclusion

We have surveyed various nonlinear and linear equations as possible substitutes for the Neumann series solution of the transport equation. We have tried not to forget the motivation for studying these equations, that of producing a simpler computation than the Neumann series.

The details that we have been able to give are possible because of the existence of exact linear equations among whose solutions are all the solutions to the nonlinear equations. We have been able to give existence and uniqueness results as well as results relevant to the stability problem for numerical computations. This wealth of detail is primarily a result of the assumption of homogeneity of the atmosphere. All of the results have been [52, 54], or can readily be, extended to the anisotropic but homogeneous atmosphere.

We will not rate the various numerical methods. Since we have made no estimates on the rate of convergence of iterative methods for nonlinear equations, it is not possible to compare them with the computations based on the linear Fredholm equations. Nor have we given any quantitative measure of the seriousness of the instabilities discussed in Sec. 6. We have shown that instabilities put bounds on the accuracy of numerical computations in certain cases. But it may be that satisfactory accuracy can be attained before instability sets in [14] .

As we have remarked before, the linear singular equations are a result of the assumption of homogeneity, as clarified in Sec. 2. Numerical methods for solving equations (3.13) or equations (3.14) and (3.15) perhaps have the greatest potential since analogous equations can be formulated for inhomogeneous problems [10, 19, 74]. The detailed analysis of the linear equations for homogeneous problems and the ensuing results for nonlinear equations is of value, if for no other reason, in giving indications of behavior to be expected in a study of the more complicated inhomogeneous problems.

REFERENCES

1. Ambartsumian, V. A., "Diffusion of Light by Planetary Atmospheres," Astron. Zhur., Vol. 19, 1942, p. 30.

2. ________, "Diffuse Reflection of Light by a Foggy Medium," Doklady Akad. Nauk SSSR, Vol. 39, 1943.

3. ________, Theoretical Astrophysics , Pergamon Press, London, 1958, (Gosudarstv. Izdat. Tehn. -Teor. Lit., Moscow, 1952.)

4. Anselone, P. M., "Convergence of the Wick-Chandrasekhar Approximation Technique in Radiative Transfer, Astrophys. J., Vol. 128, 1958, p. 124.

5. ________, "Integral Equations of the Schwarzschild-Milne Type," J. of Math. and Mech., Vol. 7, 1958, p. 557.

6. ________, "Convergence of the Wick-Chandrasekhar Approximation Technique in Radiative Transfer II," Astrophys. J., Vol. 130, 1959, p. 881.

7. ________, "Convergence of Chandrasekhar's Method for the Problem of Diffuse Reflection," Monthly Notices Royal Astron. Soc., Vol. 120, 1960, p. 498.

8. Bailey, P. B., A Rigorous Derivation of Some Invariant Imbedding Equations of Transport Theory, Sandia Corporation, Albuquerque, New Mexico.

9. ________, and G. M. Wing, A Correction to Some Invariant Imbedding Equations of Transport Theory Obtained by "Particle Counting," Sandia Corporation, Albuquerque, New Mexico.

10. Bellman, R., and R. Kalaba, "On the Principle of Invariant Imbedding and Propagation Through Inhomogeneous Media," Proc. Nat. Acad. Sci. USA, Vol. 42, 1956, pp. 629-632.

11. Bellman, R., R. Kalaba, and G. M. Wing, "Invariant Imbedding and Neutron Transport Theory I," J. of Math. and Mech., Vol. 7, 1958, pp. 149-162.

12. ________, "Invariant Imbedding and Neutron Transport Theory II," J. of Math. and Mech., Vol. 7, 1958, pp. 741-756.

13. ________, "Invariant Imbedding and Mathematical Physics, I: Particle Processes," J. Math. Phys., Vol. 1, No. 4, 1960.

14. Bellman, R., R. Kalaba, and M. Prestrud, Invariant Imbedding and Radiative Transfer in Slabs of Finite Thickness, The RAND Corporation, R-388-ARPA, February 1962. (ARPA Order Number 189-61.)

15. Busbridge, I. W., "On the H-Functions of S. Chandrasekhar," Quart. J. Math., Oxford Ser. (2), Vol. 8, 1957, pp. 133-140.

16. ________, The Mathematics of Radiative Transfer, Cambridge Tracts, No. 50, 1960.

17. ________, "On Solutions of Chandrasekhar's Integral Equation," Trans. of Amer. Math. Soc., Vol. 105, 1962.

18. ________, "On the X- and Y-Functions of S. Chandrasekhar," Astr. J., Vol. 122, 1955, pp. 327-348.

19. ________, "On Inhomogeneous Stellar Atmospheres," Astr. J., Vol. 133, No. 1, 1961, pp. 198-209.

20. Carlson, B., "Numerical Solution of Neutron Transport Problems," Amer. Math. Soc. Proceedings of Symposia in Applied Mathematics, Vol. XI, 1961.

21. Case, K. M., "Elementary Solutions of the Transport Equation and Their Applications," An. Phys., Vol. 9, 1960.

22. Chandrasekhar, S., Radiative Transfer, Dover, New York, 1960. (Oxford University Press, 1950.)

23. ________, "On the Diffuse Reflection of a Pencil of Radiation by a Plane-Parallel Atmosphere," Nat. Acad. of Sc., Vol. 44, 1958, pp. 933-940.

24. Chandrasekhar, S., and Donna Elbert, "The Illumination and Polarization of the Sunlit Sky on Rayleigh Scattering." Trans. Amer. Philos. Soc., (N.S.) Vol. 44, pp. 643-728.

25. ________, "The X and Y Functions for Isotropic Scattering, II," Astr. J., Vol. 115, 1952, pp. 269-278.

26. Chandrasekhar, S., Donna Elbert, and Ann Franklin, "The X and Y Functions for Isotropic Scattering, I," Astr. J., Vol. 115, 1952, pp. 244-268.

27. Churchill, S., C. Chu, L. Evans, L. Tien, and S. Pang, Exact Solutions for Anisotropic, Multiple Scattering by Parallel Plane Dispersions, The University of Michigan, DASA-1257, 03675-1-F, September 1961.

28. Coulson, K. L., J. Dave, and Z. Sekera, Tables Related to Radiation Emerging from a Planetary Atmosphere with Rayleigh Scattering, University of California Press, Los Angeles, 1960.

29. Crum, M. M., "On an Integral Equation of Chandrasekhar," Quart. J. Math. (Oxford), Vol. 18, 1947, p. 244.

30. Davison, B., Neutron Transport Theory, Oxford, 1957.

31. Fox, Charles, "A Solution of Chandrasekhar's Integral Equation," Trans. of Amer. Math. Soc., Vol. 99, 1961, pp. 285-291.

32. Gross, Kenneth I., "Discussion of an Iterative Solution to an Equation of Radiative Transfer," J. of Math. and Phys., Vol. XLI, No. 1, 1962, pp. 53-61.

33. Hilbert, D., Phys. Zeitschr., Vol. 13, 1912, p. 1056.

34. Hopf, E., Mathematical Problems of Radiative Equilibrium, Cambridge Tracts, No. 31, 1934.

35. Kagan, R. I. and M. I. Yudin, "Approximate Solution of the Equation of Dispersion of Light, Izv. Akad. Nauk. SSSR. Ser. Geofiz. 1956, pp. 968-975.

36. Kourganoff, V., and I. W. Busbridge, Basic Methods in Transfer Problems, Oxford, 1952.

37. Leonard, A., and T. W. Mullikin, Solutions to the Criticality Problem for Spheres and Slabs, The RAND Corporation, RM-3256-PR, 1962.

38. Lehner, J., and G. M. Wing, "On the Spectrum of an Unsymmetric Operator Arising in the Transport Theory of Neutrons," Comm. on Pure and Appl. Math., Vol. 8, 1955, pp. 217-234.

39. ________, "Solution of the Linearized Boltzmann Equation for the Slab Geometry," Duke Math. J., Vol. 23, 1956, pp. 125-142.

40. McFarland, J. E., "An Iterative Solution of the Quadratic Equation in Banach Space." Proc. Amer. Math. Soc., Vol. 9, 1958, pp. 824-830.

41. Mayers, D. F., "Calculation of Chandrasekhar: X- and Y-Functions for Isotropic Scattering." Monthly Notices Royal Astron. Soc., Vol. 123, 1962, pp. 471-484.

42. Melzak, Z. A., "A Scalar Transport Equation," Trans. Amer. Math. Soc., Vol. 85, 1957, pp. 547-560.

43. Melzak, Z. A., "A Scalar Transport Equation, II," Michigan Math. J., Vol. 4, 1957, pp. 193-206.

44. ________, "Entire Operators and Functional Equations," Proc. Amer. Math. Soc., Vol. 10, 1959, pp. 438-447.

45. Mika, J. R., "Neutron Transport with Anisotropic Scattering," Nuclear Sci., and Eng., Vol. 11, 1961, pp. 415-427.

46. Milne, E. A., "Thermodynamics of the Stars," Chap. II, Handbuch der Astrophysik, J. Springer, Berlin, 1930.

47. ________, "Radiative Equilibrium in the Outer Layers of a Star: The Temperature Distribution and the Law of Darkening, Monthly Notices Royal Astron. Soc., Vol. 81, 1921, p. 361.

48. Mitsis, G. J., Transport Solutions to the One-Dimensional Critical Problem, Argonne National Laboratory, ANL-6459, December 1961.

49. Mullikin, T. W., "Principles of Invariance in Transport Theory," J. of Math. Anal. and Appl., Vol. 3, 1961, pp. 441-454.

50. ________, "Estimates of Critical Dimensions of Spherical and Slab Reactors," J. of Math. Anal. and Appl., Vol. 5, 1962, pp. 184-199.

51. ________, "A Complete Solution of the X and Y Equations of Chandrasekhar," Astrophys. J., Vol. 136, 1962, pp. 627-635.

52. ________, Radiative Transfer in Homogeneous Plane-Parallel Atmospheres, The RAND Corporation, RM-3209-NASA, 1962.

53. ________, Chandrasekhar's X and Y Functions for Homogeneous Atmospheres, The RAND Corporation, RM-3376-JPL, 1962.

54. ________, Radiative Transfer in Homogeneous Anisotropic Slabs, The RAND Corporation, RM-3558-PR, March 1963.

55. ________, A Type of Instability of an Integro-Differential Equation for the Scattering Function in Radiative Transfer, The RAND Corporation, RM-3548-PR, March 1963.

56. ________, Singular Solutions of an Integro-Differential Equation in Radiative Transfer, The RAND Corporation, RM-3575-PR, April 1963.

57. Muskhelishvili, N. I., Singular Integral Equations, P. Noordhoff, Groningen-Holland, 1953.

58. Preisendorfer, R. W., "Invariant Imbedding Relation for the Principles of Invariance," Proc. Nat. Acad. Sci. USA, Vol. 44, 1958, pp. 320-323.

59. ________, "A Mathematical Foundation for Radiative Transfer Theory," J. Math. and Mech., Vol. 6, 1957, pp. 686-730.

60. ________, "Time-Dependent Principles of Invariance," Proc. Nat. Acad. Sci. USA., Vol. 44, 1958, pp. 328-332.

61. Rall, L. B., "Quadratic Equations in Banach Spaces," Rendiconti del Circolo Matematico di Palermo, Serie II, Tomo X, 1961, pp. 1-19.

62. Redheffer, R., "Novel Uses of Functional Equations," J. Rational Mech. and Anal., Vol. 3, 1954, pp. 271-279.

63. ________, "On the Relation of Transmission Line Theory to Scattering and Transfer," J. Math. Phys., Vol. 41, 1962, pp. 1-41.

64. Schwarzschild, K., "Über das Gleichgewicht der Sonnenatmosphäre," Gottinger Nachr., Vol. 41, 1906.

65. ________, "Über Diffusion und Absorption in der Sonnenatmosphäre," S.B. Preuss. Akad. Wiss., Vol. 1183, 1914.

66. Sekera, Z., and E. V. Ashburn, Tables Relating to Rayleigh Scattering of Light in the Atmosphere, NAVORD Rept. 2061, U. S. Naval Ord. Test Station, Inyokern, California, 1953.

67. ________, and G. Blanch, "Tables Relating to Rayleigh Scattering of Light in the Atmosphere," Sci. Rept., No. 3, Contract AF 19(122)-239, Air Force Cambridge Research Center, 1954.

68. Sobolev, V. V., "A New Method in the Theory of the Diffusion of Light, Russ. Astr. J., Vol. 28, 1951, p. 355.

69. ________, Transfer of Radiation Energy in the Atmospheres of Stars and Planets, Moscow, 1956.

70. Stibbs, D. W. N., "On the H-Functions for Isotropic Scattering," Monthly Notices of the Royal Astr. Soc., Vol. 119, 1959, p. 512.

71. Sykes, J. B., "Approximate Integration of the Equations of Transfer," Monthly Notices of the Royal Astron. Soc., Vol. 111, 1951, p. 337.

72. Ueno, Sueo, "The Probabilistic Method for Problems of Radiative Transfer, IX: Diffuse Reflection and Transmission in a Finite Atmosphere with Isotropic Scattering in the Non-Conservative Case," Ann. Astrophys., Vol. 22, 1959, p. 468.

73. ________, "On the Scattering and Transmission Functions of S. Chandrasekhar," Ann. Astrophys., Vol. 22, 1959, p. 484.

74. ________, "The Probabilistic Method for Problems of Radiative Transfer, X: Diffuse Reflection and Transmission in a Finite Inhomogeneous Atmosphere," Astrophysical Journal, Vol. 132, 1960, pp. 729-745.

75. ________, "Stochastic Equations in Radiative Transfer by Invariant Imbedding Method, J. of Math. Anal. and Appl., Vol. 2, No. 2, 1961, pp. 217-222.

76. ________, "The Invariant Imbedding Method for Transport Problems, II: Resolvent in Photon Diffusion Equation," J. of Math. Anal. and Appl. Vol. 3, No. 2, 1961, pp. 361-372.

77. Weiner, N., and E. Hopf, "Über eine Klasse Singularer Integralgleichungen," S. B. Preuss. Akad. Wiss., 1931, p. 696.

78. Wing, G. Milton, "Transport Theory and Spectral Problems," American Mathematical Society, Proceedings of Symposia in Applied Mathematics, Vol. XI, 1961, pp. 140-150.

79. ________, An Introduction to Transport Theory, John Wiley & Sons, New York, 1962.

80. Zelazny, R., "Exact Solution of a Critical Problem for a Slab," J. of Math. Phys., Vol. 2, 1961, pp. 538-542.

This paper is based on research performed for the United States Air Force under Project RAND and reported in other forms. Any views expressed in this paper should not be interpreted as reflecting the official opinion or policy of any of RAND's governmental or private research sponsors.

INDEX

K

L

M

N

O

P

Q

R